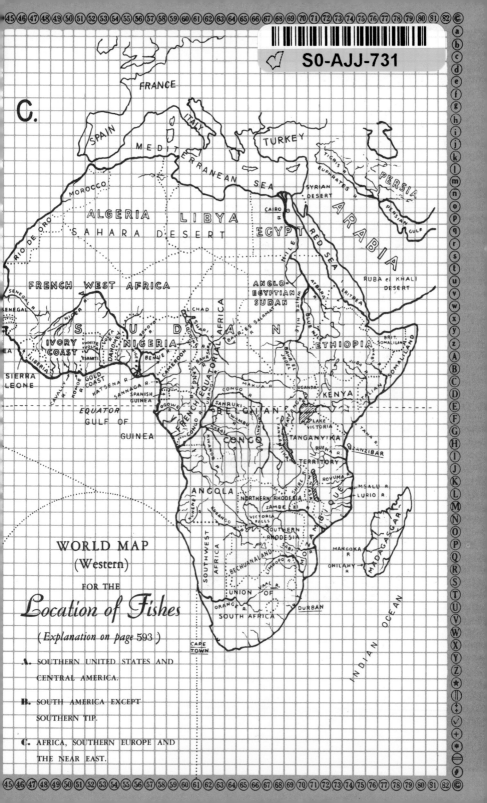

C.

WORLD MAP
(Western)

FOR THE

Location of Fishes

(*Explanation on page* 593)

A. SOUTHERN UNITED STATES AND
CENTRAL AMERICA.

B. SOUTH AMERICA EXCEPT
SOUTHERN TIP.

C. AFRICA, SOUTHERN EUROPE AND
THE NEAR EAST.

Rasbora heteromorpha

EXOTIC AQUARIUM FISHES

A Work of General Reference

By WILLIAM T. INNES, L.H.D.

Founder of *The Aquarium Magazine*
Editor of *Aquarium Highlights*
Author of *The Modern Aquarium*
Goldfish Varieties and Water Gardens
and *Your Aquarium*

The 19th edition of *Exotic Aquarium Fishes* was edited by George S. Myers, A.M., Ph.D., Professor of Biology, Stanford University; Editor *Stanford Ichthyological Bulletin;* Past-President, American Society of Ichthyologists and Herpetologists; Sometime Ichthyologist, U. S. Fish and Wildlife Service; formerly in charge Division of Fishes, U. S. National Museum and Advisor in Fisheries and Ichthyology to the Brazilian Government.

The 19th edition of *Exotic Aquarium Fishes,* Revised, edited by Helen Simkatis as indicated, Technical Editor, *The Aquarium Magazine.*

METAFRAME CORPORATION
DIVISION OF MATTEL, INC.
MAYWOOD, NEW JERSEY • MOUNTAIN VIEW, CALIFORNIA
UNITED STATES OF AMERICA

[Pronounced In'ess]

Printed in U. S. A.

Author-Publisher's Introduction

THE AUTHOR and editors have to thank thousands of correspondents from all parts of the world for their part in letting them know what kind of an aquarium book they need and want. In sifting their letters, it is not difficult to tell.

Particularly is clear detail wanted regarding those practical principles, which, when applied, keep the aquarium and the fish in health. In responding to such needs we have devoted a great deal of space to that general topic, so arranged and cross-indexed that any subject may be quickly located.

We should always remember that aquarium management is as much of an art as it is a science, which is what Weir Mitchell said of the practice of medicine. Then, too, we have the hobbyist who is not consciously aware of either science or art, but whose passion is simply to enlarge his collection. To be inclusive of these diverse interests is more simple than it might seem, for whatever individual tastes may be, we all need the same sound groundwork on which to build, each to his own inclination.

Next, aquarists want to be able to recognize and classify species. With proper helps this can be most interesting. Photographs, taken for clearness of detail, without regard to pictorial effect, furnish the best and truest medium of expression. They are especially useful when the author has himself taken the photographs and places them before him when writing, so that he can, when necessary, intimately interpret them to the reader, explaining various points—and sometimes, shortcomings. We began photographic portraiture of aquarium fishes in 1905 and first introduced it as a basis of illustration in 1917. As nearly all our plates up to 1930 showed only single specimens, we discarded the work of a quarter century and began all over in order to show fishes in pairs, whenever feasible, in *The Aquarium Magazine*.

The placing of the illustration and the text together in every instance is one of the main features of this book.

It will be noted that greatly varying amounts of text accompany different fish illustrations. This is deliberate. Where little is known of a species, or where its habits have just previously been described for another member of the same genus we believe blank paper is better than needless repetition. Those species which are especially interesting or popular, or whose life habits require extra space to describe, receive it.

3

A point to which we attach importance, and which has received much care, is one that the casual reader might easily overlook. This is the arrangement of the fish families in their correct order of precedence, those lowest in the scale of development being first, and the highest, last. The reasons for this are very interesting. They are explained as simply as possible under the heading, Classification of Fishes. This is followed up and briefly supplemented through the book at those points where main family headings occur. A little study of this subject will dispel much of that fog in which aquarists usually find themselves when attempting classification. They will know just why each fish is placed in its own family. Yes, they will themselves be able to correctly place many species which had previously puzzled them. This feature is capable of being used in schools in the systematic study of fishes.

While such points as the pronunciation of scientific names, the 7 family distribution maps and the 2 master location maps are new features, they are so easily understood that no elaboration on them is necessary.

"Exotic" has been used because in every way it is a better word than "tropical." Tropical gives the false impression that all these fishes come from torrid climates, and that they must be kept at a steaming temperature. In many instances this idea works to their injury and also creates in the public mind the belief that they are delicate, and difficult to keep. "Exotic" expresses that fascination we expect of anything from distant parts, and which our aquarium fishes possess in such full measure.

Through numerous editions we have found that (from the hobbyist's viewpoint), certain species of fishes become practically obsolete. Such numbers are at least temporarily dropped from time to time, and replaced by obtainable new favorites. This works in with our belief that while a volume of this character must be kept up to date, the bulk ought not be much increased.

It has not exactly been our object to write so that "he who runs may read," but rather to express ourselves so simply at all times that any who take the trouble to read can understand. Scientific terms have been avoided whenever common words would serve the same end.

By fully setting forth every detail which the beginner wants to learn, we may at times bore the advanced aquarist, who knows the answers. However, a truth already known, but freshly stated by another, may be given new life. In any case, it is well to remember the words of a certain wise old Frenchman, who wrote: "If you would be thought agreeable in society, you must consent to be taught many things you already know."

From the first edition (and before) the author has had the good fortune to have had the cooperation of Professor George S. Myers of Stanford

University on matters pertaining to identification, classification and distribution of fishes, and indeed in many related matters, for Dr. Myers is himself another of those born, dyed-in-the-wool aquarists.

W.T.I.
Edited by H. S.

A Foreword to the 19th Edition, Revised

ALTHOUGH the basics of the aquarium hobby have changed very little since the first edition of Dr. William T. Innes' *Exotic Aquarium Fishes* appeared, refinements of techniques have been developed, and new products, and new interests on the part of the hobbyist make revisions of the work necessary from time to time. The 19th edition, revised, reflects some of these changes without disturbing the format or style of the 19th edition as it was written by William T. Innes, L.H.D. and edited by George S. Myers, A.M., Ph.D.

On going over the book, we realized that its manner of presentation lends itself to such revision very well, and that actually very little in the original text required rewriting. The basics of fishkeeping as presented by Dr. Innes have never been expressed more clearly in subsequent literature on the subject, and it is not our purpose to alter that which has become classic. Our task has been relatively uncomplicated, and we have merely added species that have become sufficiently popular within the hobby in the last years to warrant recognition, and to point out new methods which have become possible only because of the technological advancements made in all fields in recent years. As a matter of interest to the reader, and as a relief from responsibility for both Author Innes and Editor Myers, the above-mentioned additions are indicated by our initials wherever they happen to occur. The changes in the original text are so limited that identification as such would be redundant and confusing.

It is our sincere wish to fulfill Dr. Innes' desire that his book be perpetuated in a manner that will maintain for it the recognition it has earned in the past as the standard work in its field. We hope that when he browses through the pages of the 19th edition, revised, Dr. Innes will be of the opinion we have succeeded.

HELEN SIMKATIS
Technical Editor,
The Aquarium Magazine

Contents

Aquarium Principles

"The best way to be free of the law is to obey it."

PRIMARY PRINCIPLES

THE principles of correct aquarium management are based on a few easily-learned natural laws. To take advantage of them is to succeed. It is our hope to explain these laws so simply that none who follow them can fail.

The ideal aquarium is one which is self-sustaining, except, of course, for feeding the fishes. It should stay in good condition with little care. This is possible if five fundamental factors are observed. They are:

Liberal Water Surfaces   **Right Temperature**
Enough Light   **Water Quality**
                    Correct Feeding

Let us take the five factors in order and see how they apply.

Water Surface
Oxygen and Carbon Dioxide

At the surface of every inhabited aquarium two seeming miracles are constantly occurring, both vital to the life of fishes. One is the dissolving of air into the water to replace that extracted by the gills of the fishes (lungs to them). Like land animals, fishes sustain life by the use of the oxygen content in that air. Then the action of oxygen on the body tissues results in the creation of the harmful gas, carbon dioxide. It is exhaled by the fishes. This gas, in concentration, causes suffocation, rather than does the lack of oxygen. Happily it is carried off at the water's surface. The larger the surface, the more rapidly the double action of dissolving of air and the releasing of carbon dioxide takes place.

The importance of water-air contact can be strikingly demonstrated by the experiment of floating a sheet of paper so that it completely covers the water surface. Soon the fishes show signs of distress, and in several hours they will be dead of suffocation. Water surface is truly the "window of the aquarium."

This double action can be further promoted by mechanical aeration; also plants under the action of good light contribute a little towards this exchange of the gases. These helps will be considered separately.

7

The soundest principle is to have only enough fish in an aquarium so that the air-surface-per-fish is sufficient to give them ample oxygen and to discharge carbon dioxide without depending on any other source.

Aquarium Proportions
From what has been said, it will be seen that those aquariums which are designed so as to give liberal air-surface to the water are best for the fishes. Tall, narrow tanks for window sills or for special spots in decorative schemes should be populated only on the basis of water surface measurement, disregarding the depth altogether.

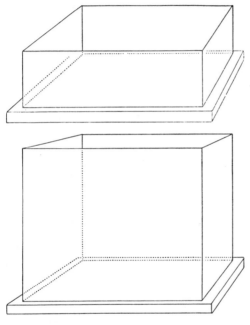

These aquariums have equal water surface areas. In theory, without the aid of plants or artificial aeration, each can maintain the same number of fishes.

The larger one, due to its extra capacity, has a greater initial supply of dissolved oxygen held in the water. In this tank the evil results of overcrowding would merely be longer postponed.

It will also be clear that when ordinary "fish globes" are used they should be filled only a little more than half way, so as to get as much water in contact with air as possible.

Aeration
This is one of the modern developments in aquarium convenience. A small electric pump forces the air through a tube connected to a liberator at the bottom of the aquarium, sending up a spray of small bubbles. It is a common impression that some of this air is *forced* into the water, but such is not the case. It is all picked up by absorption, some from the bubbles, but mostly at the surface, which is steadily circulated by the rising column of bubbles, thus distributing the fresh oxygen through the whole aquarium.

Aeration is particularly valuable to turn on at night in aquariums partly depending in the daytime on the oxygen from plants, for at night they make no oxygen and give off carbon dioxide, a gas that should be gotten rid of. It is also particularly valuable in hot weather, when the natural oxygen capacity of the water is low. Then, again, when overcrowding of fishes is unavoidable, a stream of air through the water has the effect of practically doubling the fish capacity of the aquarium. Sometimes a cloudy gray (not green) tank can be cleared in a few days by constant aeration.

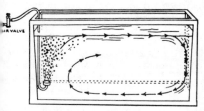

Indicating the beneficial circulation of water which is set up by aeration.

The chief disadvantage of aeration is that, if applied continuously and freely, it makes the fishes so dependent upon it that they are apt not to do so well when removed to still water. Usually a thin stream of bubbles is sufficient for ordinary purposes. Small bubbles, using a given quantity of air, are more efficient than large ones.

Number of Fish per Aquarium? Most of our exotic fishes will take a lot of punishment before coming to the surface to whisper their complaints by breathing atmospheric air. They can be overcrowded without any such demonstration. The author is in constant receipt of letters stating that the correspondent's aquarium is in beautiful condition, but that the fishes do not grow. Inquiry nearly always brings out the fact that the fishes have neither enough "elbow room" nor oxygen. (They are also often underfed. That point is covered under the heading of "Feeding," and especially in the paragraph on "Forcing Growth.")

After making a series of studies of aquariums under average conditions, it is believed the following forms a satisfactory but flexible basis of computation. For fish the size of grown pairs of Guppies, 3 square inches of air surface per fish. That is to say, an aquarium 9 x 20 inches, with an air surface of 180 square inches, can safely support 50 grown Guppies, giving each over 3 inches. Other exotics the same size rate a bit more, as Guppies have great powers of standing crowding. Labyrinth fishes (Bettas, Paradise, Gouramies) need about half the amount of air surface calculated for other fishes of the same size.

Fishes like grown Swordtails, large Platies, etc., need about 8 square inches per fish (4 x 2 inches, or equivalent).

The medium Barbs, like *conchonius*, in 3½-inch size, and other fishes of equal weight should have 20 square inches per fish (4 x 5 inches, or equivalent).

Large Barbs, like grown *everetti,* and Cichlids of 5-inch length require a minimum of 54 inches per fish (6 x 9 inches or equivalent). Big pairs of "Scalares" need at least 10 gallons with surface of 208 square inches. More if other fish are present.

The computations are made from aquariums that have neither plants nor aeration, and at a temperature of about 74 degrees.

The foregoing figures are *minimum* requirements. For health, growth and first-class condition, the air-surface per fish should be doubled or even trebled these suggestions.

A large aquarium can support a little higher percentage of fish in proportion to its size than a small one.

Dishpans Added water surface is usually available by pressing into service the humble enamel dishpan. It can solve problems of temporary overcrowding; it makes a fine hospital unit; it serves as a quarantine for newly-acquired fishes; it is perfect for ripening raw water; it is ideal for storing live foods; it can be slid into the refrigerator (if nobody is looking!) so that the life of such foods is greatly prolonged; it is easily sterilized with hot water; it is easily lifted; it is universally obtainable at low cost; if not dented it is everlasting.

Many breeders use dishpans for spawning fishes and for giving fry a good start in life. White pans are particularly valuable in which to examine catches of Daphnia so as to remove insect enemies otherwise so hard to see.

Some fishes newly placed in any low container are apt to jump out. A glass or screen cover prevents that. Plenty of plants in the water seem to give the fish a sense of security, so that there is less desire to leap.

Effects of Plants While the subject of plants is a very important one in itself, the reader will notice that it is treated here as a sub-heading under "Oxygen." This is as it should be. Their main purposes are to supply oxygen (which they do under the influence of light) and at the same time to absorb the injurious gas (carbon dioxide) which the fish (and all other animals) give off in breathing.

Besides their decorative value they serve another important end. That is the absorption of certain concentrations which are bound to accumulate where animal life is maintained in any confined space. For that reason alone an aquarium with healthy plants is better than one without them. It is this reciprocal reaction between plants and fishes, each to the benefit of the other, that gives rise to the very good, if not accurate, expression, "balanced aquarium."

Plants, besides being one of the most important subjects, is also one of the largest. To dwell in detail on it at this point would interfere with the continuity of this brief outline of the main features of "Primary

Principles." Having shown their place in the scheme of things, we will defer details for the present and place them in later sections on "Plants" and "Planting."

Light

Aquarium Location
Location depends upon whether or not the aquarist intends to use plants. If not, then the problems of placing are simplified. All that is needed is a spot where the temperature does not go to extremes and where there is enough light for the fishes to easily see their way about. While some few species (top fishes) require light for health, most of them can live satisfactorily in quite a subdued light. It should be kept clearly in mind, however, that no plants should be used where the light is very poor, for there they are a positive detriment. By "very poor" is meant a location where a newspaper cannot easily be read by daylight.

For plants of mixed varieties there should be a medium light. A position by a window where there is a good diffused light and about 2 hours of direct sun is ideal, but not indispensable. A strong north light without sun is satisfactory and, on the other hand, a position by a south window is likely to give too much sun, and a certain amount of shading becomes necessary. The great difficulty about excessive light is the growth of too much algae, resulting either in green water or a green mossy coating on glass and plants. Also too much summer sun is apt to overheat small aquariums. Altogether it is really a nice problem securing just the amount of light needed to stimulate the plants into that action which is so valuable, and yet not develop other unwanted growths. Light is like many virtues. In excess it may become a liability.

Of course, it is better being over- than under-equipped with illumination, for we can always find means of cutting it down.

Exotic fishes should not be placed in draughty locations, nor where room temperature varies greatly, as in winter-ventilated bedrooms.

To those who do not mind the slight expense of electricity, the question of location, so far as light is concerned, is an easy one, for with modern electrical equipment, daylight may be completely ignored.

Artificial Light
Artificial light in the aquarium has one great advantage. It gives us accurate control, so that it is easier to furnish needed plant stimulation without encouraging algae.

The ordinary artificial illumination of a living-room, even though it penetrates into the aquarium, is worthless to plants. Electric light, to be of value to them, must be *very close*, and *preferably overhead*. Various devices are manufactured for holding bulbs in position over aquariums.

Some of them have reflectors completely covering the frame. A home-made job will do. A socket can be fastened to a board to be laid across the aquarium, the bulb pointing downwards and the wires coming through holes in the board from the top. The light may be just above or *in* the water, so long as it is not up to the socket. Bulbs will not break in the water unless placed there while heated. The life of fila-ments in submerged bulbs is greatly increased.

Roughly the amount of electric light needed per aquarium per day is as follows: For a 10-gallon tank of ordinary shape, 40 watts for 8 hours or 75 watts for 4 hours. For a 15- to 25-gallon tank, 60 watts for 6 to 8 hours. For a 25- to 50-gallon tank, 75 watts for 8 to 10 hours. These figures must be reduced if there is help from weak daylight. The efficiency of clear and frosted bulbs is about the same, the latter being more agreeable.

Ultra-violet lights have no more effect on plants than ordinary bulbs. Plants are benefited more by the red end of the spectrum.

There is one important thing about artificial light that may be either an advantage or a disadvantage. It supplies heat. This is very good when needed, but in warm weather when the temperature is already in the eighties, it is dangerous to fishes. Fluorescent tubes (not quite as benefi-cial to plant life as incandescent bulbs) make far less heat. The "warm white" tubes are more effective than the blue-white "daylight" type.

Temperature

The name tropicals, as has before been remarked, places too much emphasis on the idea of high temperature for all exotic fishes. A number of them are not from the tropics and quite a few of them from the tropics do *not* come from particularly warm water. It is true that most of our exotic aquarium fishes cannot stand chill, but, on the other hand, many of them do not prosper in the higher temperatures because they need more oxygen than such waters carry. Placing them all in water in the neighborhood of 80 degrees is not sure to be the kindness that is intended by the aquarist who is a high-temperature fiend.

Nor should it be believed that there is an exact degree of heat which is best suited to each species. Most of them have a toleration of at least 10 degrees, and can stand a 5-degree change overnight without injury. That is to say, if a fish has a safe toleration range of from 70 to 80 degrees (and most of them have), it would be all right for them to experience a drop from 75 to 70, spread over a period of several hours.

The one practical thing to work out, as far as individual species is concerned, is to place the tender fishes in the warmest and most uniform places, and the hardier ones in the cooler spots. The list of fishes, later in the book, gives the approximate temperature range for each species.

The author believes a great deal of needless worry and expense is given to trying to keep aquariums or aquarium rooms within 2 degrees of a fixed point. Almost nowhere does Nature supply such an environment, and it has often been observed that fishes are stimulated by a reasonable change of temperature.

Nor should aquarists be too seriously concerned about the variation between the heat at the top and the bottom of the aquarium. This difference in native waters is often considerable, but the fishes negotiate it without trouble. They have the choice of selecting the level they like.

It is to be hoped that these unorthodox opinions will give no one the idea that it is a workable idea to acclimate fishes to a new temperature range. That is an old experiment which has always failed.

In practice, it all comes down to this: The average exotic aquarium fish is perfectly happy at an average temperature of 72-76 degrees. For short periods it can go down to 68 or up to 85 degrees without trouble. Even these extremes may be safely passed in aquariums which are in extra fine condition, and where the fishes are not crowded. If, through uncontrollable causes, the temperature drops to the extreme danger zone of the low 60's, or even the 50's, the thing to do is to slowly raise it to about 80, and keep it there for 24 hours or more.

Heaters The common form of artificial heat for aquaria in rooms liable to become dangerously cool is a partially submerged tube in which there is an electric coil, usually placed at the lower end so as to contact the cooler strata of water and thus produce circulation in the tank. Glass tubes are best. Any chromium-plated apparatus in water is dangerous to fishes (see paragraph "Metals in Water"). Glass tubes are often sold as being "submersible." Our observation is that, under water, moisture eventually seeps in at the point where the wires are sealed into the tube, thus ruining it. We advocate keeping upper part of tube above water line. Aeration equalizes top and bottom temperature.

The common question as to what sized heater is required for a given gallon capacity cannot be intelligently answered without knowing the amount of cold to be overcome. A good general rule is 2 watts for raising each gallon 5 degrees above surrounding temperature. That is, if a 10-gallon tank is to be raised 5 degrees, use 20 watts. For 10 degrees, 40 watts. We favor conservative sized heating units. Then if a thermostat fails to function, the fishes are not likely to be "cooked."

Sudden Changes While fishes may safely swim from warmer to cooler strata in an aquarium, it is an entirely different matter changing them from a tank at one temperature to another having a difference of several degrees—either up or down. This is one of the things that just *must not be done.* The effect may not be apparent at once, but it is seldom escaped. It usually brings about the "shakes" or "shimmies," Ichthyophthirius ("ick"), fungus or a general decline. Changes should be made within 2 degrees of the same temperature.

Thermometers As average thermometers are liable to be wrong to the extent of 4 degrees or more, they should all be checked.

Scum on Water The cause of this disagreeable condition is often puzzling. It may come from new aquarium cement, decomposing vegetation, oily food, atmospheric settlings or from domestic frying or greasy cooking. Persistent removal by drawing a paper over the surface may overcome it. Covering tank with glass helps. Mechanical aeration of the water dispels it. A thin film causes no trouble.

Fishes Outdoors In many temperate parts of the world, certain fishes from tropical countries can, to advantage, be placed in outdoor pools during the summer months. They can stand a greater temperature variation in large bodies of water where the general conditions are virtually perfect. Fishes that, in an aquarium, are in danger at 65 degrees, can stand 60 in a good pool. Of course, it is not wise to tempt fate too far, but the fishes are so benefited by an outdoor vacation, and often breed so beautifully, that it is a temptation to try it. The great dangers are in placing them out too soon and leaving them too long. Also, of course, they must be placed in pools where they can be caught again when wanted. The placing of aquariums outdoors in a changeable climate is not recommended.

In returning the fish to indoor tanks after being outdoors for the summer, it is *most important that the same water in which they have lived during the summer be used in the tanks to which the transfers are to be made.* Later, if desired, this can gradually be changed.

The Nest Builders all breed profusely in warm lily ponds, as do most of the Cichlids. Separation of breeding pairs from their young in large bodies of water having ample plant refuge is unnecessary. The mixing of different kinds of breeders, however, is inadvisable.

Some professional breeders, mostly south of the Mason and Dixon line, set wooden tubs in the ground and place single pairs of fishes in them for summer breeding. The tubs are covered on cold nights with sashes.

Except with hardy fishes like Bloodfins, White Clouds, Medakas and Paradise Fish, there is considerable risk in placing them in outdoor pools in locations having unseasonable cold spells in summer, such as in our Middle and Northern States. These risks can be minimized by covering the pond with glazed window frames or sheets of Celloglass (to be had from leading seedsmen).

Water Quality

Average aquarium fishes and plants have considerable tolerance as to the type of water in which they are kept. Ordinarily its quality is likely to be the last thing considered when looking for cause of failure, yet with some of the more "fussy" species it may be very important, not only for their breeding, but in actually keeping them alive.

The average water furnished by the public systems of cities and towns is reasonably well-suited to our needs. Perhaps the most serious fault, from our standpoint, is extreme hardness.

If the natural water of a community is so hard that housewives would have difficulty in making soap suds, this is usually corrected at the pumping stations, or by private water-softening equipment. Water having been so treated is fit for aquarium use.

However, where trouble or failure persists after running down the common causes (overcrowding, faults of temperature, light and feeding) the difficulty may be that the kind of water is unsuited to the affected fishes and plants. Occasionally we hear of aquarists who are in general successful, but fail with certain fishes or plants. This could very well be found to result from water unsuited to the species affected. For instance, if light and soil conditions are good, and Vallisneria habitually turns yellow, while other plants prosper, the fault is probably in the quality of water. The aquarist then has the choice either of correcting it or of taking the easier course and giving up the troublesome species—either plants or fishes.

As the subject of aquarium chemistry is a rather complex one, and usually does not deeply concern the average reader, it seems advisable not to go into it at length at this point, but to cover it amply in our last pages, under "Miscellaneous Information," thus leaving us free to take up at once the following related chapter.

In order to prevent tooth decay in people (mainly children) many large cities are placing fluorine in their municipal water systems. In answer to questions as to whether this is injurious to fishes or plants, our answer is that there seems to be no evidence to support that possibility. The standard dilution being used is only one-part-per-million. If it hardens teeth in humans, it *might* be beneficial to fishes!

General Management

Green Water   The facts about green water appear to be so simple that this should be an easy matter to control, but it is not. The green cloudiness unaccountably rises to confound the ablest aquarists and the humblest of authors—even those who tell others how to keep water clear!

We know that the color is produced by microscopic vegetal cells that must have food and light in order to develop. By taking away either or both of these stimulants, we would have no green water, but that is not easy when we have fishes present which enrich the water both by their breathing and their droppings, and which themselves, along with plants, require light.

Yet, on the other hand, it is perfectly true that there are numberless aquariums which are healthy and clear, year after year. It would seem we should be able to reproduce the same condition at will. To a great extent, we can. In such aquariums we nearly always find plenty of strong, growing plants, usually Vallisneria or Sagittaria. The reason is that they successfully compete with the green cells (suspended algae) for both food and light.

In these perpetually clear tanks, two other things will be observed. The fishes are not crowded and there is only enough light to keep the plants in good condition. That is another way of pointing out that if there is only enough supply of life elements to keep the plants going, and with practically no excess left, then the green organisms are kept in subjection.

Slightly acid water tends to check most vegetable growth. While it produces cleaner water, it also discourages the plants.

Many of these green water cells go through periods of activity. If allowed to subside naturally, the water may remain clear for a long time.

Oppositely, many of them are only stimulated by a partial change of aquarium water, and start out on a fresh rampage.

To maintain clear water one should have no more fish than the tank can easily support *without aeration*. Use only enough light to keep plants healthy. It can, if necessary, be reduced in several ways: by interposing suitable thicknesses of paper on the light side, by applying tinted crystal varnish to the outside glass, by using a thick mantle of floating plants, such as Duckweed, Salvinia or Water Fern. Such a blanket will not cut down the action of the water in absorbing oxygen or in liberating carbon dioxide. Difficult to explain, but true.

Remember that green water is not an unmitigated evil. In moderation it is healthy. Depleted fishes sometimes improve in it.

Remove some fishes if crowding is suspected. Feed less. Every scrap of food becomes fertilizer. Siphon the bottom frequently. Use only enough new water for replacement.

When green water reaches the "soupy" stages and is very opaque, it is dangerous, especially in hot weather. It is liable to suddenly decompose and kill the fishes. A change to a slightly yellowish tinge is the danger signal. This calls for an immediate change of water. Minutes count.

Cloudy Water Green water is cloudy, but cloudy water is not necessarily green. There is a difference with a distinction. Both are frequently caused by unabsorbed organic matter in the water, due to too many fishes and an excess of fish waste. Suspended algae feeding and prospering on it cause green color, while gray cloudiness is produced by bacteria doing the same thing. Nature is always trying to balance the water. In light places she uses algae; in darker ones, bacteria. The treatment for both, up to a certain point, is the same. That is, the use of more plants to absorb the organic matter, and a reduction in the number of fishes producing it. On the other hand, there may already be enough plants but insufficient light to stimulate them into action, so that in this case *more* light is needed.

Newly set aquariums are likely to be clouded from sand that is not well cleaned. Also they are particularly subject to gray cloudiness because the plants have not yet begun to fully function. For every reason it is better to have an aquarium planted and in a favorable light a week before the fishes are introduced. Even then the aquarium should not be taxed with its full limit of fishes in the beginning. A small start is better, adding a few from time to time.

Clearing Water Correction of underlying causes has been indicated for the different kinds of cloudy water, but there are ways in which clearing can be hurried. Gray cloudiness can be reduced in a few days by constant aeration. If fishes are temporarily removed from a green-water aquarium, it can be cleared by putting in many live Daphnia. Filtering, described hereafter, will improve conditions caused by larger particles of organic matter in the water. No aquarium filter will completely remove algae nor cloudy-water bacteria, but they can be precipitated chemically. One method is to dissolve ⅛th grain by weight of permanganate of potash into each gallon of aquarium water. At this strength nothing needs to be removed. The water clears in a day or two, but it will cloud again if the same conditions continue.

Filters   A number of good aquarium filters are sold commercially; some fit into the inside corner of a rectangular aquarium, some on the outside. The outside kinds are usually larger and are perhaps more easily cleaned and serviced. The aquarium water is raised by the action of pumped air, dropped in the top of the filter, where it drops by gravity through various layers of porous materials, such as sand, glass wool and activated charcoal. It is then picked up by a constant siphon and returned to the tank proper, largely cleared of coarser particles and objectionable gases, but not of microscopic life. Filters should be cleaned every week or two, either by reversing the current of water, or by complete washing. A wad of glass wool placed every two weeks on top of the filter material, just below the point of water entrance, catches most of the dirt and greatly increases the time between filter washings.

The mechanical action of most of these pumps works on either of two principles. In one a motor drives a piston in a cylinder as a positive air compressor. This produces a pulsating supply unless an equalizing storage tank is placed in the air line.

The other type, usually less expensive, and less durable, operates an electrically driven vibrating bar against a rubber diaphragm. These pumps produce a slight buzzing sound.

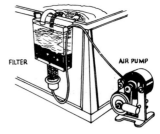

Filters use much more air than do air stones. With simultaneous use of a dozen or more of them, a large commercial compressor is advisable.

Glass tubes in filters sometimes gather an internal slimy deposit. This is easily removed by soaking tube in a pint of water containing a teaspoon of Clorox. Rinse before returning.

Air pressure used to lift aquarium water in filtering, or for any other purpose.

Metals in Water   Metal in contact with aquarium water should be avoided where possible.

There is no paint, varnish, asphaltum, shellac or compound that will permanently protect aquarium water from a harmful metal. For temporary coatings we have found the modern rubberized coatings to be very good. Paraffin is poor, but mixed hot with 25% of lubricating grease or vaseline it makes a soft but durable water resistant. It waterproofs tin cans effectively.

When iron or sheet iron instead of slate is used as an aquarium base, a sheet of glass should be laid on the inside, cemented at the edges.

Sometimes the cement chips away from the corners of a brass-framed aquarium and exposes the metal to the water. Re-cementing is needed.

Trouble sometimes occurs when water of condensation collects on defectively plated or aluminum top reflectors, and runs down into the aquarium. Even such water that gathers between glass covers and the aquarium frame can, in time, poison the tank, especially if brass is exposed. Nickel plating does not last well in water.

Algae on Glass A green film of Algae on glass is one of the aquarist's greatest griefs. It is bound to occur if strong daylight is used. In weak light, even when augmented by electric illumination, it is negligible. Active snails keep down the soft kinds, but presently a hard species develops which they cannot touch. A razor blade scraper can be used to remove it in a few moments. Also a piece of stiff felt or a ball of steel wool is good for the purpose. Many of our fishes, especially Mollienisias, Swordtails, and Kissing Gouramies are extremely fond of Algae, and it is undoubtedly a beneficial food. These fishes do much towards keeping the glass and plants clear.

It should be remembered that Algae is not an unmixed evil. It is an active oxygenator and on the light side of an aquarium is a shield against too much sun. In this respect it has a tendency to keep the water clear. Judgment should be used in its removal.

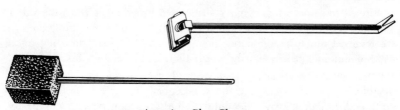

Aquarium Glass Cleaners

Rusty brown Algae are obnoxious and hard to eliminate. No snail or fish will eat them. Some aquarists declare that salt in the aquarium at the rate of two level teaspoons to the gallon of water inhibits the growth of brown algae. If true it is good news.

Very much the same comments apply to the smelly blue-green algae (*Oscillatoria*) which sometimes infests tanks kept at tropical temperatures. If left alone it makes a mantle over everything and suffocates the plants. It is soft and easily wiped off. Only Goldfish eat it.

Long, hard, hairy Algae or Confervae that cannot be rubbed from the plants sometimes take possession of a tank. The only remedy is to remove fishes, destroy plants, disinfect the aquarium with a wash of weak ammonia or strong salt, and start again with clean plants, using less light thereafter.

Scavengers Many aquarists, especially beginners, ask too much of so-called "scavengers." It is unreasonable to expect any creature to take all undesirable matter out of an aquarium and utterly destroy it—or keep the glass cleaner than would the aquarist himself.

The original aquarium "scavengers" were Fresh-water Snails. Other important assistants have appeared in the persons of Weather-fishes, Armored Catfishes, Tadpoles, Fresh-water Mussels and Fresh-water Shrimp. All except the Mussels hunt out and eat particles of food which have been missed or rejected by the other occupants of the aquarium. This is a very important service. It prevents the evil chain of conditions and events following the decomposition of that food. It has foolishly been argued that they only convert it into humus. True, but it is then practically harmless. Snails, in addition, keep down the film of green algae from glass and plants, but none of them get *all* of it. They cannot, unassisted, make a polished plate-glass parlor of the aquarium.

Many fishes kill small kinds of snails. Big "Mystery" snails fare better. Snails eat fish spawn, but never attack live fishes, even very small ones. This fact makes them valuable in cleaning up uneaten food in the nursery.

Tadpoles and Weather-fish are not much favored because they agitate the water too strenuously.

Mussels to some extent remove suspended green algae from the water, but they require watching to see whether they are alive. Altogether we are inclined not to recommend them, especially as heat does not agree with them. The risk is hardly worth their doubtful benefits.

It is generally believed that several species of the fishes called *Corydoras* are the best aquarium scavengers. These are illustrated and described under their own headings. Admitting their general popularity, as well as effectiveness in cleaning up left-overs, it must be conceded that their rooting activities tend to cloud the water by keeping sediment in a state of suspension.

Loricaria and *Plecostomus* are vigorous algae eaters, but are apt to grow unpleasantly large for the average aquarium. Two *Plecostomus* together will fight. The little *Otocinclus* is the best plant cleaner, working on both sides of the leaves, but it is not very hardy.

An interesting recently introduced fish of the Goby type (see *Evorthodus breviceps*) picks up food from the bottom without disturbing anything.

Snails The popular EUROPEAN RED RAMSHORN SNAIL *(Planorbis corneus)* continues to hold interest. Bright red ones, free from chippings or blemishes, are always in demand, and their breeding is a matter of some commercial value. In order to get them clear red, they must be grown rapidly, and to be grown quickly they must

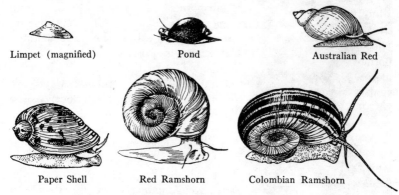

Limpet (magnified)   Pond   Australian Red

Paper Shell   Red Ramshorn   Colombian Ramshorn

Popular Aquarium Snails

have plenty of room, warmth and food, together with slightly alkaline water. The preferred foods are spinach, lettuce and boiled oatmeal containing powdered shrimp. They should be fed as much as they can possibly eat. This has a tendency to foul the water, which, in turn, produces erosion of the shells. Therefore, the bottom of the tank should be siphoned off frequently and fresh water added. Daphnia tends to clear the water and to prosper at the job. The flat, amber egg-masses appear freely in the early spring. If properly raised, snails will be ready for the market in October, although the demand is greater in midwinter. The eggs hatch in anywhere from 10 to 40 days, according to temperature. Nearly all fishes destroy newly hatched Red Ramshorn Snails.

FRESHWATER LIMPETS are very small snails, completely covered by translucent shells, like low parasols, rather oval in outline, usually about ⅛ inch across. They are really miniature "scavengers," and quite harmless. They appear unaccountably, often coming in with aquarium plants.

POND SNAILS *(Physa)* are the best of all, in the writer's opinion. Their clear, jelly-like spawn brings forth young that are too hard for most small fishes to eat. Some consider this snail a pest, it multiplies so freely.

COLOMBIAN STRIPED RAMSHORN *(Marisa rotula)*, reaching a diameter of 1½ inches, is the best of several South American introductions. It is very handsome, but eats the softer plants.

THE AUSTRALIAN RED SNAIL is a most prolific breeder outdoors, and a handsome creature, with yellowish red body.

The handsome and once popular Paper-shelled Snail dislikes warm water. It breeds rapidly, but lives only a year. Like the native snails, such as *Physa* and *Lymnae*, it survives winters outdoors if not actually encased in ice.

Ampullaria spawning on glass above water line. Arrow shows egg in transit from under the shell.

THE APPLE SNAILS are the big, round "four-horned" Ampullarias from South America and Florida. All except one are ravenous plant-eaters. They are sometimes known as "infusoria snails" for the reason explained under the heading "Cultivation of Infusoria." The exception is *Ampullaria cuprina,* for some mysterious reason known in the trade as the "Mystery Snail." It does not eat living plants, and is a fair scavenger. If not getting enough pick-ups it should have some boiled spinach.

It may be distinguished from the destructive Ampullarias by the depressed channel around the turns of its rather high spiral. The destructive Ampullaria *(paludosa)* has a low spiral and no channel. All these snails spawn great masses of eggs above the water, generally at night. Young fall into water as they hatch. Hatching in about two weeks requires a warm, moist atmosphere. (Plate subject is *A. cuprina.*)

THE JAPANESE LIVE-BEARING SNAIL like Goldfish, prefers cool water, and is therefore popular mainly among Goldfish fanciers. Being large and meaty, they are also relished in Japan as food. The young, about the size of a pea, are born alive and fully formed. The right horn of the male is slightly shorter. It serves as a sex indication. A female once impregnated, appears to be fertile for life. Identification of species is by the high spiral and slightly raised keels on the big turn. The so-called American Potomac Snail, sometimes sold as the Japanese species, is generally similar, but has no keels. It is sluggish, spending most of its time buried in the sand.

JAPANESE

Covers   Principally owing to the tendency of many fishes to jump out of the water during excitement, it is advisable to keep them covered. Sheets of glass are usually used, but fine screen is satisfactory. The cover is usually laid directly on the aquarium frame, which not only makes sure that no swift-leaping fish can find an opening, but also keeps the water a little warmer. Unfortunately it tends to rust the frame.

The idea of tight-fitting cover glasses usually causes the beginner aquarist some mental suffering, for it seems opposed to all our theories about oxygen. The answer is that the amount of dissolved oxygen in water is extremely small, and it would take a long time for an aquarium to exhaust or appreciably diminish the amount in an inch layer of air in the top of the aquarium.

The writer personally believes in having the glass very slightly raised or else using screen covers, not for a fresh supply of oxygen, but to better carry off some of the stale gases. Also the increased evaporation cools the surface of the water, making it heavier. As it sinks, a mild but beneficial circulation is thus set up. The young of bubble-nest-builders, need covers up to the age of 3 months.

Plastic screen covers are particularly good in summer.

Fishes are especially apt to jump after transfer, or other fright. They are less likely to leap when they enjoy the safety of dense vegetation.

In our many fish problems we should try to *think like a fish*, much like the wise simpleton who found the lost horse when others had failed. Asked how he did it, he answered, "I started from the barn and tried to think like a horse."

Gases   Water absorbs not only the beneficial oxygen, but injurious gases and fumes as well. One of the worst and commonest is coal gas, prevalent in many homes at night when coal stoves are improperly banked. Often human noses fail to detect the presence of this poison. Polished silver is very sensitive to it. If this oxidizes in a few days, there is too much coal gas in the house and something should be done about it. Tight aquarium covers help in such situations. Fumes from varnishes, varnish removers, paints, turpentine, shellac, insecticides, or anything containing wood alcohol, are all injurious to aquarium water. Not infrequently they are fatal. An excess of tobacco smoke does no good.

Rockwork Beautiful effects in the aquarium can be had by the clever arrangement of rocks. They can be used to construct terraces, grottos, arches, or other natural formations. Smooth, weather-worn stones are much to be preferred, for fresh broken surfaces are likely to injure the fishes. Coral is extremely rough and should only be used with such marine fishes as are used to it in Nature.

Catching Fishes Approach the task with confidence but not conceit; also with a determination not to lose patience, nor to ruin the plants. Any fish can be outwitted and out-waited by man. Each species has its peculiarities. Once captured, all individuals of that species can be caught by the same method. Many species yield to very slow movement. It is the first thing to try. When a fish seems nearly caught by the slow-motion method, it is almost sure to dash away if the net accidentally taps the glass. This is often difficult to avoid, but should be kept in mind. A net in each hand often helps, a large one for a catcher and a small one for a persuader. In large greenhouse pools or other places where it is almost impossible to catch fishes without drawing off the water, it is surprising to find what can be done with a minnow trap. It is an article sold in sporting goods stores. It is made of glass and is about the size of a rat trap. Bait is placed in it and the trap is laid on the bottom of the pool, attached to a cord.

Very small newly hatched fishes had best not be handled at all, but if it must be done, a good way to raise them near the surface with a fine net and then dip fish and a little water out in a spoon. Sometimes they are lifted in a dip-tube, in the same manner that dirt is drawn from the bottom of an aquarium.

Nets Except for use in globes, all nets should have straight edges. Suitable Nylon netting is preferable to knotted threads. Net rots rapidly in a moist atmosphere, especially when laid down wet on a sheet of glass. They should be hung up when not in use. It is a good practice

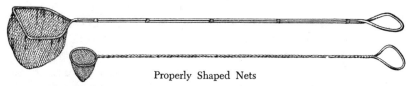

Properly Shaped Nets

to rinse all nets in clear water before drying. Every aquarist loses fishes by having them leap while being transferred from a net. We can only suggest extreme care. A net should be deep enough so that a little bag enclosing the fish may be made by the free hand. Oppositely, a net ought not be deep enough to entangle the fish so that in its struggles it will tear its fins. Small nets, up to about 3 x 4 inch frames, should be as deep as they are wide. Larger nets can be proportionately shallower.

"Glass nets" shaped somewhat like large clay smoking pipes, are used by some European aquarists in catching small fishes. They can be purchased from some American dealers. In certain situations the author likes them very much. With them, young fish can readily be lifted without danger, and at the bottom of plant thickets, where netting is almost impossible, the "glass net," being nearly imperceptible, can often be slipped over 2-inch adult fish without difficulty. The water and fish are removed as in the use of a dip-tube, by placing the thumb over the end of the tube.

With large aquariums a large net is almost indispensable. Professionals who must catch their fishes without wasting too much time about it often have a square net nearly the full width and depth of the tank. With this the fishes are raised to the surface and then removed by a smaller net. Splendid large net frames (about 8 inches square) of heavy aluminum wire can be purchased cheaply.

Effective Net for Use in Large Tank

**What to do with
Newly Received Fishes**
If fishes come from healthy tanks where they were thoroughly acclimated, and have not traveled more than half a day, and have had no marked change in temperature, then they need no attention beyond two very simple things. One is to see that the new water in which they are placed is within 2 degrees of the same temperature as that in which they traveled. This applies to all transfers under all circumstances. If the new fishes come in small containers and there is a noticeable difference in temperature between the two waters, it is a very good plan to float the container in the aquarium until the temperatures are equalized before making the transfer.

The second point is one that may be neglected without great risk, but careful aquarists should take it into account. Most fishes are injured by a too sudden change in the degree of acidity or alkalinity of the water. Fishes from other aquariums, especially those from a distance, are liable to be used to water which is quite different in that respect. Therefore, if the aquarist is equipped to take a pH reading and make needed adjustments slowly, it is the prudent thing to do. Such simple precautions sometimes prove to be the well-known ounce of prevention. For many years experienced aquarists have utilized the water of shipment to mix with the aquarium water. Unknowingly they have been adjusting the pH. This is a very practical way of doing it if there is sufficient volume to make it count. See remarks under "What is pH?"

While the same things apply to fishes that have traveled one or more days, other points must also be taken into consideration in their behalf. Experienced shippers do not feed fishes prior to expressing them. After this fast they should be fed *lightly* for a few days, preferably making Daphnia or other live food a part of their diet.

New arrivals from a distance should be looked over as to general condition, particularly as to their fins and any indication of Ichthyophthirius, the Pepper and Salt disease. If there are suspicious signs the new arrivals should be quarantined, given a dose of permanganate of potash, ⅛ grain (by weight) to the gallon of water, and have their temperature slowly raised to 85 degrees, keeping it there a few days.

Many aquarists pump air into bags of fishes for several hours before making the transfer. This refreshes the travelers and gives the water time to become equalized in temperature with its new surroundings.

It is generally a good policy to introduce new fishes among others *after* feeding those which are already established in the aquarium. This is especially true in placing small fishes with larger ones. The world over, a good meal makes for mellowness.

Emergency Aquarium It takes resolution to resist regularly using any well-planted aquarium in beautiful condition, but it pays in the long run to keep at least one emergency tank. In such a container all new arrivals should be placed, regardless of apparently clean bills of health. Too often do we hear the mournful tale of an aquarium that was a paradise until some new fish or plants were introduced, and, along with them, disease. Strangers ought to have at least 2 weeks' probation.

A healthy aquarium, balanced with plants, containing no other fish, is the very best place to put one that is a little out of condition, or that has been bullied; or for a female live-bearer needing protection and rest after delivery of her young.

Seasoning Tanks New wooden or concrete tanks to be safe must be seasoned. Without artificial help it takes at least 3 months to season wood by occasional changes of water. This may be hurried by slaking a large piece of lime in the tank while it is filled with water, stirring it and allowing it to stand a few days. Rinse well and use. Powdered lime (fertilizer) does equally well. Use plenty. Any mild alkali, such as bicarbonate of soda, should serve the same purpose.

Wooden tanks should not be painted, either inside or out. Cypress is the best wood.

Probably the best medium for neutralizing the free alkali in concrete pools is phosphoric acid. An ounce to 50 gallons should be sufficient. Stir well and allow it to stand about 48 hours. Wash well and use. Otherwise the pool may be made safe for fishes by 4 changes of water over a period of a month. An old pool showing hair cracks can be safely waterproofed and beautified by a coating or two of aluminum paint. For larger leaks, moisten surface and apply Portland cement mixed without sand. When dry, swab new cement gently with 50% solution of liquid glass (silicate of soda). Rinse well before use. If medium sized cracks are numerous, both operations can be done with a cheap paint brush.

New wooden tanks and concrete pools may be tested by introducing tadpoles or minnows. The water is safe if they live 3 days.

Tapping on Glass There seems to be about as much sense to tapping an aquarium glass to gain the attention of the fishes as there is in speaking in a loud tone of voice to someone who does not understand our language. The result is the same—fear and confusion.

Bullies Sometimes an individual fish, possibly of a peaceful species, learns that other fishes will flee if chased. This becomes a sport with that fish, to the misery of its fellows and the discomfiture of their owner. It should either be disposed of, partitioned off, (perhaps

in a corner, like a dunce), or placed in another aquarium with larger
fishes, where, among strangers, it may reform. Like the rooster taken
out of its own barnyard, it will not fight so well.

Sudden Light Along with the petty cruelties to fishes which might be mentioned is the thoughtless practice of suddenly placing them in powerful light when they have gotten used to darkness. This is done both by switching on full electric light at night, and by suddenly lifting the lid of a shipping can in bright sun. The fish give every evidence of experiencing the same distress we ourselves would feel under like circumstances. A little care in this matter is a kindness that is not misspent.

Changing the Water The most popular question put by the beginner is "How often must I change the water?" From what has earlier been stated, it will be seen that, theoretically, the water in a properly planted and populated aquarium does not need to be changed at all, except for making up the losses of volume due to evaporation and siphoning.

Regardless of theory, water must, for good reasons, sometimes be changed, either in whole or in part. There is much difference as to what may be safely done in winter and in summer. This difference is caused not so much by temperature as it is by quality of water. Fresh winter water is dangerous, being charged with various gases and germicides. It should stand uncovered in an enamel or glass container a day or two before use. The length of this precaution is governed by the amount to be used. If only about 10 per cent of the volume is to be changed, water from the tap, brought to the right temperature, is safe. If half is to be renewed, the water should be ripened a day or two. For a complete change (we are still referring to winter) the new water should stand at least 3 days before use, preferably 5. Most successful aquarists keep ripened water ready at all times. Gallon milk bottles are excellent.

As stated in the paragraph on "Filling," hot water drawn in a bath or laundry tub, and cooled over night, is ripened more rapidly.

In most places where the water supply is of a quality favorable to fishes, changes of considerable volume may be made in summer without risk. We would say that a 25 per cent volume of new water from the tap (at the right temperature) is perfectly safe in the majority of districts in summer. This is usually enough to make up for the water loss in siphoning off dirt.

It is the experience of many leading aquarists that a systematic replenishing of water in small quantities is of marked benefit to most aquarium fishes—say 10 per cent weekly in winter and 25 per cent in summer.

FEEDING

"Now, good digestion wait on appetite, and health on both."

How fishes are fed is quite as important as *what*. A poor food properly handled may give better results than an excellent one used without judgment.

How Often to Feed Temperature and oxygen directly influence the amount of food a fish can properly consume. The life processes (metabolism) of all cold-blooded animals are very much affected by temperature. The warmer they are, within their own established limits, the faster they breathe, digest, eliminate and grow. Such animals as frogs, turtles and alligators offer extreme examples of this law. With a few degrees deficiency in temperature they will refuse food for months on end. Lizards, lightning-fast in the sun, are torpid in the cool of the morning and can be picked up. A warm water aquarium fish has an indifferent appetite at 67 degrees, a good one at 72, and a ravenous one at 77. It does not increase above 80 degrees because of the diminished oxygen content of the water at the higher temperature. Appetite and digestion are twins, and both require oxygen, as well as warmth.

Upon reflection it will be realized that exotic fishes, mostly from tropical countries, and normally leading a life that is well speeded up, need a fair supply of fuel, delivered frequently. The practical application of this thought is to feed at least twice daily instead of once. This will double the pleasure of most aquarists (for they like to feed their charges), increase the sales of the food manufacturers and make fishes bigger, better and happier.

If it is only possible to feed once daily, the morning is the best time, especially if the aquarium contains healthy, growing plants. The oxygen they develop during the day aids digestion. At night they give off carbon dioxide, which does the opposite.

Should an aquarium be kept at the lower end of its allowable scale— say 67 to 70 degrees—one feeding daily is sufficient. It is only when we get up into the 73-80 range that we need be concerned about extra feedings.

Frequent small feedings of live Daphnia are even more important than of prepared foods. The Daphnia compete with the fishes for the oxygen in the water. When their numbers are too great over a period of several hours, they do more harm than good, in extreme cases even suffocating the fishes, for they can live in more impoverished water. Give only enough Daphnia at one time so that they will all be eaten in 2 hours

29

or less. Several still smaller feedings are better, if convenient.

Mosquito larvae are different. They breathe atmosphere and take no oxygen from the water. A fairly large supply may be given the fishes, provided one is prepared to deal with the mosquitoes which are likely to hatch from the uneaten larvae.

How Much to Feed Regardless of all other rules, theories, practices or printed instructions, the aquarist should stick tenaciously to this one: *Feed only enough prepared food at one time so that practically ALL of it is consumed within 5 minutes.*

The rigid application of that rule will avoid many mysterious ills, and much clouding of water.

On the other hand, light feeding is another one of those virtues which may easily become a vice. The writer favors frequent feedings, especially in well heated aquariums, but more especially if ALL of the preceding meal has been eaten and the fishes show signs of real hunger.

Floating feeding rings for dry foods have the advantage of concentrating the food within a small area, so that it does not scatter about the aquarium. However, they are not important accessories.

As all dried foods swell considerably when moistened, it is just as well not to at once give hungry fishes all they can eat. The fishes may experience the same disastrous results as the boy who bolted a pound of dried apples and then drank a pint of water. It is better to feed them slowly. If there are several aquariums, make two rounds of the feeding when using dried food. Some aquarists wet the food beforehand, but it always seems that the fishes prefer the flavor before it has been soaked.

Care During Absence If one must be away for a few days it seems to be safer to let the fishes go hungry rather than entrust their feeding to someone without experience. It is quite extraordinary what a number of things can go wrong when aquariums are in unfamiliar hands. In leaving the fishes unfed it may relieve the mind to remember that when they are shipped and are on the road several days they arrive without signs of starvation. Should the aquarist be away two weeks or more and it is necessary to call in a substitute, let the person first do an actual feeding under instructions.

Substitute caretakers should tend towards *under*feeding, and also be most particular to replace glass covers.

A very good plan is to leave with the novice caretaker a set of one-meal packets of food, designating the aquarium in which each is to be used.

When fishes must be kept without food for several days it is better to maintain them at a temperature of 70 rather than the high range.

FISHFOODS

"The stomach is a helpless slave, but, like a slave when abused,
it takes sly and sometimes deadly revenge."

It is generally conceded that living foods produce the best results, and it is therefore the ideal of every amateur or professional maker of prepared foods to produce a compound that will be approximately as satisfactory as a living food, such as Daphnia. This is a fine ambition, for a prepared article that is perfect would answer every aquarist's prayer. Each manufacturer of food believes his own to be the best, but as yet no impartial, competent comparison has ever been made. Aquarists, bewildered by a chorus of claims, often use several brands, hoping thus to combine the merits of all. Not a bad idea if one has no time to make systematic tests. The fishes surely give evidence of enjoying a change, so why not let them have it?

PREPARED FOODS

There are those who, like some cigarette smokers, prefer to make their own. It never pays the small user for his trouble, but here are a few suggestions for those who would like to try it. First, puppy biscuit is not a bad fishfood and will do very well in an emergency. It only needs to be ground to suitable size. A household coffee-mill is the thing. All ground fishfood should be sifted, so that the dust-like particles suited to baby fishes will be separated from the grains intended for adults. Most large fishes do not eat the powder, and unless snails or scavenger fishes are present, it has a tendency to foul the water. Sifting through cheese-cloth removes the powder. Muslin sifts a fine flour, suited to those young which are extremely small, such as Bettas.

Here is a simple recipe which has long given satisfaction:

> Two tumblers powdered puppy biscuit
> One tumbler powdered dried shrimp
> Three pinches salt

Mix together and moisten with water which has had an egg beaten into it. If necessary, add enough more plain water to bring the mass to a stiff but workable consistency. Then spread it about a quarter inch deep on tins, such as pie-plates. In summer it can be sun-dried, but radiator drying in winter is preferable. After the surface has somewhat hardened, it may be turned over in sections with a broad knife and the drying completed. When dry, it is broken into pieces suitable for milling. Grind and sift to desired sizes.

31

Another recipe consists of equal portions of powdered shrimp and either soy or whole wheat flour. Pea or lima-bean flour are also good. These last may be had in health food stores. To this 50-50 mixture is added a flavoring portion of dried salmon eggs and a bit of salt. This is then mixed to a stiff paste with water containing beaten raw eggs, using about one egg to a pint of dry mixture. Finish as in previous recipe.

Baking makes food more bulky if baking powder is added, but it is the best modern opinion that heat drives off important elements, and that cooking should not be resorted to.

Partially dried shrimp can be bought in ground form at low prices, but should be further pulverized for use in these recipes. Complete drying is best done in Winter when the air is dry. It is easily milled if dried.

Pablum, that splendid food for human babies, is enjoyed by many fishes. It may also be used as a major ingredient in any cooked or un-cooked food. It is sold in large drug stores. "Gerber's" is also good.

These dried fishfoods are rather concentrated. Theoretically they might be constipating. To avoid this tendency some manufacturers of high-grade foods add powdered agar-agar, an insoluble, gelatinous, vege-table substance made of seaweed. It may be had at the larger drug concerns. Two heaping teaspoons would be sufficient for adding to a pint of the dry mix.

One heaping teaspoon of powdered or precipitated chalk makes a desirable addition of lime, equal, let us say, to the bones when one fish swallows another! And, after all, as our old friend Poyser once tersely put it, "The best food for fish is fish."

Any dried fishfood, or its ingredients, should be carefully protected from flies and moths. Their eggs turn into wormy larvae that eat the food and riddle it with their cocoons. When a large quantity is made up, it is better to keep the bulk of it in lump form in tins or other closed receptacles and only grind a month's supply at a time.

Not enough soft algae grow in aquariums to satisfy those fishes that need it. Chopped boiled spinach is a beneficial substitute. It has been found that many fishes can be educated to eating these greens. Try small portions when they are hungry, especially on the live-bearers.

Mead's Cereal, an article to be had in large drug stores, is good for the more vegetarian fishes when cooked to a thick paste, or mixed 50-50 with powdered shrimp for the omnivorous species.

"Strongheart" and other canned dog or cat foods make excellent food for medium-sized and large fishes. Some prefer canned cat food. Both are very cheap. Keep opened cans in refrigerator.

Chicken eggs as fishfood may be prepared by beating them, adding a teaspoonful of water per egg, and then pouring slowly into boiling, moderately salted water which is being stirred. The resulting edible flakes are gathered by straining.

It is risky to state what the temperamental Scalare will eat, but they have been found to like scrambled eggs, and grow rapidly on it. For "fresh" foods that are not living, see paragraph under "Winter Feeding."

Wholesale Feeding Those having really large quantities of fishes to feed, and who manufacture dried food for sale, are like our friends, the doctors. They do not take their own medicine. In both cases there is good reason! The drying of fishfood is merely a convenience to the amateur aquarist. There is no other reason why it should be dried. Visitors at wholesale establishments are mystified in seeing the fishes nibble at a kind of porridge which has been given them, and imagine it to be some kind of secret preparation.

Such a food is easily made and, as with dried foods, considerable latitude ingredients is safe. The base is usually one of the quick-cooking oatmeals. A simple and satisfactory recipe consists of 2 parts of oatmeal and one part of powdered shrimp, slowly boiled and stirred for about 10 minutes over a mild fire, until the mass is thick. Start with about twice as much water as the measure of the dry ingredients. Salt as for domestic oatmeal. Pour into saucers, cool, and place in refrigerator until used. One batch will keep fresh about 5 days. Drop a portion of suitable size into each aquarium, allowing the fishes to pick it to pieces. Enough to last them 5 minutes is not too much.

Grocers now carry small jars of strained infant foods containing liver and vegetables, too soupy to place in aquarium water, but can be cooked into any of the above. Meat packers make small cans of cooked, chopped beef liver that may be fed direct, or crumbled for small fishes.

A splendid moist food, a bit of trouble to make, suited to all but very small fishes, is made as follows:

One pound of beef or calf liver, finely chopped and put through a Waring Blendor twice. Strain through fine wire sieve. Add 1-level tablespoon·of salt. Mix with Gerber's (or other) junior baby size spinach. Add 14 level tablespoons of Pablum and six of wheat germ (Kretchmer or other). Stir well, pack in small screw-top jars. Pasteurize 30 minutes. Cool and store in refrigerator. This is known as the "Gordon formula."

LIVE FOODS

Daphnia Except in a few cases, live foods are not indispensable, but they are always desirable. They are important to baby fishes and they round out a needed something which few, if any, prepared fishfoods possess.

Daphnia are the best known of the living foods. They are of almost universal distribution. However, one can not go to any body of water anywhere and get what the fish might describe as a delicious dish of Daphnia. It is not as easy as that.

Daphnia pulex, About Twice Natural Size

While it is true that this little aquatic crustacean (about the size and general shape of a flea) occurs in fresh water almost everywhere, it only appears in concentrated numbers in a comparatively few places— rather unpleasant places, as a rule. It is at the margins of the pools sometimes present on city dumping grounds that we find the true "fish fan," enveloped in a cloud of mosquitoes, patiently swirling a net through evil-looking water, hoping to land a few million of the "bugs." What none but the initiated can understand is that they *like* to do it.

Collecting Daphnia It is always difficult to tell a person what Daphnia look like and how to gather them, but let us try. The one best short-cut to this knowledge is to go out once with an experienced collector. Perhaps a member of a local aquarium society would oblige. But let us assume the worst, and start from scratch. Our photograph shows Daphnia as well as a photograph can, which is none too well. They vary in color through green, gray and red. We like them red —the redder the better. We always *hope* to find them in colonies sufficiently thick so that the mass colors the water. From a few feet away, if red, they look like a dull red or rusty cloud in the water. Perhaps the cloud will be only 2 inches across. If we are lucky, it will be 2 feet; or, if luck is running high, the whole surface of the water will be red with them, "like liver," as the Daphnia hounds gleefully describe it.

The cloud formation is not unusual, but often there are plenty of "bugs" with none in sight, and again there really are none. The Daphnia gatherer provides himself with a special kind of net, made of cheesecloth of medium-fine Nylon. It should be about 10 inches wide, 14 inches deep and of seamless pattern, with rounded bottom. Some are made with a seam and pointed at the bottom like a reversed foolscap, but this design injures the Daphnia by concentrating their weight into a ball, if the catch is a good one. For convenience in carrying, the net should be attached to a stout, jointed pole, usually to be had in sporting goods stores or departments. A 9-foot length in 3 sections is about right.

The net is dipped into the pond and its contents reversed into a large carrying pail of water, which should be liberally iced if the weather is hot. If the Daphnia are in sight in masses, the net need only be dipped, but usually a little gentle churning is necessary. The net is moved in a figure 8 at the surface of the water for perhaps a half minute. If the Daphnia are at the bottom, this brings them up.

The uncertainty as to whether Daphnia will be found, and where, is both the vexation and fascination of the collector. Ponds go through cycles. They may be good for a time and then die down, to again ripen later. *When*, none can predict.

Daphnia need a fair amount of oxygen. Like fishes, when it is deficient, they rise to the surface. This is apt to be the case in hot weather or

Collecting Daphnia from a Characteristic Dump Pond

on humid days. Early morning, before the wind has started to stir, also finds them at the top. Where collecting competition is sharp, the true fish fanatic starts out for live food at daybreak. Future generations may smile at our working hours, but this schedule also enables Mr. Fancier to get to his salaried occupation at 8. At any rate, the point of this paragraph is that on crisp days the Daphnia are apt to be down, while on heavy days and early mornings they are up where they are more easily taken. When overcrowded they will come to the surface, no matter what the weather.

In cities like Philadelphia, having the average mixed temperature zone climate, Daphnia begin to be plentiful in April. They diminish in hot midsummer, do well again in October, and in favorable years can be had in reduced numbers in mild periods through winter.

Ponds, of course, can be fished-out of Daphnia, but it is believed that moderate fishing prolongs the cycle rather than shortening it. It prevents the Daphnia from overcrowding themselves.

There are many species of Daphnia. A few kinds live in acid water, but they are not the kinds which multiply by the billion. Those gathered by aquarists live in neutral or slightly alkaline waters. This valuable food can be purchased from many aquarium shops or semi-professional collectors.

Where to Collect Water conducive to the production of Daphnia in quantity contains active organic decomposition. From the human standpoint it should be bad, but not *too* bad. City aquarists usually seek out ponds at the "dumps" on the fringes of their towns. Rural collectors may find a good culture in fishless dirty water in an old quarry, or in a pool getting drainage from a barnyard.

Storing Daphnia Again, like fishes, Daphnia should be given as much air surfaces to their water as possible. They should also be kept as cool as possible—best in the family refrigerator! If not overcrowded they will last several days in a cool cellar.

Food Value of Daphnia Daphnia, named for a beautiful Greek goddess, receives blind homage by many aquarists. It is considered to be the one perfect food, and the more of it that can be fed, the better. In riding a theory, as well as a hobby, it is well to keep the eyes open. Daphnia is truly an important fishfood, but it is not magical, nor without defects, nor even dangers. Owing to its soft but insoluble shell it acts as a laxative, and too much laxative produces a fish which is not plump. This tendency can be overcome by alternating with fishfoods containing starchy substances, such as wheat or oatmeal.

Occasionally fishes die from gorging on Daphnia. This can be true of other foods, but it is more likely to happen with Daphnia, for they are excessively fond of them. As has been pointed out, aquarium fishes may be robbed of oxygen by long presence of an excessive number of Daphnia. The most serious objection to Daphnia is the company they keep. In those pools, feeding on the Daphnia, are many enemies of fishes. They are mostly larvae of small size, impossible to detect, but which grow apace when feeding on valuable aquarium fishes. Some of these are described under "Enemies." Furthermore, in recent years we are observing more and more of strange maladies attacking our exotic fishes: lumps on the body, open sores, bloody excrescences, worms emerging from the bodies or eyes. Possibly some of these distressing (and as yet incurable) maladies are brought in with the fishes from the tropics in a state of incubation, but it seems more likely that they come from some ripe Daphnia pond where thousands of forms of life swarm. In the majority of instances where these rare diseases appear, Daphnia are being fed to fishes. Having pointed out the disadvantages of Daphnia, the fact remains that their merits far outweigh their faults.

Dried Daphnia These little crustaceans shrink astonishingly in drying, and theoretically ought to be wholesome, concentrated food. How much of their virtue is retained in the processing is unknown. At any rate, fishes are extremely fond of Daphnia that have been rapidly dried. This form has the advantage of being independent of seasons and of hidden fish enemies. The commercial supply is small.

Frozen Daphnia Daphnia and other live foods, like Tubifex, White Worms or Mosquito Larvae when rapidly frozen in concentrated bulk retain their nutritional values well. Refrigerated they keep indefinitely, but are dead when thawed, and must be used at once. *Any uneaten excess quickly clouds and may foul the water.* Small icy chunks may be placed with the fishes, or the frozen food can be shaved down, which is particularly effective with oysters and clams.

Other Frozen Foods Frozen grown Brine Shrimp (about ⅜-inch size) are now processed commercially, frozen solid in small containers. A wonderful fishfood for those having facilities for storing them frozen. Rinse the mass briefly before feeding. Baby fishes the size of baby Guppies pick them to pieces. Frozen Earthworms are recently marketed. Easily broken into bits. Should be good. Home-frozen oysters, clams, shrimp, fish, when sliced, make excellent variations on the bill-of-fare for aquarium fishes.

Artificial Propagation of Daphnia

While Daphnia are raised in large quantities by wholesale breeders having outdoor pools, and although we sometimes hear claims of persons who have raised enough in a tub to supply their fishes over winter, it may be put down for a fact that with our present knowledge of the subject it is not possible to breed enough in a tub, either summer or winter, to satisfy an average amateur's collection of fishes, even though they were fed 50 per cent on other food. It would be quite an achievement to comfortably feed a pair of 2-inch fishes for a year entirely on Daphnia grown in a tub. If we do not look for too much and are satisfied with an occasional light feeding, it can be done and is interesting to try. An old wooden tub or trough is best. It should be in a bright light.

The best food for Daphnia is green water. This can be produced in unlimited quantities when not wanted! However, slightly alkaline water, plenty of light and a little sheep manure mixed with rotted leaves will produce either green water or other conditions favorable to the growth of Daphnia. Water lightly clouded by yeast feeds them well.

Open Daphnia ponds may be enriched by the decomposition of almost any vegetable or animal substances.

Wholesale breeders requiring large quantities of Daphnia often have several culture ponds for the purpose. They are approximately 2 feet deep and have soil bottoms. Average size, about 50 feet square. In order to be assured of a constant supply, they are fertilized and used in rotation. The dry soil is heavily fertilized with liquid manure and soy bean flour. This is exposed to the sun until dry, thus eliminating most aquatic enemies. The pond is then filled. If Daphnia have previously been in the pond, they will soon start breeding again. If not, a few breeders should be introduced as soon as the water has turned green. Multiplication will be rapid. Ponds may be fertilized with stable litter and dead leaves, partially covered by earth.

Daphnia introduced into a duck pond usually do very well.

Drainage from a barnyard or pig-sty emptying into a pond produces a rich culture medium for Daphnia.

Midsummer heat is hard on Daphnia. Some protection from it would be an advantage. A source of fresh water to be used during dry periods is desirable, as the water becomes too "thick" at times.

In the Fall dark frost-resisting egg capsules form on the bodies of the females. They drop off, and in spring they hatch. Summer females are born fertile, and deliver their young alive. Males appear in the fall.

Plastic Cone Shrimp Hatcher
with aeration

Brine Shrimp Eggs Dried eggs of the small marine shrimp, *Artemia salina,* now sold by most dealers, are indeed a Godsend to all breeders of aquarium fishes. About the size of ground pepper, they are sprinkled on salted water (7 level tablespoons to the gallon) and they bring forth, in a day or two at temperatures between 70 and 80, tiny, but visible thousands of new shrimp, tidbits of food for baby fishes and those up to and over an inch long.

The eggs come from both Utah and California. The Utah eggs sink in water and should be kept moving by aeration, the bubbles coming from the lowest point in the vessel. A tilted jar is suitable, but a device such as the gallon size inverted plastic cone shown here is convenient.

Clouds of shrimp are drawn off and concentrated by passing the water through fine nylon netting. They are now fish food and can live a few hours in fresh water. Avoid overfeeding.

Horizontal Hatcher for California Shrimp Eggs

California eggs, hatched or unhatched, float. Aeration desirable, but not imperative, for hatching. Use stick to dam back eggs and keep end surface clear so that a light can be used to attract hatched shrimp into masses, where they can be lifted with a baster as shown, concentrated in a fine net and used. Bottled, dry and cool, shrimp eggs keep indefinitely, even years.

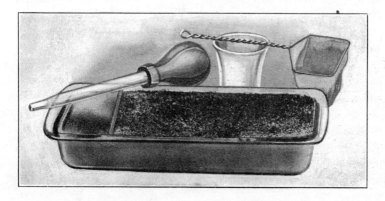

Mosquito Larvae Here we consider a living food which is often present in Daphnia pools, but in many others besides. In season it is found in almost any pool that is free of fishes, especially in water containing decaying vegetation, such as old leaves. In many instances Mosquitoes place their eggs in rain puddles, which is the reason we have more Mosquitoes in rainy seasons. The eggs hatch in a few days and become "wrigglers." They are usually dark, straight, have a big head at one end and a Y-shaped ending at the other. In length they average perhaps a quarter-inch when fully developed. When not eating they congregate in masses to breathe at the surface of the water, but ready to wriggle to the bottom when alarmed. For this reason it is necessary to approach them rather carefully and make one quick sweep with the net. They can be carried in water in a crowded condition. Ice is unnecessary. Mosquito larvae are good for fishes large enough to

swallow them readily. Fishes about an inch in length have been known to strangle, and larger ones to overeat on them. Vessels containing stored mosquito larvae should be

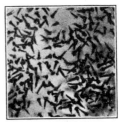

MOSQUITO LARVÆ AND PUPÆ
(Side view, somewhat enlarged)

At the surface line are 4 larvæ and 3 pupæ, the latter ready to split at the back, liberating a mosquito. One empty case shows. The 2 lower larvæ are wriggling through the water.

Above—Mosquito larvæ, natural size, as they look in masses, top view. They are resting at an angle to the surface, heads down, thus appearing shorter than they really are.

covered with gauze to prevent escape of the flying pests. Their egg "rafts" look like ⅛ inch bits of floating soot. It is well to learn to recognize and collect them, for on water they hatch into numerous very small larvae that make splendid food for any fishes the size of newly-born live-bearers.

When larvae are collected from suspiciously foul pools it is just as well to give them a rinsing in fresh water before feeding or storing.

Flies House-flies, freshly swatted, are very fine food for larger species. Once fishes become used to them, they are always on the lookout for their owner to give them a few as a special treat.

Tubifex Worms Sometimes in Daphnia pools we find a rusty edge around the shore that looks hopefully like Daphnia, but which turns out to be a mass of wriggling, threadlike worms called Tubifex. When they are alarmed they become quiet and draw back into their cases for a short time. These are the worms that sometimes infest the soil of aquariums. They are good fishfood, increasing in popularity.

In some localities where they are more plentiful than Daphnia they are utilized as a substitute for them. It is only practicable to collect Tubifex Worms where they occur in numbers so that they form a mass. The best places for collecting are upon the filthy flats of the streams about a half mile below the point at which sewage is discharged. The surface mud is

TUBIFEX WORMS
(Life size)

The Gourami is enjoying a meal from a ball of worms newly dropped in the aquarium. If uneaten, they soon scatter and establish themselves singly in the sand as shown, weaving perpetually. Corydoras can completely eliminate them.

lifted by a shovel and placed in coarse cheesecloth or fine wire net. A stream of water is then run through the mass so that the mud is washed away. The worms may be completely separated from the remaining dirt at home by placing the mass in shallow water, where they collect in bunches. They can then be lifted and stored for use.

The best way to store these worms for use is to place them in a pail under a small stream of water from a tap. The worms remain in a mass in the bottom of the container. This mass should occasionally be broken up by a strong stream, and the dead worms washed away. The colder the water, the longer they last. Obtainable the year round from professionals. Artificial propagation of these worms is not practicable.

Earth Worms Having considered various natural foods from the water, let us give some attention to that choice morsel from the land, the lowly worm. It is known as the Earth Worm, Garden Worm, Rain Worm, or Fishing Worm. It is the one grand food of practically all fresh-water fishes. Nature's gift to them. Man cannot improve upon it. Even vegetarian fishes take it with relish. Game fishes probably suspect the hook but cannot resist the worm.

Not much need be said about collecting this choice food. That is a matter for local experience. The one thing to avoid is taking the evil-smelling Dung Worm, usually inhabiting manure piles, and exuding a disgusting yellow secretion. Even wild fishes will not touch them.

Small worms are more tender and generally preferable. Most of them should be chopped for aquarium fishes, except for such as large Cichlids. A pair of old scissors does it very well. These worms are fine for putting fishes into breeding condition. Gather a big supply of them in the fall for winter use. Keep in damp earth, but not wet. Feed lightly on mashed potatoes, corn meal or rolled oats. They may be cleansed by keeping for a week in moist sphagnum moss, or for a day in water. They don't drown. For safety some scald them. Most live-bait stores sell Earthworms.

Glass Worms In many lakes and ponds throughout the land one may break the ice in midwinter and net out a liberal supply of live food called Glass Worms. They are the larvae of a fly, are about half an inch in length and are nearly transparent. From a top view

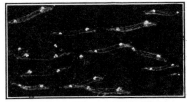
GLASS WORMS (*Life Size*)

they look something like a miniature Pike. Although popularly called Worms, they are not worm-like in appearance. They last remarkably well in crowded conditions and will keep for weeks in cool water. Food value, fair. They have been known to eat fish spawn and newly-hatched fry.

Blood Worms Often in Daphnia ponds and other bodies of water one sees deep red, jointed worms, about half an inch long, wriggling awkwardly through the water. They are Blood Worms, the larvae of Chironomus midges. Wild fishes eat them ravenously and they are good food for all except the smaller varieties of aquarium fishes. Instances have been reported of their eating their way out of fishes that had not chewed them. These worms build themselves cases, especially on decomposing wood.

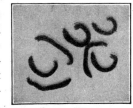
BLOOD WORMS
(**Life size**)

White Worms These little relatives of the Earth Worm are about an inch long. They are cultivated. Cultures may be had commercially. Under proper conditions they may be multiplied rapidly. Keep in covered damp soil of a spongy character, containing plenty of leaf-mold, etc. Every 2 days stir in as much dry Pablum or oatmeal as it is found they will consume in that time. Or they may be fed a variety of foods placed in holes in the soil and covered over. Mashed potatoes, cheese, bread wet with milk, or shelled boiled Lima beans are some of the offerings they like and prosper on. Overfeeding sours the soil. Mite-like creatures usually accompany them, but do no particular harm, nor are they related. The principal enemies of White Worms, or *Enchytraeids,* are ants, mice and heat. They like a temperature of about 60 degrees. It is difficult keeping them over the summer. Most amateurs buy a new culture each fall. There are many methods of getting out the worms for feeding, but a pair of tweezers dipped into a mass of them seems to be about as good as any. As worms in general are hosts to various parasites, it is good practice to cleanse and purge any of them in clear water for an hour or more before using. They won't drown.

WHITE WORMS
(Enchytraeus albidus Henle)

Cyclops Usually in Daphnia ponds we find Cyclops, a slightly smaller animal which moves rapidly in a straight line by a series of jumps. Sometimes there is a double tab on the end of the body. It is the egg-pouch of the female, and presently drops off. In German publications we are told to feed "Sifted Cyclops" to young fishes. Here we could not ordinarily gather enough Cyclops to sift. If we could, we would not use them. Scientific authorities assure us Cyclops are vegetarian and have no jaws with which to attack, but we have found Cyclops on young fishes. It is the general opinion among American breeders that they are dangerous in breeding tanks. To such fishes that can catch

CYCLOPS
Female with
egg pouches
(Magnified)

them, they are good food. Tub cultivation of Daphnia usually ends by the disappearance of Daphnia and the survival of Cyclops. Having one central eye, Cyclops was named for the similarly-equipped giant of mythology.

Other Live Foods While there are many good live foods other than those here described, such as Asellus; Fresh-water Shrimp, Fairy Shrimp, May Fly larvae and others, they only amount to interesting conversation for aquarists when other subjects give out—if they ever do. They cannot ordinarily be gathered in quantity. Some cereals, such as pancake flour, are apt to get wormy, especially in summer. If one wishes to take the trouble to sift out these fat little white worms, they are enjoyed by the fishes.

Brown Meal Worms, such as are sold in pet stores for feeding to birds, are good food for strong-jawed fishes like the Cichlids. If placed in plenty of bran in a large, covered tin box, and allowed to go through their natural beetle stage, they will multiply greatly in a few months.

Crushed small aquatic snails of any kind are good fishfood, and are especially valuable in winter when other living foods are scarce. Newly hatched red Ramshorn Snails (Planorbis) are greedily eaten whole by almost any fish.

Infusoria To the fish-breeder the word "Infusoria" means almost any aquatic animal organism that is of a suitable size to feed young fishes before they are large enough to negotiate small Daphnia. Many of these little animals, such as the important group of Rotifers, are not Infusoria at all, but we aquarists are used to making scientific blunders without embarrassment, so without apology we are going to use the word in its popular sense. "Animalcules" would be correct and inclusive.

Averaging in size something like small dust, a finer net is needed to catch them. Fine Nylon cloth is very good for the purpose. Fine muslin is also very good. Infusoria in quantity is even more uncertain of being present than Daphnia. The spring, up till hot weather, is usually a favorable time, but it appears intermittently through the summer and

Two Foods in One
(Greatly magnified)
Valuable rotifers, *Brachionus rubens*, taking a ride on *Daphnia pulex*. The ovals seen in Daphne's body are young that hatch before delivery.

fall, and some species live through the winter. The larger kinds are apt to form into misty groups that can be seen as a kind of haze in the water. One of the most important species *(Brachionus rubens)*, a rotifer that sometimes attaches itself to Daphnia, can be seen as a rusty film at the surface of the water. Often these little fellows encrust a Daphne so completely that it takes on a rounded appearance and keeps up its hopping motion with apparent labor. Under these conditions, if the rotifers are not swimming through the water, it is a simple matter to collect them by first getting the Daphnia, placing them in a very fine sieve and running water through them. The rotifers are knocked off and pass through the screen, which is too fine for the Daphnia to go through. Wonderful food.

COLLECTING "POND INFUSORIA," THE BEST FOOD FOR TINY FISHES
Photo by Barry Funnell

Cultivation of Infusoria
There are two general methods. One is to set up a mild decomposition in water and wait for infusoria spores from the air to settle on the water, there to multiply on the products of decay. A handful of roughly crumpled lettuce placed in a quart of water produces results in about 4 days. So does chopped hay. One of the best mediums we know is dried Anacharis sprinkled on the water. Many organic substances may be used. A tank containing those lettuce-devouring snails, *Ampullaria paludosa* ("Infusoria snails"), soon brings forth infusoria that prosper on their half-digested droppings. Cultures depending on decay should be started in rotation every few days if a continuous supply is needed. Aeration freshens such cultures, and prolongs their life.

A laboratory method is to prepare a boiled and cooled culture medium which is then inoculated with selected organisms, usually Paramecia, commonly to be found in old aquarium water, barnyard drainage, etc. Biological laboratories sell it. Only a little is needed. Boiled cultures do not foul, and last well. Rice, chopped hay, canned pea or black bean soup, dried lettuce leaves are among many suitable stocks for boiling. Use about 3 tablespoons of mixed ingredients to a quart of water. This may be kept covered as stock and further diluted with water when poured into culture vessels (preferably shallow trays) for inoculating.

A new Frings method, now popular, has dried skim milk as a culture medium, about 2 pinches to a pint of boiled and cooled water. The milk and the seed micro-organisms should be put in at the same time. A rich growth takes about 4 days. A pinch of milk powder added every 3 or 4 days keeps the culture going. We have also used liquid skim milk, a teaspoon to a quart of water. "Infusoria tablets," too, have their advocates. Do not place them with fish. Make culture water and dip as needed.

To the left is the "Slipper Animalcule" or Paramoecium (pronounced Para-mee'see-um), much the commonest organism produced in the artificial culture of Infusoria. It thrives on the products of organic decomposition and can live in either foul or good water. Its food value to newly hatched fishes is fair.

At the right is the Rotifer, *Hydatina senta* (pronounced High'da-tie'na sen'ta), one of the best of microscopic live foods. It occurs in Daphnia ponds and elsewhere; most abundantly in the early Spring months. The two figures are shown in their relative sizes.

Well-established aquariums with old settlings, contain infusoria, but only enough to give the fish a start. A separate rich supply is needed. It is impossible to specify exact feedings; 3 tablespoons daily of good culture to a 5-gallon aquarium with 50 fry would be conservative. The nursery needs a constant supply, to be determined by magnifying a drop of its surface water. Youngsters are kept on this diet until they have about doubled size. Infusoria are too small for livebearer or Cichlid babies.

How TO JUDGE THE RIPENESS OF A CULTURE is one of the most difficult (and important) things to impart to the inexperienced. The organisms usually seek the top surface towards the light. Touch the tip of the finger there and place a drop on a piece of glass. Hold glass over something dark, and with the light coming across the drop, examine with a magnifying glass, preferably a folding "thread-counter." If it is swarming with life, the culture is ready. Or the water may be examined in one of those thin pill phials. This slightly magnifies the contents, so that a sharp pair of eyes can detect life moving about like particles of fine dust. Or, use a microscope magnifying not over 10 diameters.

"Mikro" Worms These tiny worms (*Panagrellus silusiae*), barely visible to the naked eye, were originally found in beer felts, in the presence of yeast fermentation. They serve the same purpose as newly-hatched Brine Shrimp in feeding baby fishes that have outgrown the need for infusoria. They nicely supply the next step upward in size, and are far less expensive. A constant supply is easily kept. Many dealers sell them. The growing culture is usually 4 parts of Pablum (or boiled oatmeal) to one part of yeast, either in granulated or paste form. This is diluted with water to the consistency of thin paste, and kept about ¼ to ½ inch deep in a covered glass container. Temperature, 70-80 degrees. The worms are live-bearing and multiply fast, once well started. They creep up the sides of the glass, or will cover blocks of water-logged wood which are thick enough to stand just above the level of the liquid. From there they are easily rinsed off into the aquarium water. As they sink rapidly, it is advisable to drop them into a small net suspended just under the surface of the water. Nylon with openings of suitable size does nicely. Through this the worms escape gradually, and are eaten as they fall. These worms are also well suited as a *first* food for the larger fry, such as Cichlids or the Livebearers. Also Goldfish.

Even a fresh culture has a mild odor of yeast sourness, but if it becomes offensive, save a portion with which to seed a new batch, and discard the remainder. Life remains in the culture, even though the appearance is bad.

Cypris This common crustacean is not very important to aquarists, but readers often describe it and want to know whether it is friend or enemy. It is really neither. We often find it in the ponds when collecting Daphnia. They are about the same size, but the color of Cypris is purplish-brown, becoming paler indoors. It stands pretty bad water and a degree of heat that kills off Daphnia. Goldfish breeders sometimes use it in summer when Daphnia are scarce. They call it "Hardshell Daphnia," which of course it isn't. The animal is encased in a clam-like covering which is so firm that most small exotic fishes refuse to eat it. It is particularly fond of swarming on rotting boards. A scavenger.

Cypris, magnified

Gammarus
Life Size

Gammarus A widely distributed, hard, shrimp-like creature, sometimes coming in on plants. Hovers about bottom of aquarium, ploughing through sand, loosening leaves of Vallisneria, etc. Otherwise harmless. Multiplies rapidly. Too tough for small fishes, but is eaten by Cichlids. Remove by passing the sand through fine net.

Feeding Baby Fishes A particularly effective minister whose sermons had practical and lasting meaning to his congregation was asked how he was able to make his messages so convincingly clear. His reply was, "First I tell them what I'm going to tell them. Then I tell them. Then I tell them what I've just told them."

It is with somewhat the same idea in mind that the following condensed feeding schedule for young fishes is presented. The same directions will be found elsewhere (mainly under "Spawning the Egg-layers") and at scattered points, but it is believed that in most instances this summary will prove helpful. It should be remembered that success is also possible with well chosen changes and substitutions. There are good foods besides those proposed.

Menu

VERY SMALL FRY, such as Bettas, Chanda lala, etc.

PREFERRED FOODS

First Stage Green Water	Second Stage Fine pond infusoria	Third Stage Larger pond life, especially Brachionus rubens	Fourth Stage Sifted Daphnia, Brine Shrimp Mikro

SECOND CHOICE FOODS

Flour-size prepared food	Infusion of boiled yellow of egg	Cultured infusoria	Chopped White Worms, grated shrimp, fish or crab, small dry food

MEDIUM-SIZE FRY, such as Barbs, Brachydanios and the larger Characins

PREFERRED FOODS

First Stage Pond Infusoria	Second Stage Brachionus rubens	Third Stage Sifted Daphnia or Brine Shrimp, Mikro.	Fourth Stage Adult Daphnia Frozen Brine Shrimp

SECOND CHOICE FOODS

Cultured infusoria Egg infusion Fine prepared food	Fine Grated shrimp fish or crab Fine dry food	Chopped White Worms or next size larger prepared dry food. Larger sizes fish, shrimp, crab, etc.	Small whole White Worms, or larger sizes of 3d stage foods

LARGE FRY, such as Cichlids and the Tooth Carps, like Panchax. Also suited to the young of most livebearers

PREFERRED FOODS

First Stage Sifted live Daphnia, Brine Shrimp. Mikro, Brachionus Rubens	Second Stage Medium Daphnia	Third Stage Adult Daphnia Frozen Brine Shrimp	Fourth Stage Mosquito larvae, chopped small earthworms, adult Daphnia

SECOND CHOICE FOODS

Small dry food Egg infusion	Grated shrimp, fish, crab, etc.	Larger sizes prepared foods, or larger sizes of shrimp, crab, fish	Continue 3d stage foods. with occasional addition of finely chopped or scraped raw liver of chicken or beef

A "stage" merely indicates that the baby fish is big enough to eat the size of food indicated. ("Sifted Daphnia" means living small sizes that have been separated from the larger ones by passing them through a fine tea-strainer vibrated just below the surface of the water.)

Conditioning for Breeding Under this heading we necessarily repeat some statements made elsewhere, but as there is a popular belief that this is an important subject requiring special treatment, we are glad to focus the different factors at this point.

Anything that produces good health sets up favorable breeding conditions. There is no special routine, but there are some arts by which we can better get the cooperation of Nature.

First, most of our exotic aquarium fishes are not seasonal. One of their great advantages is that they can be bred whenever given the proper conditions, but the requirements of some species still baffle us at all times of the year.

The main points in "conditioning" are obvious: frequent meals of good food, a comfortably warm temperature and plenty of water-per-fish. Aeration may help. If possible a fair proportion of the food should be either living or fresh, the latter meaning such as scraped lean meats, liver, fish, shrimp, crab, clam, minced earthworms, etc., especially live Daphnia.

Under such stimulation females obviously fill with spawn and the males become more plump than usual. Ordinarily fishes in prime health will breed if given a fair chance under conditions described for their kind, but action sometimes needs to be stimulated. Professional breeders with whom success is a *must* try to keep the sexes of the egg-droppers separated. Placed together in the evening there is a good chance that ripe fish will spawn in the morning, especially if placed in water that has been drawn from the tap about 24 hours previously. If not successful in 2 days, separate and later try again.

The use of hormone extracts in stimulating breeding is inadvisable. Livebearers, as we all know, need no stimulation, but they do best if given frequent small meals, varied in content. A ripe female, apparently unable to deliver, is helped by a partial addition of new water and a bit of salt. A few inexperienced aquarists believe that the presence of the male helps the female in her delivery. This, of course, is not true. His assistance, if any, is liable to be in helping her eat the young!

How Often to Breed This subject is briefly covered in the section on Livebearers, but we can well add here "the voice of experience," referring again to the practices of our friends the professionals, especially in breeding Angel Fish. Here, perhaps more than with any other species, we have accurate records of individual fishes, tabulated by their owners. They are allowed to spawn as often as they will. Although there is a great difference in the performance of individual females, the frequency of spawning appears to have no corresponding effect on their lives, nor on the vitality of their young.

BAIT WITHOUT A HOOK *(See next page)*

Winter Feeding However excellent any dried food may be, fishes should have an occasional change, especially in the long winter months when not much live food is to be obtained. Desirable variation can be had with little trouble. Chopped raw fish, shrimp, crab or clam are very good, or may be used boiled, exactly as they come from the dinner table, reduced to bits. Mincing them in the hand with scissors is easily done. Blot up clam or oyster juices before feeding. Minced raw liver of chicken or beef is a good change. Fishes enjoy fowl, boiled sweetbread, or other meat delicacy that is not highly seasoned or greasy.

One of the standbys for winter feeding is canned shrimp. It is obtainable in all grocery stores. Small cans at a very low price can be had at chain stores. Practically all aquarium fishes like it and it agrees with them. When the can is opened, all the shrimp should be removed, rinsed, drained, placed in a covered saucer and kept in a refrigerator, where it will last about 4 or 5 days in good condition; indefinitely if frozen. For use, cut the shrimp into thin slices with scissors, cutting across the grain. Canned salmon, which should be handled in the same way, is also a very fine fishfood. White Worms and Glass Worms, generally regarded as winter foods, are covered under the heading of "Live Foods."

Small fishes can have lots of fun picking at a mashed raw oyster crab suspended from a string. Marine Puffer Fishes are gluttons. A friend of the author's has one that became thin and nearly died on an apparently good mixed diet. Half-a-dozen oyster crabs a day, swallowed whole, made a magical cure. It may be that this is exactly what that species needs, but it seems as though oyster crabs must be a very good food, and one to try when all else fails. They parallel the oyster season, and can be purchased separately.

A boiled, lightly scored shrimp suspended on a string hanging from a light stick crossing the aquarium frame gives the fishes sport and exercise. Leave in as long as they enthuse over the work and consume the fallen bits. *See illustration on previous page.*

Winter need not be devoid of live food. Bottom scrapings from ponds, if carried home and brought up to house temperature, yield an amazing amount of life of many kinds. The surface of decaying wood is particularly likely to yield a harvest of Blood Worms. After the worms are revived in this way, the same care must be exercised as in summer for the exclusion of fish enemies, but, if present, they are easily discovered when the water life awakes. Blood Worms keep best in cotton rags in a cup in a refrigerator, using only a little water to keep the rags wet.

Mealworms, to be had in the larger bird stores, are available throughout the winter season. For most aquarium fishes they should be chopped or split. They may be bred in wheat bran. Keep container closed.

Forcing Growth The growth of almost any aquarium fish can be forced by the combination of ample room, aeration frequent feeding, warmth and cleanliness. For best results a fair proportion of live food *must* be used. Daphnia, Mosquito larvae, chopped Earth Worms, Tubifex and White Worms, frozen Brine Shrimp are the main standbys. With this heavy feeding and general speeding up, it is necessary to siphon off sediment frequently; that is, about every 2 or 3 days. Used seasoned water for replacement. Feeding 4 to 10 times daily is not too much, if it is done sparingly. Artificial light induces eating at night.

All fishes become more robust by steady, fairly fast growth, but there is doubt as to whether actual forcing, such as described, pays in the long run. Forced fishes frequently fail when removed to normal conditions, especially if taken from aerated to still water.

ENEMIES

Fortunately there are few serious enemies of fishes in the aquarium. The three outstanding ones all smuggle themselves in with our supply of live foods. Since one of these enemies is far more destructive than all others combined, we will give it first consideration.

Water Tiger   This sleek, spindle-shaped creature is the larval form of a large Water Beetle (Dytiscus), which itself is also a powerful enemy of fishes. There are several species, but in effect, as far as the aquarist is concerned, they are all one. Our illustration gives a clear idea of its formation, but the great difficulty is that in its smallest size it is hard to pick it out from among the Daphnia upon which it feeds. The pincers, or mandibles, are hollow, and through these they rapidly suck the blood of their victims. Growth is rapid and they soon attain a size where they attack tadpoles, fishes or any living thing into which they can bury their strong bloodsuckers.

Water Tiger and Victim

Theirs is one of those appetites which "grows by what it feeds upon," and they move steadily from victim to victim. In a size such as illustrated they would soon clear an ordinary aquarium of its fishes, but these big ones are not so dangerous because they are easily detected. It is the half-inch fellows, moving quietly about among young fishes, that do the wholesale damage. In a few days entire hatchings are liable to disappear, and all that remains is a Water Tiger, which, by that time, is probably an inch in length. What helps make these larvae so deadly is that they are good swimmers.

Vigilance is the only protection against them. Large, hard-mouthed fishes will eat them. Destroying them gives double pleasure to parent Cichlids while tending their flocks of young.

The victim in our illustration was a medium-sized female Guppy. She was dead in a matter of seconds and within a minute was shriveled and pale. The Water Tiger breathes air through its rear end and, therefore, must occasionally come to the surface. This one maintained a breathing position during the bloodsucking.

Dragon Fly Larvae Although not nearly so deadly as Water Tigers, these larvae have a more widely heralded reputation as killers. Their disadvantage is that they have to lie in wait for their victims and seize them from below with a much smaller and less

Dragon Fly Larva Holding Live Fish
(The Floating Plants Are Large Duckweeds)

effective pair of pincers. These pincers are on the end of a "mask," a contrivance having hinged joints, so that it normally lies folded just below the head, but ready to be extended in an instant when within striking distance of a victim. When attacking a fish as large as that in the illustration, the pincers frequently fail to penetrate the scales, and slip off. It was not until they finally caught on the lower edge of the gill plate that a fastening was secured. While holding the fish with the pincers, the larva slowly chewed at the side of the fish with a mouth better equipped for swallowing small victims. After a minute in this position the fish was released by the photographer and it soon recovered from two slight wounds. This account is not intended to minimize the danger from these larvae, for in a little longer time the fish would have been killed and consumed. Smaller larvae are effective in proportion.

Damsel Fly
Larva
Much smaller
but of same
habits. Catches
fry up to ½
inch size. Iden-
tified by feath-
ery gills at rear
end.

Dragon Fly Larva With "Mask" Extended (Viewed from below)

Although there are more Dragon Fly Larvae than Water Tigers, they are less likely to be collected with Daphnia, for they usually lie half concealed in the mud, whereas the Water Tigers are swimming about.

Damsel Flies are about half the size of the Dragon Fly, and when at rest the wings lie parallel to the body. Their larvae are proportionately smaller and more slender, but they are also killers. They may be identified by three long bristle-like gills at the rear end of the body.

The flies themselves have their uses to man. Dragon Flies ("Devil's Darning Needles"), while flying, devour mosquitoes. Damsel Flies also creep along plants, eating plant lice (Aphis) as they go.

Hydra These low forms of life are enemies of any small water creatures that can be caught by their peculiar method. So far as the aquarist is concerned, Hydra catch baby fishes up to a size of 3/16 of an inch. They also devour Daphnia.

In form they are extremely variable. The fact that they can contract themselves almost to the point of invisibility makes it impossible to detect them in a can of Daphnia. Even worse is the fact that any broken bit of a Hydra soon develops into a new, complete individual.

The usual appearance of a colony of them is like pendant, slowly swaying gray or green hairs, about a half-inch long or less. From the main thread are from 3 to 7 tentacles, spread starlike. They are usually found attached to the glass and the plants. It is rather surprising to find that

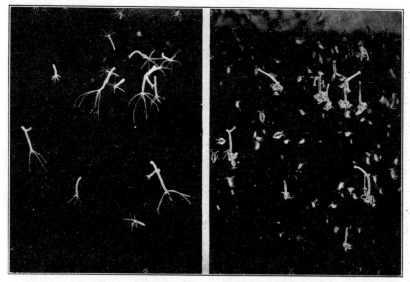

HYDRA *(slightly enlarged)*, Before and During Dinner

Left: Hungry Hydra, poison tentacles spread. *Right:* Taken from same position a minute after live Daphnia were introduced. Each Hydra, so changed in appearance, holding at least one victim, can be traced to the same spot.

they can move about. They use alternately their tentacles and their suction foot in a clumsy kind of locomotion, but they eventually arrive.

The body, and especially the tentacles, contains many sharp barbs, filled with a numbing poison. As a prospect passes near, the apparently inert Hydra springs into action, injects a "shot" into its victim, draws it into a mouth from which the tentacles radiate, digests it and presently discharges the undigested portions from the same opening. When business is brisk, a Hydra may have a Daphne or a young fish held by each tentacle, to be swallowed at leisure.

Immediately following a "strike" the creature undergoes a marked change in form, becoming much more compact. This lasts until digestion is completed. Multiplication usually takes place by budding, and, under the influence of plenty of food, is rapid.

The larger young livebearers, like Mollienisia, are a little too big for them to negotiate. Their favorites are the babies of the different egg-laying species.

The easiest and safest way to get rid of this rather interesting pest is by introduction into the aquarium of several Three-spot, Blue or else Pearl Gouramies. Give them no other food and they will soon devour

the Hydra. A complete change to fresh water from the tap usually puts
an end to them in a day. Remove all fishes during treatment. An
effective chemical treatment consists in dissolving 5 grains of the
common fertilizer, ammonium nitrate, in each gallon of aquarium water.
Remove nothing.

Other Enemies Two questionable intruders which sometimes enter with
Daphnia are Water Boatmen (Corixidae) and Back-
Swimmers (Notonectidae). They may be introduced while very small
or in larger sizes. It is a well established belief that they are enemies
of young fishes. The writer has con-
ducted experiments with a view to
settling the question. To date the
verdict is "Not guilty," but in view
of the generally accepted contrary
opinion, we include a picture of one
of them in our Rogues' Gallery. Dr.
G. C. Embody, a noted fish culturist,
says that Back Swimmers are danger-

BACK-SWIMMERS

ous, but that Water Boatmen are harmless. Both swim with a rowing
motion of the 2 long, oar-like legs.

Beetles Most Water Beetles live on other insects or animals. They
seldom get into the aquarium, but should be immediately
removed when discovered, whether small or large.

Fish Lice (Argulus) Free-swimming, translucent, tenacious, wafer-like parasites
that become fatally epidemic mostly in Goldfish pools, July
to October. Argulus are about 3/16 inch across, and may
attack exotic fishes. Three treatments, each a week apart, of
dissolved permanganate of potash, ⅛ grain by weight to each
gallon, usually eliminates them without harm to fishes or
plants. "The Aquarium" for November, 1940, contains a com- ARGULUS
plete, illustrated article on this "Fish Louse." Still available.

Anchor Worm While in the small free-swimming stage this repulsive
parasite embeds itself in the flesh of Goldfish and some
exotics. It develops a big anchor foot from which hangs a ⅜ inch visible
thread-like body, so tough that it does not break with the hard pull
necessary to extract the anchor. It can be destroyed in its free-swimming
stage by the permanganate treatment just described for Argulus.

Thread Worms Hair-like wrigglers, propelled through water by serpentine vibration. There are many kinds. To the
aquarist most of them may be rated as repulsive but harmless. They may
be eliminated by treating planted tank as described for "Disinfecting
Plants." Many small fishes, such as Guppies, eat them.

Planaria, or Flatworms About ⅛ inch long, gliding like snails, these pale, repulsive little creatures sometimes distress aquarists by appearing in large numbers on the glass sides of tanks. Of a carnivorous nature they live on microscopic organisms, and might fairly be

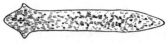

rated as "scavengers." Placed in clean water they presently starve. In an immaculate aquarium they do not last long.

FLATWORM, GREATLY MAGNIFIED Like Threadworms, their exit can be hurried by the permanganate treatment for disinfecting plants. Fishes should be temporarily removed, but may be returned in about 12 hours without changing the water.

Like leeches, they may be trapped overnight on a piece of raw meat, but of course it is necessary to in some way shield this bait from the fishes. Repeat until all are gone. Some small fishes eat Planarians. Certainly Guppies and Dwarf Gouramies do.

Leeches Reports of leeches found in aquariums are not rare. Aquarists do not always recognize them. While there are other animals that travel like the measuring worm, it is a good guess that anything in the water travelling that way is a leech, especially if it has the ability to contract and extend its length. The illustration is typical, but the markings vary with different species. They sometimes come in on new plants. In North America there are about 15 genera, divided into 30 species. Only

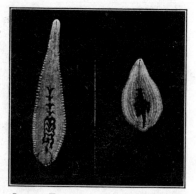

LEECH, EXTENDED AND CONTRACTED

a few attack fishes. Most of them are parasitic on snails, or consume small worms, etc. Some prey on each other.

It is rare to see one attached to an aquarium fish, but it is a possibility, so that it is good policy to get rid of any such suspicious characters if possible. They are extremely tough. No known chemical affects them that may not also kill the plants. They hate salt; also nicotine. If things become too unpleasant for them, they climb out of the water.

After a meal, and at night, they seek a dark spot, such as under a stone. If an inverted saucer is placed loosely on the bottom of an aquarium, and leeches are present, they will likely be found in the morning, clinging to the dark side. Destroy them and continue until no more appear. Most leeches carry their young on the underside of their bodies.

Outdoor Enemies   In outdoor ponds or pools the fishes have to contend with special enemies. Frogs will eat any moving thing nearly as large as themselves. Then we have Snakes, Rats, Cats, Kingfishers, Blackbirds, Starlings, Water Turtles and Boys. Ground-level ponds are more subject to some invaders. Walls less than 16 inches high offer little hindrance to frogs, snakes and rats. It is remarkable from what a distance frogs will sense a body of water. Open hatcheries in rural districts lose many, many fishes to predators, especially Goldfish ponds, where, in addition, they are neatly picked off by Cranes and Herons. A handy shotgun is part of the equipment at these places.

Such enemies as the adult sizes of the Predacious Diving Beetle, Giant Water Bug (Electric Light Bug), Dragon Fly Larva and Water Tiger, which are easily detected in the aquarium, are much more difficult to control in planted ponds, or where the water is not clear. Here, again, vigilance, helped by screening, is our best weapon.

DRAGON FLY, FRIEND OR ENEMY?

This gorgeous, speedy fly lives on insects, mostly mosquitoes, expertly caught "on the wing." It deposits eggs in the water that turn into the fish-destructive larvae described a few pages back. Some people fear Dragon Flies, but they are harmless to man. *Inset:* adult Damsel Fly. At rest the wings are held parallel to the body. Dragon Flies never do this.

DISEASES

Fortunately, far fewer diseases and parasites attack our fishes in the aquarium than they do in Nature. This is probably because the aquarium does not furnish favorable conditions for the life cycles which many of them undergo.

Ichthyophthirius   The only very common disease which gives us much concern is popularly called "Ick," being short for Ichthyophthirius, the name of the parasitic protozoan causing the trouble. The malady by some is aptly called the "pepper and salt disease," because in the advanced stage the small white specks on the fins and body of the victim resemble seasoning. At first only a few specks are seen, but unless treatment is given they multiply rapidly until the body and fins are almost covered. A coating of fungus appears, and death soon follows the fungus.

A TILAPIA ATTACKED BY ICHTHYOPHTHIRIUS

The cause of attacks of Ichthyophthirius is usually chill or exposure to the parasite. An affected new fish can wreak havoc in an entire tank. Chill works doubly against the fish. Its own resistance becomes reduced, while the vitality of the parasite is increased at lower temperatures.

The organism causing the trouble is one of the low forms of animal life, being a simple cell covered with swimming hairs. It burrows just below the outer skin of the fish, the irritation causing a tiny pimple. In this the parasite prospers on the fluids and tissues of its host, causing an itching, which is evidenced in the early stages by the efforts of the fish to scratch itself against objects in the aquarium.

In a few days it has reached its maximum size of one millimeter, leaves the fish, drops to the bottom, forms a cyst and breaks up into from 500 to 2200 young. Not all these young succeed in reaching a host, but enough do so that the progress of the disease sweeps on "like wildfire."

The important thing, of course, in checking the parasite is to break into its life cycle at the weakest point. This is in the early free-swimming stage. Several methods have been developed. Most of them call for heat, about 85 degrees, either with or without medication. Some aquarists are of the opinion that simple heat is not only the best, but the only effective remedy. Against that extreme view most of us believe in the value of other aids. An old and popular treatment is to raise the temperature to about 85 degrees and add 3 or 4 drops of 2% Mercurochrome to each gallon of water. A growing suspicion has developed that this drug has a delayed bad after-effect on the fishes. It does not harm plants.

Methylene Blue, 2 drops of 5% aqueous solution to the gallon, has no such reaction, but it is deadly to plants. Therefore treatment with this dye should be in a bare container. One of the best remedies.

The use of quinine at a proper strength has neither of those disadvantages, and can be used without high temperature. A half grain of quinine sulphate to each gallon of aquarium water is approximately correct. Place the required amount of powder in a cup, add a few drops of water and with the point of a spoon mix it into a thin paste. Add warm water to fill the cup. A short stirring will then fully dissolve the powder. Empty into the aquarium and stir gently.

For the amateur it is best to purchase from a druggist 3 grams (45 grains) of the powder and have him make it up into 15 packets of 3 grains each. One packet is about right for 5 gallons.

The quinine treatment, originated in Germany, and generally accepted there as being the best, has its critics, both as to its reaction on plants and fishes. Perhaps it has sometime been used in too strong concentrations. A strength of one grain to the gallon is highly effective, but injures plants.

Acid water of 5.8 readings (see "What is pH?") is said to make life hard for the parasites. Also sea salt, one heaping teaspoonful to the gallon of water, is recommended in conjunction with high temperature.

The germs of this organism are not carried through the air like the spores of fungus or of green-water algae. In an absolutely sterilized aquarium, fishes will die of chill without developing Ichthyophthirius, but in ordinary practice it is difficult to produce or to maintain water in that condition. Biologists state that the microscopic young die in 60 hours if they fail to find a host, but if this is true there must be some unknown way in which the life of the organism can be indefinitely suspended, for an epidemic has often been produced by chilling an aquarium that had been subject to no recent contamination, and which for a long preceding period had not been attacked. In any case, all aquarium implements should be well sterilized and water splashings into other tanks avoided when handling a case.

Aquarists are often puzzled as to why, in a tank of mixed species, only certain kinds may be affected by "Ick." This is for several reasons. The parasites prefer certain hosts. Some fishes withstand chill better than others. Certain species in an aquarium will be in better health than their companions. There are several species of Ichthyophthirius, which probably accounts for variable results in treatment.

It should be remembered that it is by no means a sure indication of "Ick" if fishes scratch or rub themselves against objects. It could very well be "Flukes" or some other parasitic disease. Treatment for Ichthyophthirius should not be given unless the little white spots are observed. When these are seen, no time should be lost.

Itch   This is different from "Ick." The fishes seem to itch but do not develop white spots, nor do they dash about as with Flukes. Neither is it usually fatal. The cause arises from numerous organisms which develop from too many settlings and uneaten food in the aquarium. Remove nothing and give the aquarium a ⅛-grain-to-the-gallon permanganate of potash treatment for 2 hours. Siphon the bottom, drawing off about half the water, and replace with clear, seasoned water. The remaining permanganate will soon clear itself.

Dropsy   One of the strangest of our fish diseases is dropsy. It is also one of the most unpleasant in appearance. The fish becomes puffed and the scales stand out at an angle to the body. Sometimes the eyes have a tendency to bulge. The puzzling thing about the malady is the unaccountable way in which it singles out individual fishes. It is never epidemic. Although some aquarists believe that the trouble arises from faults in diet, the fact remains that it strikes without apparent regard to what the fish has been fed, and it is just as likely as not to single out a fish in a pool where the conditions seem to be perfect. The illustration of the male *Pachypanchax playfairii* suggests the disease.

Some species seem to be more subject to dropsy than others. *Colisa lalia, Danio malabaricus* and *Brachydanio rerio* are among the more susceptible.

The disease is fatal in from one to three weeks. Most fanciers destroy the unfortunate victims at once. Reports of cures by the use of extract of digitalis have persisted for many years, but apparently without a basis of fact.

Flukes   A malady not often attacking aquarium fishes. It is caused by a parasitic animal called Gyrodactylus, which lodges in the skin and gills. The fish dashes wildly about and comes to a sudden stop, exhausted. There are other maladies which cause fishes to act in this way, but since we know little or nothing about them, the treatments here described may as well be applied. Highly contagious.

Flukes can be cured in a bath of one part of glacial acetic acid to 500 parts of water (one drop to an ounce), the treatment lasting 20 seconds and being repeated in two days.

Another treatment is 20 drops of formaldehyde to a gallon of water. Leave the fish in this bath until it shows signs of exhaustion, which is usually in from 5 to 10 minutes. Repeat as in previous formula.

Pop-eyes   Dr. Ross F. Nigrelli says the commonest cause of pop-eyes or exophthalmus in fishes is hemorrhage produced by gas in the capillaries in the eye socket. Place fish in later-described progressive salt treatment over a period of 36 hours. Keep fish in full strength 24 hours, then swab eye with 5% Argyrol, Silver-sol or similar drug. Repeat if necessary while slowly substituting fresh for salt water.

Fungus   A white, slimy coating on fishes, usually following the first stages of Ichthyophthirius, but it sometimes appears independently. In either case it is caused by a Fungus called Saprolegnia. Use following "progressive salt treatment." Mercurochrome is useless for fungus.

Fishes are made susceptible to Fungus by bruises, attacks of other fishes, sudden temperature change, chill, overfeeding and poor general condition.

Salt   Salt is Nature's remedy for many ills. It is effective in most troubles of freshwater fishes, has no bad reactions, and is safe to try on obscure cases or when in doubt. Its one fault is that when strong enough to check disease, it is too concentrated for plants. Place fish in bare tank or enamel receptacle in seasoned water containing 2 level teaspoons of salt to the gallon. Gradually over 24 hours build it up to 4 measures. If no improvement appears by the third day go to 6 measures if the fish shows no signs of distress. Species vary. Guppies and Mollies can stand 8. In case of long treatment in mild solution, change to new salted water of same strength in about 3 days if it starts to smell stale. Aeration helps. At end of treatment, slowly add fresh water until the salt content is low before returning fish to aquarium.

Sea water is still better than salt crystals. One part to 5 of fresh is a good strength, about equal to 3 level teaspoons of crystals to the gallon.

Mouth Fungus This is a wicked disease, of which we know little. A
------------------ cottony fluff appears at the lips, gets into the mouth
Aureomycin and soon starts eating the jaws away. Unless action is
taken very quickly it is likely to kill all the fish that have been exposed
to it. The disease seems usually to start from fishes that have had their
mouths bruised in shipment. It then becomes highly contagious and
epidemic. Bettas and Mollienisias are particularly subject to Mouth
Fungus. For long no remedy was known. The new wonder-drug, Aureomycin, cures it, as well as other stubborn parasitic diseases.

Dosage, 50 milligrams to each gallon of water. Follow dissolving
procedure described under "Ich" for dissolving Quinine. Cure is usually
effected in a few days. At specified strength this will be no harm to
plants nor fishes. Expensive but effective.

Fin Rot Fins sometimes become frayed without having been bitten by
other fishes. Treatment is the same as for Fungus.

"Velvet" A comparatively new disease among domesticated fishes,
affecting mostly labyrinth fishes and members of the Carp
family, such as White Clouds, Brachydanios, Barbs; also the live-bearing
Tooth Carps. It first shows as a yellowish brown patchy film, usually
beginning on the body near the dorsal fin. If untreated this spreads
quickly and develops into a series of small raised circular crusts. Fry
usually succumb before the disease is detected. The trouble is caused by
a protozoan parasite (probably *Oodinium limneticum*), which has a free-
swimming stage before becoming parasitic. It yields to most of the dye
treatments, Acriflavine being one of the most satisfactory. Dissolve a 0.46
grain tablet in 8 ounces of water. Use one teaspoon of this solution to
each gallon of aquarium water. The cure is apparently effected in a few
days, but a second treatment ought to be repeated in six days. No charcoal filter should be used while any dye treatment is in process.

It is believed that the disease has been brought in with Daphnia from
infected ponds.

Permanganate of Like salt, this drug has many uses. Although marked
Potash "Poison" by druggists, there is no danger in using
it in moderation. Physicians have prescribed it, in
weak solution, as an astringent gargle, and even as a nasal douche. Its
uses in the aquarium remind one of the multiple claims on bottles of
patent medicines.

At a strength of ⅛ grain-to-the-gallon it is perfectly safe for temporarily
clearing green water, or as a mild antiseptic in treating fungus diseases
and some of the parasitic ones. For the latter, or for a safe sterilizing
bath, hold the fish in a net and dip it for a full minute into a quart

of water into which one grain (by weight) has been freshly dissolved. This oxydizing drug has the advantage that in the presence of organic matter it soon exhausts itself; and that its effects are not cumulative. Mild doses may be repeated, after the magenta and the following yellowish color disappears, without building up concentration.

Crystal permanganate of potash at photographic supply houses is cheap, or it may be had in convenient measured grain tablets from druggists.

Wounds Nothing seems to be better for wounds than touching them with 2% Mercurochrome, or with 10% Neo-silvol or Argyrol. Repetition may be necessary.

Shakes or "Shimmies" A description of this trouble is not easily made, but most aquarists have seen it, and once seen it is always remembered. The fish usually stays stationary, wabbling its body from side to side, in a slow, clumsy motion. It is like swimming without getting anywhere. There are several causes, but the principal one is chill. Many aquarists declare their fishes to have been afflicted in this way without having been chilled, but probably they are mistaken. A short drop in temperature may do it and the effect lasts long.

Fishes with Ichthyophthirius are apt to "shimmy." This shaking is merely a manifestation of trouble and is not a definite disease in itself, any more than chills are with people. Aside from treating the disease causing "shimmies," the usual successful treatment is a persistently applied temperature of about 78-80 degrees.

Indigestion is, no doubt, another cause. There is reason to believe that a too dirty aquarium gives rise to quantities of microscopic organisms which cause the fish to act in this way, for cases have often been instantly cured merely by a complete change of water, the new water, of course, having been duly seasoned.

Wasting Like "Shimmies," wasting is not a disease, but a symptom, although it may be caused by internal parasites. In any case there is little or no hope for a hollow-bellied fish with a big head and shrunken body. Usual causes are lack of fresh or living food, infrequent and too small feedings, over-crowding, and continued cool water. The trouble *may* be from old age.

Whatever the cause, an emaciated fish seldom survives, although it may last for some time.

Swim Bladder Trouble The great majority of fishes are equipped with a very wonderful mechanism which enables them to remain balanced, almost without effort, in any reasonable depth of water. It is a flexible bladder, filled, not with air, but with gas generated by the fish. It may be seen elsewhere in our picture of *Chanda lala*. For this balancing system to be effective the amount of internal pressure must be precisely right. With too little gas the fish sinks; with too much it floats. Sometimes floating is temporarily caused by intestinal gases. Usually floating or sinking is caused by some derangement of the swim bladder, and is incurable.

Crooked Bodies It is probable that deformed spines in fishes sometimes result from constitutional or tubercular weakness similar to rickets in man, and are just about as incurable. Malnutrition and vitamin deficiency are contributing causes. Often the body assumes a crescent shape. It may accompany swim-bladder or other internal disturbance. In our many years of experience we have never seen or heard of a recovery from any of these deformities, and usually death is not far off.

Other Troubles There is a list of rare troubles of which we aquarists know little or nothing. Cysts, lumps on fishes, blindness, partial paralysis, worms eating through from the inside, sudden death with no outward sign of disease, are all things we hear of and hope some day to learn more about. No doubt there are internal parasites which defy treatment. Many of them must have free-swimming stages in which they can be killed.

Sudden Deaths Occasionally a fish, in apparently perfect health, is found dead in an aquarium that seems to be in ideal condition, in which other fishes are in good health. This *could* be the result of a "stroke." Man is not the only creature subject to that malady, nor to the sudden results of over-eating. Unless this little tragedy is repeated too often, it seems best to file it under "unsolved mysteries."

Springtails Aquarists are sometimes worried by seeing little black creatures, about half pinhead size, hopping over the surface of the water. They are vegetarian and harmless. To remove, wipe inside corners and glass above water. Draw sheets of paper over water as in removing scum.

Chlorine Chlorine in varying amounts is placed in municipal water systems for destroying sewage bacteria. If strong enough to taste or smell, it is bad for fishes. It does no harm to man in drinking water, and fortunately is easily removed for aquarium use. Most of it evaporates when exposed to the air for 24 hours. If heated to 110 degrees, the water is fit for fishes as soon as cooled.

Passing the water through a filter of activated charcoal promptly removes the chlorine. It can also be neutralized by a small amount of photographic "hypo," which is very cheap. A small pinch to each gallon of aquarium water is enough. If time is a consideration this enables one to use fresh tap water (at the right temperature). It serves no other magical purpose. Convenient tablets of the chemical are widely sold in the trade as "water conditioners," or under similar names.

Inbreeding Aquarists sometimes become worried as to the possible weakening effects on progeny by mating together closely related fishes. Generally speaking, this fear can be dismissed.

Deliberate, continued inbreeding of fishes for the development and fixing of peculiarities in a strain is confined principally to the live-bearers, especially to the Guppy and some hybrids, such as the Red Swordtail. Just how far this may be carried without reducing natural size and vigor is a question. It would take many generations to show any bad effects.

Per Cent **Solutions** Dosage of drugs, such as Methylene Blue, Acriflavine, Mercurochrome, Gentian Violet, Malachite Green, etc., are usually given in terms of a specified number of drops placed in each gallon of aquarium water. The strength of the drops themselves is expressed in per cent, such as "2% Mercurochrome." An easy way to figure the per cent is to allow 4½ grains of the chemical by weight to a fluid ounce of water. That makes a 1% solution. A 2% strength would require 9 grains, and so on.

The three most-used drugs fortunately come in tablets of a specified number of grains. These are Mercurochrome, Methylene Blue and Permanganate of potash. Liquid medications are best when freshly made. If mixed, keep cool and dark.

Check-ups It not infrequently happens that aquarium conditions seem to be ideal, the aquarist has been careful about feeding and temperature, yet the fishes are low in vitality or otherwise ailing. All conditions have their causes, however obscure they may be. Sometimes these causes are beyond the range of our knowledge, but there are several important points on which a re-check can be made.

Is there a possibility of dead fish or snails?

Has the water an unpleasant smell? If so, it should be partially changed and aerated, either by pump or hand pouring. A sprinkling pot serves temporarily. If the cover is down tightly, raise it a little.

Is there enough light for the plants? Have they a good green color? Are they growing? Are there plenty of them? Plants which are not prospering are a detriment.

Is there any chipping away of nickel or chromium plating at any point in direct or indirect contact with the water? Poisonous.

Unsuspected overcrowding is the commonest trouble. Re-read our paragraph (page 9) on "Number of Fish per Aquarium." When in doubt, use fewer fish.

Has the water been thickly green and then turned yellow? In that case it should be changed. The microscopic suspended plant life is dying.

Have the fishes been chilled within a month, or are they being kept at 68 degrees or a little lower?

On the other hand, there are heat fanatics who never let the aquarium water drop below 80. If and when the fishes weaken in this tropical temperature, try something about 74-76.

Has filter been cleaned not less than weekly?

What about coal gas, paint fumes, or even excessive tobacco smoke?

Has water possibly become too hard, too acid or too alkaline by long making up for evaporations by adding water from the original source without taking any out of the aquarium? If this is suspected, change half the water, using soft water, such as distilled, clean rain or melted snow, that has not been in contact with metal or new wood.

One of the commonest of mysterious troubles is caused by the use of copper boilers and piping in residences. Try water from some source not so contaminated.

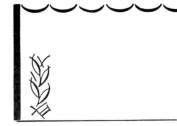

Plants and Planting

$\mathcal{W}$E now come to the point of considering plants, not only as renewers of life, but as purifiers and beautifiers. As it is with garden flowers, a few old friends are the ones we find to be best. In 90 years of organized aquarium study, only 5 kinds of plants (with their variations) have come into general use. Several other good plants are growing in popularity but are not yet universally available.

Three of the 5 favorites have running stems, to which leaves are attached. These are Myriophyllum, Cabomba and Anacharis. The other two are in grassy form, Vallisneria and Sagittaria. Each has its own uses and its admirers. Each is easily obtained and propagated, two of the qualifications for any popular plant. Enormous quantities of all of them are marketed annually. As those 5 plants are the most important, we will consider them first, and follow with others which have special uses.

VALLISNERIA SPIRALIS
(Eel Grass, Tape Grass)

Perhaps the author allows himself the pleasure of personal preference in heading the list with this beautiful plant. Its tall, graceful, grass-like form with narrow, silken, light green leaves, rises vertically in undulating lines, and gives a charm to an aquarium which is both aquatic and artistic. The plant in moderately good light multiplies rapidly and forms a dense but not impenetrable thicket or screen. It is one of the very best oxygenators and its roots tend to purify the soil.

Propagation is principally by runners. The plants are male and female and, peculiarly enough, the plants from runners are all the same sex as the parents. Nearly all of them are female. Their little floating, white cup-shaped flowers are on the ends of long, thin spirals, rising from the crown of the plant. The word *spiralis* refers to the shape of these flower stems. The flowers of the rare male plants are close to the crown. Pollen rises from them and fertilizes the floating female flowers. The seeds from these fertilized flowers may produce both male and female plants, but very few of the seeds ever germinate. In planting Vallisneria care should be taken to keep the crown just at the surface of the sand.

A THICKET OF VALLISNERIA

Showing characteristic reproduction by runner; common also to the Sagittarias and other grass-like aquatic plants. The depth of this aquarium is 16 inches.

Common wild Vallisneria is not well suited to aquaria. This is true of most of our native aquatic plants.

A giant species with leaves about five-eighths of an inch wide and several feet long, with bristly edges, is propagated in Florida. It is splendid for aquariums of 50 gallons and upward.

There is a stripe down the center of Vallisneria leaves dividing them into 3 nearly equal stripes of 2 shades of green. This makes an easy way of distinguishing it from Sagittaria.

"CORKSCREW" VALLISNERIA

An attractive mutation from the tall *Vallisneria spiralis,* but instead of growing from 15 to 20 inches and sprawling on the water surface of small tanks, its charmingly twisted leaves average only 7 to 12 inches. Very popular. Prefers hard water and fairly strong light.

SAGITTARIA
(Arrowhead)

This famous old aquarium plant is another one having grass-like form. It comes in many more species than Vallisneria, most of them being bog plants, rather than pure aquatics. Their barb- or arrow-shaped aerial leaves, common along watery borders almost everywhere, are responsible for the naming of the plant after the mythological Sagittarius the Archer.

About half a dozen species, some of them of doubtful identity, are being successfully used as aquarium plants. The 3 most important are *Sagittaria gigantea* (believed to be a cultivated form of *Sagittaria sinensis*), *Sagittaria natans*, and *Sagittaria subulata*.

The strong green leaves of *Sagittaria gigantea* are a half inch or more wide, and from 7 to 18 inches in length. They are rather firm and withstand a fair amount of buffeting by nets, once they are well rooted. As their roots are eventually quite vigorous, they should be planted in sand about 2 inches deep. The plant is a comparatively slow grower in the aquarium, but aquarium-grown specimens are best. These are easily distinguished by a large mass of yellowish roots, whereas those grown in ponds have fewer, shorter and white roots. It takes about a year to get pond-grown plants acclimated to the aquarium.

Sagittaria natans. This is the original Sagittaria of the aquarium, and was at one time very popular, especially in the early days of the fancy Goldfish. In the Goldfish tank it was largely replaced by *Sagittaria gigantea*, which was better for that purpose. Since the advent of "tropicals" it has again come into its own, for it has advantages which make it welcome in the small aquarium. The main point is that it does not grow very long and, therefore, does not easily get into a tangle. The 6- to 12-inch leaves are tough and the plant is a very good oxygenator.

While not quite as beautiful nor as long as Vallisneria, we believe that, all things considered, it is the most valuable plant for use in the average household aquarium. Among its other merits it is long-lived.

Several Sagittarias are shown in the accompanying natural-color photograph. The pointed leaves in the frontispiece are *Sagittaria natans*.

Sagittaria subulata. This is a species which has in recent years become very popular. It is different from the 2 foregoing kinds in 3 respects. The leaves are narrower and thicker. They are straighter and they are darker green. Under favorable conditions this plant propagates rapidly. The leaves are from 5 to 10 inches long, and are rather wiry.

A vigorous 2-inch *Sagittaria "microfolia"* has its appropriate uses.

All these truly aquatic species of Sagittaria throw up summer stalks which develop long, lance leaves above the water. Flower stems bear trusses of pretty cup-shaped white flowers with a yellow ball in the center. Sagittaria and Vallisneria are rivals. Both seldom prosper together.

COLOR PLATE PAGE 587

THREE KINDS OF SAGITTARIA　　↑

The larger plants are Giant Sagittaria; the small ones in the foreground are Dwarf, while the single plant above the arrow is Subulata. The two stems of reddish leaves at the top are the red phase of Ludwigia.

As this is the first successful natural-color photograph of a populated aquarium interior, a few words regarding it may prove of interest. It is the outcome of original experiments proposed by Mr. Arthur J. Sweet, of the Westinghouse Lamp Company, and which were carried out by the author at the Company plant at Bloomfield, N. J.

Photographing only a pair of fish in a small space by the natural color process (Agfa) requires a great amount of light, but to do an aquarium interior in detail with the lens "stopped down" to give sharp focus everywhere there must be an enormous flood of illumination.

Carefully-placed flashlight bulbs were used, generating 18,000,000 lumens for a period of about 1/50 second. Mr. Sweet worked out this interesting comparison in order to present to the popular mind what that volume of light means. He says: "It would require 1,200,000 ordinary paraffin candles to produce this amount of light. Placed close together they would occupy a space of 90 feet square. If they were lighted at the rate of one every 2 seconds, it would take a man 27 days, working 24 hours a day."

The photograph is shown in a size of about ¼ diameter. The young Scalares are 65 days old and were raised with the parents, although that is not common practice. The adult to the left is the female.

Hygrophila (Pronounced Hy-grof'i-la) *polysperm*

This popular and comparatively new addition to aquarium plants is one of the most important. From India, it adapts itself remarkably well to a wide variety of conditions, especially to weak light, either natural or artificial. Propagates easily from rooted cuttings. It is the only aquatic member of an otherwise terrestrial genus. Introduced to aquarists through the late Joe Johannigman, Jr.

Cabomba   Myriophyllum   Anacharis

THREE POPULAR FAVORITES

Among those aquarium plants having leaves attached to a running stem, these 3 are by far the best known and are in the most general use.

CABOMBA
(Washington Plant, Fanwort, Watershield)

While we by no means claim this to be the best of aquarium plants, it is the most largely sold, and has its good points. It fell out of fashion in the Goldfish aquarium because those husky fishes picked it to pieces, for it is brittle. Very few of our exotics munch on plants, and so that objection to Cabomba is removed, as far as they are concerned. Certainly when in good condition it is one of the brightest and most beautiful of aquarium greens. It is used chiefly on account of its attractiveness, coupled with the fact that it is always in supply.

The fan-shaped, light green leaves on a running stem form good refuge for young fishes, but they are not sufficiently dense to make a satisfactory spawning plant. Cabomba is apt to become long and stringy unless kept in a strong light. It is a fair oxygenator.

MYRIOPHYLLUM
(Water Milfoil)

A plant of delicate beauty. Its fine leaves make a perfect maze for catching the adhesive eggs of egg-dropping fishes, or a wonderful refuge for newly hatched fish babies. Broken or cut-off bits of its feathery leaves precisely suit the needs of those fishes which entwine a bit of such material into their nests (Dwarf Gouramies and Sticklebacks). It is beautiful in the aquarium but requires strong light to avoid becoming thin and leggy. Long a popular favorite, it is generally in good supply. Rinsing well under a tap of water removes most of the possible fish enemies from wild stock.

Sold bunched, it should not be kept that way unless used as a spawn-receiver.

ANACHARIS
(Elodea, Ditch Moss)

Early dealers claimed that Anacharis was the best of oxygenators. This was generally accepted and has become something of a tradition, although the claim is open to question. It is probably based on the undoubted fact that it is the most rapid-growing of all aquarium plants. An inch-a-day for a long strand is not unusual. However, growth and oxygenating power bear little, if any, relationship to each other. Rapid stem growth occurs in poor light, producing plants lacking vigor.

It is the author's observation that Anacharis is only at its best in outdoor ponds that are partially protected from the full light of the sun. In the aquarium it gradually becomes stringy and pale. Some aquarists claim that a good supply of it clears green water.

PARROT'S FEATHER *(Myriophyllum proserpinacoides)* is an interesting species mentioned here only on account of its decorative quality. The feathery plumes of the ends stand above the edges of pools in magnificent masses. Good in the greenhouse.

PLANTS FOR SPECIAL PURPOSES

Here are listed plants which are not so commonly obtainable, but which have their own values in utility or beauty. Bits not always found in the highways of trade. Advertised items of unproven value are omitted.

Ludwigia This is not a true aquatic, but a bog plant which does fairly well under water. It never completely forgets its habit of having some leaves above the water line. There are about 25 species in North America, usually growing at the shallow edges of ponds and streams, somewhat similar to Watercress, but, unlike that plant, not requiring cool water. The native kinds are not as well suited to the aquarium as a South American species, *mullerttii*. This is also handsomer, being more robust and not having as many rootlets along the stem. A very beautiful red strain of this species is cultivated in Florida, where conditions exactly suit it, but elsewhere it soon loses most of its peculiar character. This variety is shown in the color plate with the Sagittarias.

For best results Ludwigia should be rooted in earth and placed in strong light. Otherwise the leaves drop prematurely. It is easily propagated from end cuttings. Nurserymen stick these in small pots containing earth and a top layer of sand. This is not done under water, but on trays of saturated sand or ashes. As soon as growth starts, the pot may be placed in the aquarium. This is a very satisfactory method.

Cryptocoryne These long-lived Asiatic plants were once rarities, but their valuable special uses, together with intensified commercial production, have brought them into popular demand and fairly good supply. Besides an attractive individuality different from all other true aquatics, they have the great merit of thriving in situations where the light is rather weak. This obliging characteristic should not be pushed too far. They come from well-shaded jungle streams, but need a reasonably strong diffused light. Where an aquarium contains a variety of plants it may not be possible to give all of them light ideally suited to their natures. With Cryptocorynes in the picture, it is well to place them out of the full glare of strong light.

While there is a fascination (especially among beginners) about decorating aquariums with a wide variety of plants, there is also a simple, pleasing and perhaps more successful scheme in which only one or at most two kinds are used in one tank. Cryptocorynes adapt themselves well to that treatment. They are all long lived.

Cryptocoryne griffithi with two underwater flowers (about ⅔ size)

This species, the first of the family introduced, has broad dark, silken green leaves that look more like those of terrestrial plants. They are reddish underneath, tough, and stand a lot of knocking about.

In many streams in the Malay country, *Rasbora heteromorpha* spawns on the undersides of these leaves, and the tiny young hide in the roots which mat above the soil. Their native waters are strongly acid, but they tolerate a variety of aquarium conditions. Planted in sand, they live satisfactorily, but for free propagation, earth should be mixed with it, especially if grown in pots. Happily located, a few plants make a handsome grove in about a year.

Cryptocoryne ciliata (about ½ size)

Very abundant in its native Malayan waters, and freely introduced into European aquariums during the past decade, this handsome lettuce-green Cryptocoryne has only recently gotten a foothold in the esteem of American aquarists.

As will be seen in the plate, the leaves are ruffled, and more pointed than those of the *Griffithii,* which in a general way it resembles. With age the leaves become quite long and the wavy effect is increased. In the illustration of the leaves of the *Cryptocoryne* species, a few pages further on, will be found one from this plant showing these tendencies not yet fully developed. Illustration is about half life size.

In common with its numerous cousins it prefers subdued light and warm water.

Young plants appear around the sides of the parent, and can be picked off and planted.

Cryptocoryne willisii (⅗ size)

This species, with its pleasantly rippled leaf edges, is perhaps the most graceful member of the family, and certainly one of the most popular. Dealers have trouble in keeping up their stocks.

One of the things that should be borne in mind about all the Cryptocorynes is that they are really tropicals. They do not die in cool water, but do best at between 72 and 80 degrees.

The color of this species is a bright, medium green. As with the other members of the family it propagates from short runners. To the best of our knowledge this species has never been known to bloom in cultivation, even when multiplying freely.

By the way, the family name of these plants is popularly mis-pronounced Krip toe-ko-reen. It should be Krip toe-ko-rye nee.

Cryptocoryne cordata (about ⅔ size)

Becoming popular somewhat later than *C. willisii,* this species is sometimes mistaken for that plant, although the differences between them are easily told at a second glance. This one has broader, heavier leaves of a distinctly different color, being more on the order of a rusty olive green. Turning the leaves to the underside, we see a strong reddish cast not possessed by *willisii.* While undulated, they are not rippled. Flowers are very rare, and resemble those of *C. griffithi.*

The light streak appearing here along the centre of one leaf is not a marking, but a photographic highlight.

Any of the Cryptocorynes ship particularly well when carefully packed to retain their moisture—a point worth remembering.

Cryptocoryne becketti (slightly reduced)

As the illustration is approximately life size it will be seen that the plant is not a large one—in fact the smallest of the Cryptocorynes known to aquarists. It has a flattened posture, so that most of the leaves are in a somewhat horizontal position. This characteristic makes it a good choice for a small tank, particularly one in a subdued light.

In contrast to its several relatives, the leaves are plain green, with no dark blotches nor red undersides.

Multiplication is from runners and division at the roots. The plant is not commonly carried in stock except by the larger dealers.

MADAGASCAR DWARF LILY

The leaves of this plant are shown in our color plate of the fish, *Hyphessobrycon innesi*.

These are young plants taken from the viviparous leaves of the tropical water lily, "Dauben." In fertilized soil in an outdoor lily pool it has a spread of about six feet. In the aquarium it adjusts itself to cramped space, and produces small blue-white miniature flowers if given favorable conditions, meaning a temperature of about 75, direct sun for 2 hours or more, plus being placed in a small pot of fertilized soil.

Cryptocoryne haerteliana

Named for the famous Austrian aquarist, Hermann Haertel, this plant, perhaps more than most, varies tremendously in height according to conditions of light and soil. Our illustration, grown in soft light and soft water, is shown at only ⅓ actual size. Stronger light shortens it. Face of leaves, silky green; underside deep red. Reproduction is by runners.

Crinkled Cryptocoryne. *Cryptocoryne longicauda* (about ⅛ size)

Currently this is the latest of the large and popular family *Crypto-coryne* to be introduced to aquarists. Also it is one of the oddest, the light green leaves being crinkled, somewhat after the manner of spinach. Its individuality is further accentuated by the noble size of the leaves.

The white root system is extensive and usually contains several runners bearing young. As the plant is very buoyant the roots need to be well anchored in fairly deep soil; a couple of small stones laid next to the crown assure permanence until it becomes established.

Although the small trumpet-like feature in the illustration resembles the usual flower of this family, it is actually a new leaf, and from this point it will, in about 10 days, be unfolded in all its grandeur.

As might be expected, it prefers somewhat subdued light.

becketti,   willisii,   cordata,   ciliata,   griffithi

LEAVES OF SPECIES OF *Cryptocoryne*

No matter how carefully aquarium plants are arranged and photo-graphed, it very often happens that we get an edge-view of the leaves. This does not do the plant justice nor help much in identification. *Cryptocoryne* illustrations particularly suffer from that angle, so we have taken this flat view of single leaves of the five species most in use, keeping to proportionate sizes as far as possible. This includes the new, light green *C. ciliata*, which is extremely abundant in the acid waters of its native Malayan habitat. It is established in European aquariums and is just get-ting a good start in the U. S. A. Not a rapid reproducer, but very durable. Leaves are longer and more pointed than those of *C. griffithi*, sometimes reaching 8 inches with no increase in width, but with more wavy edges. However, it does well in medium sized tanks, say 10 gallons.

Bacopa caroliniana (or *Herpestis*)

A distinctive fleshy-leaved plant, native from the Carolinas to Texas. The leaves are olive green and slightly fragrant. Since its introduction from Florida as an aquarium plant by John B. Stetson, Jr., in 1913, it has gradually gained favor. A slow grower, lasts well, and prospers in medium or strong light. It may be freely multiplied from cuttings. In Nature it bears a tiny blue flower.

CAPE FEAR RIVER SPATTERDOCK

Spatterdock One of the forms of this plant from southeastern United States makes a striking centerpiece in the aquarium. The large, long leaves are of a delicate, translucent light green. Propagation is from a heavy, trunk-like root-base called a rhizome. Unfortunately, when broken off decay may set in and finally destroy the rhizome. The break heals better if planted in soil.

Seedlings from northern Spatterdocks produce smaller plants with much more rounded leaves. While the parent stocks of most of those seedlings have aerial leaves, seen by the million along the edges of rivers, they seldom, if ever, become sufficiently robust in the aquarium to reach that stage of development. Usually they are pretty little submerged plants not over 6 inches in height.

P.S.—This is our favorite plant photograph. It really seems to be **under water.**

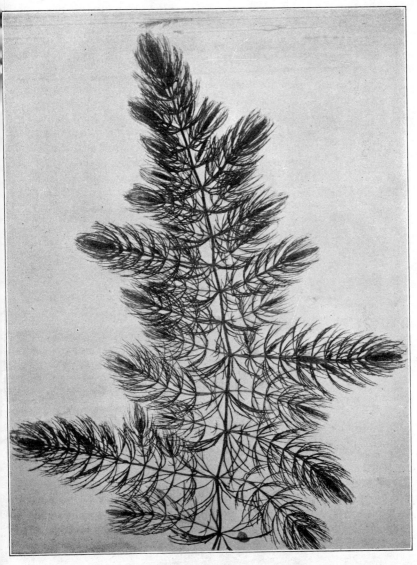

A FLOATING SPRAY OF *Ceratophyllum* OR HORNWORT *(See next page)*

Ceratophyllum   Ceratophyllum, or Hornwort, has a decided beauty that would make it one of our standard aquarium plants, but for two fatal faults. It is brittle and it has no roots. It is like a thinned-out Myriophyllum. Illustrators of fishes never seem to tire of placing a spray of it in backgrounds. Our color photograph of *Eptroplus maculatus* shows a bit of it to advantage. Placed in a concrete pool in summer, where it will receive about 3 hours of sunshine per day, it grows in magnificent scrolls, floating just below the surface.

Fontinalis or Willowmoss   A dark green plant, native to small, cool, clear swift streams. Usually attached to a stone or a bit of water-logged wood, it does moderately well in the aquarium, especially if settlings are regularly knocked off or the whole plant rinsed. The small leaves on a firm stem in Nature conceal an infinite variety of tiny crustacea, etc., mostly fishfoods. Useful as a spawn receiver, especially for fishes breeding near the bottom. Some dealers carry it.

Fontinalis gracilis, or Willowmoss, attached to a stone.

NITELLA

This is one of our native plants, distributed largely throughout temperate North America. There are several species closely resembling this one, which is *N. gracilis*. It is interesting in several ways. Classified for years as one of the algae, there is now considerable doubt on this point.

It has a great deal of sap for so slender a plant, and through its beautiful, translucent pale green walls the flow of protoplasm is easily seen with the aid of a microscope of moderate power. Used extensively in classrooms and for scientific research. There are no roots.

Young livebearers among a loose mass of NITELLA nearly filling an aquarium need no other protection from hungry parents.

When cut it smells sweet, like a new-mown lawn. Some fishes, especially *Scatophagus*, greedily eat short cut lengths of it.

Growth in a sunny situation (in neutral to alkaline water) is rapid.

HAIR GRASS *(Eleocharis)* life size

Hair Grass Growing along the edges of many ponds and streams in the eastern and southern parts of North America are short, hair-like grasses suited to aquarium culture. The majority of them propagate from runners, such as the one shown here. Others divide on the leaves, and send down rootlets.

Plants of this character offer not only interesting variety in contrast with other aquarium vegetation, but they make perfect thickets for harboring baby fishes finding themselves in a dangerous world.

This or a similar species may usually be had from dealers or specialists in aquatic plants.

WATER PURSLANE, LIFE SIZE
Didiplis diandra

Not realizing that the field has already been well worked over by experts, many aquarists, especially in their early stages, take pleasure in investigating native streams and ponds, hoping to find some new fish or plant that can be naturalized at home. Usually nothing comes of it. Attractive plants, thriving in their native conditions, seldom prosper in the aquarium, nor retain their original beauty.

Water Purslane, found by Professor Coker in Crystal Lake, Lakeview, N. C., is one of the happy exceptions. It is a member of the Loose-strife family, and does well under average aquarium conditions. Its firm leaves are medium dark green. Grows slowly, which is sometimes an advantage. Not in general supply, but can be had of aquatic plant specialists.

WATER SPRITE
(Ceratopteris thalictroides)

Based on botanical opinion of others and our own experiments we are convinced that the charming "Water Sprite" is merely Floating Water Fern (see later) held under water by having the young plants secured in aquarium soil. Under-water growth changes their form. Possibly dependent on the species, the leaves are sometimes much broader than shown here, although we have seen both broad and narrow leaves on the same plant. The genus occurs in the tropics around the world, and is most variable.

If left to itself, and untrimmed, it spreads to the surface, where the baby plants, formed on the old leaves, again assume the floating form. In a warm, moist atmosphere they pile up into veritable islands.

Another peculiarity is the stiff, narrow aerial leaves that adult submerged specimens sometimes produce. With age the parent plant becomes soft and should be replaced. Snails attack soft plants.

WATER WISTARIA *(Synnema triflorum)*

A beautiful recent introduction by Shirley Aquatics, of England. It resembles a bright green Water Sprite, to which it is not related. Propagation is either from cuttings or from runners at the base.

It forms a 10-inch, bushy plant with a central stem, preferring subdued light and slightly acid water.

"Water Wistaria" gives promise of becoming very popular, but as yet the supply is limited.

Naias (Surface View)

Aquarists receiving shipments of plants from the Southern States sometimes find masses of the above used as packing material. Of a pleasant
translucent green color, like a small Potamogeton. Grows into masses
useful to fish breeders. In a pool with soil bottom it may take possession.
Grows wild from Florida to Labrador.

AMAZON SWORD PLANT WITH RUNNERS AND YOUNG
(Echinodorus intermedius)

To get a reasonably true impression of this gorgeous aquatic plant, the reader should try to project his mind into the illustration, realizing that the water depth is 18 inches, and that the somewhat translucent leaves (each without a blemish of age or accident) are bright green, varying in shade, depending on whether the light strikes *on* or *through*. The plant seems to be Nature's special gift to aquarists as a centerpiece for a 15-to-25 gallon tank, or it will suitably colonize as a family of giants in a more massive container. Runners from the crown (a king's crown indeed) are free and far reaching. Press runners into sand at points where new plants develop. Do not cut them off until well started.

Several other aquatics with large leaves have long stems, making them rather rangy, but this Sword Plant has short stems that give a compact, sturdy effect. When this plant appeared here in 1937 it was a truly valuable acquisition by the artistic aquarist. It is now well established.

It likes a good but not powerful light. A moderate amount of indirect daylight, aided by an electric Mazda placed close to the water, suits it very well. The magnificent specimen used in the illustration was in a sun parlor, north light. It blooms and reproduces young plants from April through August.

A broader-leaved kind, *rangeri*, more lately introduced, blooms and sends out new plants from December to June.

BROAD-LEAF AMAZON SWORD PLANT *(Echinodorus rangeri)*
(see detailed leaf opposite)

This plan, briefly referred to on page 97, is particularly suited to large tanks, where its beautiful, broad leaves make a magnificent effect. It does well in either medium or subdued light, and is the show-piece in the tanks of many dealers, where it is often kept partly or wholly under artificial light.

The big Amazon Sword Plants (Broad and Narrow Leaf) are lusty, and have strong, long roots. This makes them bad competitors for other plants coming within their immediate sphere. It is well to remember this while planting. If given the opportunity the Broad-leaf will spread its leaves nearly two feet. It should have an aquarium of at least 20-gallon capacity.

If these large plants are in an aquarium that is too shallow for them, the leaves tend to float at the surface, and to become dry in spots, which spoils their appearance. A sheet of close-fitting glass on top of the tank reduces the drying tendency.

LEAVES OF BROAD-LEAF AND NARROW-LEAF SWORD PLANTS

This illustration shows not only the difference in shape and comparative size of the leaves, but also the number of longitudinal veins.

Each plant has its appropriate uses according to the size of the tank. Roughly the Broad-leaf belongs in containers of from 20 gallons up; the Narrow-leaf, 12 to 30 gallons. Actual measurement of the specimen leaf at the left, exclusive of stem, is 3½ x 8½ inches.

RUFFLED SWORD PLANT *(Echinodorus martii)*
(½ size)

Here we have a recent introduction of great merit, having marked individual character, plus unusual toughness of texture.

It reproduces in the same manner as the other members of the family.

Comparatively slow of propagation, it took some time to build a commercial supply. That desired end has now been reached, and while not widely offered, it is not difficult to secure from leading specialists.

Our photographic illustration seems to indicate leaves of dark green. Actually they are a light, rich shade.

Some aquarists rank it as the handsomest of the Echinodorus.

(One of the many "Everglades" introductions.)

PIGMY CHAIN SWORDPLANT
(Echinodorus tenellus)

This plant, one of the latest introductions among the numerous *Echinodorus* family, has several points of value. It is a first-class addition to the low-growing plants, of which we have few. According to conditions it reaches from only 3 to 4 inches in height.

Reproduction from runners is rapid, so that in a big aquarium it virtually carpets the floor in a few months. Runners should be pressed just below the surface of the soil.

Perhaps its greatest value is in small tanks (1 to 5 gallons), as there are so few rooted plants that do not soon get too tall for them. If used as a center-piece in a small aquarium the runners should be pinched off. This makes a bushy, fountain-shaped miniature Swordplant.

And lastly, it gets along well in subdued daylight or under good electric illumination held in a standard reflector over the aquarium.

Echinodorus radicans
Erroneously *Sagittaria guayanensis*

When this plant was first introduced into the trade it was believed to be a Sagittaria, having some resemblance to that family, but the botanists presently corrected this. In Sagittarias the flowers are separately male and female, but in Echinodorus the pistils and stamens occur in the same flower, making self-fertilization possible.

This firm-leaved plant, established to its liking, is a terrific grower, presently developing both floating and aerial leaves. If one has a big tank and would like to see aquatic surprises in action and variety, this is the species to put on a show. Growth of aerial leaves can be retarded by shade. When ready to reproduce it shoots up a stalk bearing beautiful white flowers having large fertile seeds. As if this were not enough, new plants form between the seed pods.

Our illustration, at a little less than life size, shows the young plant at its best stage for the average aquarium.

Aponogeton undulatum (incorrectly *A. crispus*)

The somewhat translucent leaves of this striking plant look like green swords with rippled edges. Heights, 6 to 18 inches, depending on strong or weak light. In the taller plants the leaves do not broaden in proportion, thus making them more strap-like. The illustrated specimen was about 8 inches high. Mostly grown from seed. They have a resting period in December. The plant has a shepherd's crook flower stem above the water line, bearing small white flowers.

Aponogeton ulvaceus

All things considered, we do not rate this better than the Amazon Sword Plant as a centrepiece, but for a considerable period of its life, and under favorable conditions, we regard it as the most magnificent of all large aquarium plants. The latticed, semi-translucent green leaves are truly beautiful. Since our best photographic efforts have proven inadequate at portraying the stunning grandeur of the fully developed plant, we show also a single leaf at approximately natural size. By combining both photographs in imagination, the reader should be able to construct a fairly correct picture.

The individual plant is maintained by a favorite method with us, although some aquarists succeed in other ways. It is placed when small in a 4-inch round pudding dish (chain store goods) with ¼ inch of plain, unfertilized soil on the bottom. Coarse sand is then used to nearly fill the dish. Exposure is western.

Surface runner from *Aponogeton ulvaceus*. Young plants, as well as flowers, emerge from the sheath. The white blossoms stand above the water, and in a general way are characteristic of all the Aponogetons.

Coming from Madagascar, it is said to be related to the Madagascar Lace-leaf Plant. Certainly the lattice-like pattern of the leaf is similar, but it is not actually skeletonized. One can easily imagine it to be on the evolutionary road to that odd development.

Faults: the leaves are rather easily torn, and the plants, like most, or perhaps all Aponogetons, insist upon a rest period in December and January. They die down, but presently reappear from the bulb.

Reproduction is mainly from young plants formed on strong surface runners, as shown in the two illustrations; sometimes from root separations.

LEAF OF *Aponogeton ulvaceus*, life size.

MADAGASCAR LACE-LEAF PLANT
(Aponogeton fenestralis)

Although the Lace-leaf Plant is one of the earliest used by aquarists (always by a select few) and many rivals have appeared that are really better aquarium plants, this aristocrat somehow continues to be "the class" of them all. Its very high price, its slowness of propagation and its really unique beauty easily account for the distinction it maintains. The illustration clearly indicates the peculiar skeleton structure of the leaves. Surprisingly, they are rather tough. The photograph scarcely does the plant justice, but it is used because it shows the rarely seen bud which soon terminates above the water in a large U-shaped formation, covered with small white flowers.

The plant is tricky, either succeeding or failing for reasons that are not clear. It does well in the alkaline waters of California, but poorly in the acid conditions of New England, yet at the Botanical Gardens of the University of Pennsylvania it flourished in half-casks of oak, which certainly ought to be acid. It does prefer soft water.

The snail in the picture reminds us it is desirable to have either active snails or alga-eating fishes present, as the open lattice spaces easily get choked. A moderate light is best. New plants occasionally appear at the root. Recently imported bulbs produce good plants.

Ambulia

This plant roughly resembles Cabomba, but is a little smaller, is a lighter shade of green and does better in the aquarium. The life-size drawings of sections of the two plants show the differences in leaf formation and arrangement. The alternating pairs of fan-like leaves of Cabomba form only a semi-circle, the cylindrical effect of the plant being produced by the next and opposite pair. Ambulia completes its leafy circle from one point.

Imported from India in 1932, Ambulia has grown steadily in favor, and as it easily multiplies from cuttings, it seems sure to join the surprisingly small circle of best sellers. Sold bunched. Separate the strands when planting.

Correct name, *Limnophila*.

Upper, *Ambulia*
Lower, *Cabomba*

Four Popular Decorative Plants *(drawn life size)*

Not strictly aquatics. Last fairly well in aquaria having plenty of light.

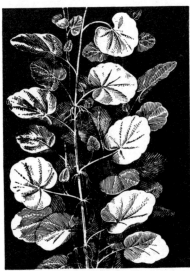

CARDAMINE *(Car-dam'-i-nee)*

A beautiful light-green moisture-loving plant from northern Europe and America, recently introduced to aquarists. Very, very good.

LUDWIGIA *(Lud-wig'-ee-a)*

A bog or semi-aquatic plant, long used by aquarists. See cultural comments several pages back. They also apply in general to all the group shown here.

MONEYWORT (or *Lysmachia*)

A common creeping terrestrial, sold in quantity to aquarists. Does fairly well under water, where it rises vertically. In time it becomes progressively weak and spindly.

HELXINE *(Helks-eye'nee)*

"Baby's Tears" often used by florists in moist terraria. In Corsica and Sardinia it covers moist rocks. Submerged, its tiny, light-green leaves make a novel and pleasing effect.

FLOATING PLANTS

Riccia To the breeder of aquarium fishes, this is one of the most valuable of plants. Its green, crystal-like formation produces masses which are compact enough to catch and hold the spawn of the surface egg-layers, yet open enough for new baby live-bearing species to use as a perfect refuge. When it is desirable to produce top shade in an aquarium, we can depend upon Riccia to do it in any desired degree.

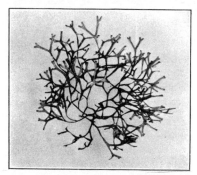

RICCIA, OR CRYSTALWORT

For some aquarists it grows tremendously, but the surplus never should be thrown away, for there are always those in need of it. When a mass grows over an inch thick, so that the sun can not force light through it, a thinning out must be effected, or it will turn yellow and soft and pollute the water.

Under the influence of sun these little plants are enormous oxygenators. Large bubbles of that precious gas become imprisoned among the massed leaves and stay there until absorbed by the water. This takes several hours and favorably affects the fishes long after sunset.

The great enemies of Riccia are algae, which get among the leaves and choke it. A plentiful supply of small snails usually keeps it clean. When used for spawning purposes, no snails should be present.

While Riccia is native to the fresh waters of the middle and southern Atlantic States, it appears to grow better in a well-lighted aquarium than it does outdoors. All-day sun seems to shrivel it.

The illustration needs to be explained in one respect. It has the appearance of being one plant with antler-like branches. This it is until broken up into small individuals. At a light touch the delicate thread fastening each plant to its parent is broken. Separating itself it in turn starts to multiply.

While Riccia naturally floats just below the surface of the water, beautiful effects can be obtained by deeply anchoring small bunches, similar to the illustration, where they will not be disturbed, and where good light penetrates. Under these conditions it develops into gorgeous green masses, even up to 6 inches across.

There are few fishes that eat Riccia, but *Scatophagus argus* is extremely fond of it. This seems strange, as nothing even distantly resembles this plant in its native salt and brackish waters.

Salvinia This is a floating plant and was originally imported from Brazil. It is much larger and handsomer than Duckweed, the

SALVINIA

leaves being over a quarter-inch across. The upper surface is covered with vertical hairs, which are probably unpalatable to fishes. At any rate, none of them eats it. It multiplies rapidly in a warm, moist atmosphere, but does not do so well outdoors, and will not survive icy winters. The leaves are ornamental.

Azolla A peculiar little floating plant, native to our Atlantic States, sometimes used as an aquarium plant. It forms a dense covering, varying in color from brilliant green to dark, velvety red. The red seems to be brought out by strong light. The individual plants are quite pretty. A few dealers stock the plant.

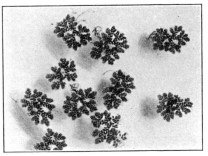

AZOLLA

Lesser Bladderwort A native plant, usually a tangled mass of thread-like stems, dotted with little bladders having openings capable of trapping living organisms such as Infusoria, young Daphnia or even the smallest sizes of newly-hatched fishes. The latter possibility was long doubted, so that the plant, otherwise well-qualified as a spawning medium for egg-layers, has often been used. No doubt the traps fail to work on baby fishes from larger-sized eggs, but recently

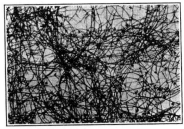

LESSER BLADDERWORT

photographed experiences of Mr. G. R. Hall of Baltimore, Maryland, clearly show trapped fishes, usually caught by the tail or head. Repeated losses of major numbers of baby Bettas in the presence of Bladderwort led to suspicions and this definite proof.

Duckweed A despised pest in Daphnia ponds, but not without its use in the aquarium. Some of our fishes like to eat it, and it is

a good producer of shade where a tank gets too much top light. No fear need be entertained about introducing it in aquariums where it can be kept under control, but in large containers and lily pools it is apt to gain too much headway and prove difficult to get rid of. A native plant of almost universal distribution. For

DUCKWEED

so small a floating leaf it develops quite long roots, if they are not nibbled by fishes. Roots show in our first plate of Dragon Fly larva.

An almost solid mantle of any of these little floating plants seems to have little or no effect in preventing the water from absorbing oxygen at the surface. Dried Duckweed is a good producer of Infusoria.

WATER LETTUCE

A beautiful floating plant about 4 inches in diameter, having fluted, velvety, light green leaves and long roots. Requires warm, moist atmosphere and diffused light. Propagation is by runners, similar to Water Hyacinth. Does exceptionally well in shallow water (3 to 5 inches) with roots dragging in earthy soil.

WATER FERN (top view) BEARING YOUNG PLANTS
(Ceratopteris deltoidea)

Water Fern This is an interesting floating plant, anywhere in size from an inch to 2 feet in diameter, according to the conditions under which it is kept. It likes greenhouse moisture and temperature. When so favored, it grows in great masses and piles itself up several inches out of the water. It is viviparous, the young plants forming on the large parent leaves. In an aquarium it keeps down to a moderate size and makes a very pretty shade plant. In this respect it is one of the enemies of green water. Bettas and other bubble-nest builders delight in placing their nests below one of the plants. A side view of the plant is shown in the colored plate of Paradise Fish.

The leaves or fronds unfold from the centre as with terrestrial ferns. It is very closely related to the submerged and rooted "Water Sprite."

In comparison with the size of the plant the roots are small.

Snails like to deposit their eggs on the under side of the leaves. This is a green of which one is apt to have either too much or none. It does best in a covered aquarium. Most large dealers carry a generous stock.

WATER HYACINTH *(Eichhornia crassipes major)*

A floating aquatic from the Gulf states, where at places its rapid growth impedes navigation. On account of its blue-black, bushy roots it is ideal for spawning fishes that drop adhesive eggs near the surface (the Goldfish and many exotics). It dies over winter unless kept in strong light in a tropical greenhouse. Cheap and easily procured in the spring. Beautiful lavender flower truss lasts a day. Primarily a pond plant.

PLANTING

Sand or Pebbles? Coarse sand is best, or a mixture of sand and small pebbles, such as Jersey gravel. Washed building sand is satisfactory. Fine sand packs too hard for the roots to easily penetrate, and allows no beneficial circulation of water.

Pebbles, stones, shells or marbles alone are bad because they have open spaces which catch and hold fishfood where no scavengers can reach it, thus causing the water to turn foul. Large and small stones, well selected, may be very ornamental and natural in an aquarium, but they should be set in sand, for the reason given.

Depth of Sand This is a more important subject than is generally recognized. The planting medium should be only deep enough to be certain of holding down the rooted plants. Vallisneria and the smaller Sagittarias need only about 1½ inches, while Giant Sagittaria requires 2 inches or more. It is a good plan to root the larger plants in deeper sand in the back of the aquarium and then let the level slope lower towards the front. This serves the double purpose of giving the smaller plants a place in the light and of working the aquarium sediment forward, where it is more easily removed. Some aquarists place a glass bar or other stop about an inch wide between the front edge of the sand and the front glass of the aquarium, making an inch trench the entire length. An excellent dirt trap. The stop may also be made of well selected small stones, placed in the form of a semicircle.

Use Earth? No. Theoretically it might be a good idea to provide soil substance in the form of a sub-stratum for plants, but in practice it does not work out well. It is apt to become foul, and any accidental stirring up clouds the aquarium. Besides, we expect the plants to get their livelihood by absorbing the waste products of the fishes. This they do. Professional growers use garden soil below the sand, but no fishes. Pulling out their plants does not cloud water to any extent. Some earth benefits potted aquarium plants.

How to Plant Enough has been said as to the characteristics of available plants for the aquarium, so that here we are concerned with the mechanics of the job.

The first thing is to make sure that the plants are kept moist while the work is being carefully done. A half-drying may set them back for weeks. If they are laid in water and covered with a wet newspaper, there will be no danger.

The water in the aquarium should be about 5 or 6 inches deep while most of the work is being done. If the sand is fairly clean, the water

112

can be kept clear by placing a piece of paper over it while filling. Pour on the paper. When rockwork is to be used, it should be placed before the plants are set. The only real difficulty is in nicely planting the grasses having spreading roots, but it is not very troublesome when the water is shallow. Spread the roots of Sagittaria and Vallisneria as widely as possible and cover them well with sand, being careful not to bury the leaves. If there are tall, stiff leaves, partly in the air, be sure to sprinkle them often during the balance of the work. Sometimes a large plant is so buoyant that it is necessary to place a small stone or two on the sand over the roots, or to wrap base of plant with a cut strip or wire of lead. Each rooted plant like Sagittaria or Vallisneria should have sufficient space so that there will be room for new runners to expand.

The smaller plants and those with long strands like Anacharis should be placed last. Old yellowish leaves should be removed before planting.

Planting Sticks   If plants must be added after the aquarium is filled, or if any of them ride up, a slender pair of sticks will be found most useful. Push the plant into the sand with both sticks, then withdraw one, and with it heap the sand about the roots. The other

PLANTING STICK WITH NOTCHED END

stick may be withdrawn and usually the plant will stay down. It is well to slightly notch and round off the sharp edges of the pushing ends of the sticks. A pair of rulers will serve in an emergency.

Bunched Plants   Plants when received in wired bundles look so attractive and it is so easy to plant them as they are; it is indeed a temptation to do so. They never naturally grow that way and it should not be done. Stemmed plants, like Anacharis, Cabomba and Myriophyllum, ought to be slightly separated so that water and light may pass between the stems at the base.

Fertilizing Plants   This is a "noble experiment," but a dangerous one. It belongs in the same category as placing a layer of soil under the sand, only it is a few degrees more dangerous. It has been proven many times that *Fish Fertilize Plants.* If there are enough fish present, the combined effects of their breathing and their droppings give the plants all the chemical stimulation they need. The author has seen many well-planted aquariums degenerate without the presence of fish life, only to revive beautifully upon the reintroduction of fishes. However, if any readers feel that their plants are in need of added stimulation, the most approved method of supplying it is by making a liquor from pulverized sheep manure (or a commercial liquid fertilizer) and shooting it into the sand about the roots by use of a pipette like a fountain pen filler, but larger. Bone meal and other fertilizers have been introduced into the sand in soluble capsules, as well as commercial tablets, like "Plant-tabs." Rabbits and Guinea Pigs supply natural fertilizer lozenges in convenient form for inserting near plant roots.

Plants in Trays   Planting in trays is practised by many of our foremost aquarists. The idea has advantages. They may be lifted from the aquarium without the slightest disturbance. This is a great convenience either in house-cleaning the aquarium or in catching elusive fishes that hide among plants, for the tray can be removed and leave the bare aquarium in which to work. Many a planting has been wrecked by the net of a desperate and maddened aquarist whose patience has been exhausted by the chase.

Earthenware trays made for the purpose are sold in many of the aquarium supply shops. These have an inside measurement of about 2½ x 5 inches and are about 2 inches deep. This size is suited to small aquariums only and allows no space for runners. Seedsmen sell propagating pans about a foot square and 3 inches deep. Also glass drip pans, used in electric refrigerators, make splendid plant trays. These sizes allow room for propagation. Chain stores often have glassware that fits the purpose. Beautiful thickets of Sagittaria and Vallisneria can be raised in this way. They are the best plants for use in trays.

The same principles may be employed as in planting the bottom of the aquarium itself. The tray can either be set on the plain aquarium floor or hidden in sand or rockwork.

In general, plants do better in soft water that is neutral or slightly alkaline, in preference to an acid condition.

Selecting Plants   As in other branches of horticulture, it is best to select young or half-grown plants rather than fully developed specimens that have arrived at the zenith of perfection. The young adapt themselves better and last longer. Avoid plants covered with algae, or "moss" as some know it. It chokes the plants and spreads through the aquarium.

Disinfecting Plants   It is of course desirable to have new plants free of germs and "bugs." Any known treatment fully accomplishing this would sicken or kill the plants. New plants should first be rinsed and then placed for a day in a shallow white tray for observation. Perhaps some unwanted snails or disgusting leeches will appear. Follow with a quarter hour bath of concentrated lime water diluted with 6 of plain water. This will get rid of most crustaceans. Lime water is the clear liquid left when the white sediment has settled after liberally mixing hydrated lime in water.

Filling   There is an art to even so simple a thing as filling an aquarium. In the first place, it should have even bearing or support all around. If the slightest rocking can be produced by raising or lowering any corner, it should be equalized before filling. An uneven strain is liable sooner or later to crack the glass or cause a leak.

We have already suggested covering the plants with paper during the filling. Fill from a sprinkling pot if convenient. A floated sheet of paper remains buoyant while a stream of water is poured on it.

Large aquariums, particularly new ones, should be filled slowly, say half the first day and the balance the next, provided no leaks appear. Here is a valuable point seldom mentioned. Like fishes, plants really ought to be placed in *old water,* especially in winter when new water is surcharged with oxygen. This is injurious to plant tissue. In winter hot water should be drawn the day before and used in the aquariums when it has come down to house temperature. Hot water, of course, should not be placed in the aquarium. It can safely be stood for cooling in a bathtub or other enamel container, or in stone laundry tubs.

Leaks   An ordinary slow leak in either a new or an old aquarium should be given a chance to cure itself. This it often does by the suspended matter in the water choking the crack. A handful of earth mixed in the water and stirred occasionally will hurry the process.

Repairs to a leaking aquarium *must* be made from the inside. Dry not less than a week, tip and support on edge, and with the aid of a medicine dropper place enough spar varnish to run into the cracks and leave a little surplus that will set in about 12 hours. Repeat on the other 7 edges and use in a week after doing the last. This takes longer than using aquarium cement, but results are better. If cement is used, scrape surfaces clean and apply a coating of spar varnish the day before.

A new caulking material produced by Dow Corning is becoming very popular among hobbyists. This material bonds well to glass, remains somewhat flexible, and does not break down in salt water or fresh. The base of this bonding agent is silicone and it is easy to apply on a cleaned, scraped surface.

Edited by H. S.

Classification of Fishes

HE pleasure of aquarium study can be doubled by organizing it. The following explanation has been prepared in the hope that it will clear up, in the beginning, a number of simple facts that aquarists ought to know, but which have not heretofore been reduced to plain enough terms for popular use, and brought together within the compass of a few pages.

These pages may be skipped without regret (but not without loss) by those who are science-shy.

Anyone who is familiar with the ordinary run of aquarium fishes, if asked whether the Red Tetra from Rio is a Characin or a Cichlid, will not hesitate to say it is a Characin. But if you ask him why, he is likely to tell you that it is similar to other Characins, that it has an adipose fin —and stop right there. Very probably he has never considered what other differences there are between a Cichlid and a Characin; *he has learned to recognize the two families by sight* without attempting to analyze the whys and wherefores. In this particular he is just like the professional ichthyologist who can place most fishes in their proper families by sight, without recourse to books.

There is more to the subject than this, however, and since we have decided to present, for the first time, the different families of aquarium fishes in their correct ichthyological order-of-precedence, a brief explanation of why this has been done should prove helpful.

Under each family heading throughout the book there are a few sentences calling attention to some of the external features which will help the aquarist recognize a member of that group. To understand *why* the families are placed in the order in which they stand, something else is required, and this is supplied by the bird's-eye-view of fish classification given in this chapter. Before this, or the notes under the families can become intelligible, we must learn a few simple names for certain parts of a fish's anatomy, especially the fins. Every aquarist ought to be familiar with these few terms, for they are used continually in describing the form and color of all fishes.

The great majority of fishes have seven fins. Of these seven, four are *paired*. That is, there is one on each side of the body opposite its mate. The first, or forward paired fins, are the *pectoral*, or *breast fins*, one on each side of the body just behind the head. These correspond to the forelegs of land animals or the arms of a human being. The second paired fins are the *ventral* or *pelvic fins*, placed close beside each other on the underside of the fish, either before, directly below, or behind the pectoral pair. Aquarists frequently misname these the breast fins. The ventral fins correspond to the hind legs of land animals and the legs of man. The remaining 3 fins are unpaired, or single, being placed exactly on the midline of the fish as viewed from the top or front. The most important

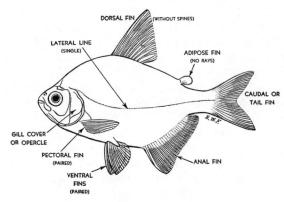

OUTLINE DRAWING OF A CHARACIN
It will be seen that there are no fin spines, and that
the ventral fins are *behind* the pectoral fins.

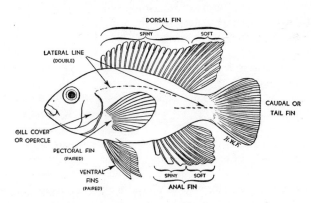

OUTLINE DRAWING OF A CICHLID
Note presence of 2 sets of fin spines, and the forward
position of the ventral fins, *under* the pectoral fins.

of the unpaired fins is the caudal, or tail fin. With most fishes it is the caudal fin that provides the chief propelling power in swimming. It may be forked, as in most swift-swimming fishes, cut off straight, rounded at the end or pointed. On the back of the fish is the dorsal, or back fin, and on the underside behind the vent, is the anal fin.

These fins are formed of a delicate *fin membrane,* supported by fairly stiff, but jointed *fin rays* which usually branch somewhat as they approach the outer edge of the fin. In certain fishes the front rays of some of the fins are bony, unjointed, and sharp. These bony rays are called *fin spines,* and in groups like the Cichlids these spines may make up more than half of the rays of the dorsal and anal fins. In such cases it is usual to refer to the two parts of the dorsal fin as the *spiny dorsal* and the *soft dorsal,* and fishes which have several spines in the dorsal and anal fins form a group called the *spiny-rayed fishes.* In the Gobies, the Silversides, and some other families, the spiny dorsal has become completely separated from the soft dorsal, so that there are two entirely separate dorsal fins, the first spiny, the second soft.

Other fishes, notably most Characins and Catfishes, as well as Salmon and Trout, have another small fin on the back, behind the dorsal and near the tail fin. This, the *adipose fin,* is unlike the other fins in that it is not usually supported by rays, but consists of fatty or adipose tissue. In the Armored Catfishes the adipose fin is supported by one stiff spine.

The similarities and differences in these fins, as well as in other, mostly internal, characters are utilized by ichthyologists in classifying fishes. In some groups, the teeth are important in classification. For groups lacking jaw teeth, see under the family headings.

All the fishes in this book, except the lung fish, belong to the great group of bony fishes, or *Teleostei,* which is split up into a great number of *orders,* the orders into *families,* the families into *genera* (singular form, *genus*), and the genera into *species.* There are good reasons for this arrangement, and the aquarist who takes a little time in spying out the similarities in his fishes can easily find out much about fish classification for himself.

The order in which the species and families are treated follows rather closely that in which the ichthyologist places fishes. Those families which resemble most closely the primitive types of fishes of bygone ages, as revealed by the study of fossils, are placed first, and the rest are arranged in an ascending order, determined by the advancing degree of complexity of their structure. This complexity is shown externally chiefly by the greater number of spines in the dorsal and anal fins and the more forward position of the ventral fins. For instance, a Characin has no spiny dorsal fin and there are never any spines in the anal fin. Furthermore the ventral fins are set well back along the belly of the fish. These are relatively "primitive" fishes and belong well towards the beginning of the series. On the other hand, the Cichlids have well-developed spiny dorsal and anal fins, and their ventrals are placed well forward, under the pectoral fins.

The Cichlids are highly developed "spiny-rayed" fishes. The Killfishes (egg-laying tooth-carps) and Gambusinos (live-bearing tooth-carps) are about midway between the Characins and the Cichlids in their make-up. They have not developed any spines in their fins, but their mouth structure and other points show that they are measurably nearer the end of the series than are the Characins. Some families, like the Snakeheads (Channidae), lack fin spines, but we know from their anatomy that they are close relatives of the spiny-rayed Gouramies, so we place them next to that group, something like poor relations who lack much that their immediate relatives have.

We now proceed with a few notes on the orders, in which the families in this book are placed.

The Herring-like fishes (order *Isospondyli*) are "primitive" bony fishes, lacking fin spines, and having the ventral fins well backward. Only one species is included in this book, the Butterfly-fish, *Pantodon*.

The true fresh-water fishes (order *Ostariophysi*) include probably three-fourths of all fresh-water fishes throughout the world. The Characins, the South American Gymnotid Eels, the Carps or Minnows, the Loaches, and the Catfishes all belong to this order. As a group, they closely resemble the Herring-like fishes, but differ from them and from all other fishes, in having a complicated series of bones (the Weberian ossicles) connecting the air-bladder with the inner ear. The exact function of this complex organ is not certainly known, but it is probably of use to its possessors as an accessory organ of hearing or in detecting differences in water pressure.

The Bill-fishes (order *Synentognathi*) are mostly salt-water fishes, but a few of them, like *Dermogenys*, are from fresh water. The Half-beaks, Needle-fishes, and salt-water Flying-fishes belong to this order. In the structure of the mouth and other characters they are more advanced than the foregoing groups.

The egg-laying and live-bearing Tooth-carps, together with some lesser families, are placed in the order *Microcyprini*, generally known as the Cyprinodonts. These are much like the Bill-fishes in the fins, but differ in the mouth and other points.

The Sticklebacks belong in the order *Thoracostei*, together with the Sea Horses and Pipe Fishes. They are remarkable for their gills and for the free spines in front of the dorsal fin.

The flatfishes (order *Heterosomata*) include the Fresh-water Soles, to which group our common Sole belongs. This is the most easily recognizable order of fishes. All its members lie flat on the bottom on one side and both eyes are on the same (upper) side of the head. All Flat-fishes start out in life upright, with an eye on each side, as we think it ought to be, but when still small they lose their balance, so to speak, flop over on one side, and the underneath eye migrates either over the top of, or directly through the head, to join its fellow on the "seeing side."

The order *Percomorphi,* or Perch-like fishes, includes the majority of spiny-rayed fishes. Among our aquarium fishes, the Silversides, the Cichlids, the Pomacentrids, the Perches, the Sunfishes, the Theraponids, the Nandids, the Monodactylids, the Archer Fishes, and the "Scats" all belong here. All of them have well-developed spiny dorsal and anal fins and ventral fins placed forward under the pectorals.

The Labyrinth fishes are now usually placed with the above families in the Percomorphi, but are often relegated to a separate order or suborder *(Labyrinthici).* They differ in having a chamber above the gills with which they breathe atmospheric air. The 3 families, Anabantidae, Luciocephalidae, and Channidae, form this order. All of them are Old World fresh-water fishes.

Another group often separated from the *Percomorphi* but which is usually included in that group as a suborder *(Gobioidei)* are the Gobies. This division includes the true Gobies, the Eleotrids, the Periophthalmids, and a few little-known families, peculiar fishes found on the coasts of all the continents. A few inhabit fresh water. The spiny and soft dorsal fins are separate, giving the appearance of a double dorsal, and the ventrals are far forward, either set very close together or united into a sucking disk.

The order *Opisthomi,* or Spiny Eels, includes elongated, long-snouted fresh-water fishes of the Old World with a great many free spines in front of the dorsal. The only fish in the book belonging to this order is *Macrognathus.*

Finally, we have the order *Plectognathi,* which includes the Puffers and Trigger-fishes. Many of them have the teeth fused together into a beak, with which they can give a bad nip. Nearly all are salt-water fishes, but a few of the smaller puffers come up into fresh-water streams. A few are used as aquarium fishes.

If the reader has scanned the foregoing with care, he will see at once that the terms "order," "family," "genus," and "species," all mean something definite in fish classification. The term "family" is the one most frequently misused by aquarists. We see many references to the "Panchax family," the "egg-laying family" or the "livebearing family." Such uses of the term family have no meaning and will not be followed by the careful aquarist. Instead of the *"Barbus* family" one should say the "genus *Barbus"* (which belongs to the Carp family). Further, all live-bearers do not belong to one family; witness the livebearing Half-beak, *Dermogenys*.

The first word in the name of a fish is the genus to which it belongs; the second is the species, and ordinarily is the last sub-division, although sometimes a less important peculiarity is taken into account and made into a sub-species, race, or variety; for instance, *Xiphophorus maculatus*, var. *ruber*. "Variety" should never be used in any other sense. It is always *within* a species.

When no specific name is given a fish, but the word "species" is used, it means that we know the genus to which it belongs, but not the species. An example would be "*Corydoras* species" or "spec." as it is often written.

It should also be noted that the singular of species is species, not "specie." The plural of genus is genera.

Sometimes after a fish has just been referred to by its full scientific name, the generic name is abbreviated on following repetitions, such as *Scatophagus argus* being repeated as *S. argus*.

Last of all, we turn our attention to that bugbear of aquarist and scientist alike, changes in scientific names. We can only say on this point that "names do change" in accordance with the progress of ichthyological research. The chief source of confusion has been the hurry and carelessness of some aquarists in clapping any name on a newly imported fish before it has been carefully identified. Later check-up usually shows such names to be erroneous, with consequent aquaristic brain-ache. Sometimes modern research has made changes necessary, but where the job has been done well, we may expect relative permanence before a particular group is again subjected to revision.

In our main heading for each fish is given the name of the scientist who first described it. This is in accord with universal practice. There is one point in connection with this which is not always understood. It will be noticed that sometimes this name is in parentheses. This means that there have been developments since the original naming which require that the fish be moved into some other genus (the first name) than that in which it was originally placed. When this is done, the original describer is retained, but his name is placed in parentheses.

Aquarists wishing to have rare or other fishes identified should preserve them in rubbing alcohol. Send to some large scientific institution having a department of fishes, giving as nearly as possible the location from which they were collected.

Pronunciation
of the scientific names of fishes

AS "rare Ben Jonson" expressed it, most of us have "little Latin and less Greek," yet we aquarists would like to be able to acceptably pronounce the scientific names of our fishes.

The writer has therefore consulted leading scientists and scholars. In the main, all agree. The few differences of opinion occur principally as to which syllables in long words take the accent.

Generally speaking, there is an accepted English standard of pronouncing scientific names. This, however, is not inflexible, nor without its exceptions. As with all language, it is influenced by popular usage.

And now a word about the modern system. English botanists, so far as we can learn, were the first large group of scientists to address themselves seriously to this matter. Nearly a century ago they decided to modernize Latin and Greek names by giving English pronunciation to the vowels. At the same time they devised a method of simultaneously indicating the vowels to be accented and whether those vowels take the long or short English sound. The very simple system consists of the use of the French acute mark (´) over the vowel to indicate the short, and the grave (`) to indicate the long sound. This system proved so satisfactory that it has continued and is now in practically universal use in all works of science written in English in which pronunciations are given. Under each fish illustration in this book we have given the pronunciation of its name by the use of the accent system, and have also spelled it out phonetically.

It will be noted that in the phonetic spellings, both single and double accents are used. The double mark shows which syllable takes the stronger accent.

The pronunciation of the vowels, long or short, according to the marks are as in the following words:

Long à as in hay; short á as in hat.
Broad ä as in bar.
Long è as in key; short é as in met.
Long ì as in tie; short í as in hit.
Long ò as in toe; short ó as in top.
Long ù as in cue; short ú as in nut.

Aquarists will be relieved to know that the consonants C and P, queerly used in the beginning of such words as *Ctenobrycon,* and *Pterophyllum* are silent. They represent Greek sounds which have no English equivalents.

Fishes

KEY TO BREEDING HABITS

IN FOLLOWING PAGES

All fishes in this book are arranged in family groups. At the start of each family its general characteristics are described. These are not usually repeated for the species comprising the group because most of them follow the same life pattern. Special traits, if any, of species, however, are covered on their individual pages.

Still further practical directions applying to the kind of fish under consideration will be found within one of 4 very important headings listed in the "Contents" (page 6), under "Fishes." They are:

> BREEDING THE EGG-SCATTERERS
> BREEDING THE LIVE-BEARERS
> BREEDING THE BUBBLE-NEST BUILDERS
> BREEDING THE CICHLIDS

Add to these the chapter on "Fishfoods," and we have a working basis which is as complete as our present knowledge can make it.

123

THE BONY-TONGUES
FAMILY OSTEOGLOSSIDAE
Pronounced Os'tee-o-gloss"i-dee

Only five species of this ancient family of herring-like fresh-water fishes still exist: *Scleropages leichardti* in Queensland, Australia, and southern New Guinea; *S. formosus* in Indo-China, Siam, Malaya, Borneo and Sumatra; *Clupisudis niloticus* in tropical Africa; and two in northern South America, *Arapaima gigas* and *Osteoglossum bicirrhosum*. All grow to two feet or more in length, the pirarucú of the Amazon *(Arapaima)* growing to about 8 feet. All are voracious and have sharp teeth, all have notably large scales, and all seem to be mouthbreeders.

Osteoglossum bicirrhosum (VANDELLI) SPIX AND AGGASSIZ

Pronounced Os'tee-o-gloss"um by'seer-ro"sum   Popular name, Aruaná or Arowaná
MEANING OF NAME: *Osteoglossum,* bony tongue; *bicirrhosum,* with two cirri or barbels
Amazon River and Guiana   Western Location Map z16 and J8 to G30
Length, to over 3 feet

YOUNG Aruaná (pronounced are-oo-ah-nah') are sometimes imported and make interesting and striking aquarium pets if kept alone or with fishes too large to be swallowed by their capacious mouths. They are probably the most graceful, smooth-flowing swimmers of our aquarium fishes. The two forward-projecting barbels, which are leaf-like though narrow, the large alert eyes, and the continuous graceful motion make this fish unique. The Aruaná likes live food. Temperature 75 to 80 degrees.

THE AFRICAN FRESH-WATER FLYING FISH

FAMILY PANTODONTIDAE
Pronounced Pan to don' ti dee

This family includes only one species, the Butterfly-fish of the aquarist, which comes from West Africa. Its nearest relatives are the members of the Osteoglossidae, a family of large fishes which includes the Pirarucú of the Amazon, one of the largest of fresh-water fishes. The chief distinguishing features of *Pantodon* lie in the teeth and certain peculiarities in the skeleton.

Pántodon bùchholzi PETERS

Pronounced Pan'to-don book'holts-eye   *Popular name,* Butterfly-fish

MEANING OF NAME: *Pantodon,* with teeth everywhere (in the mouth); *buchholzi,* after the naturalist, Buchholz

W. Africa   Western Location Map A57; x61; C64; E65   Length, 5 inches

NO finely drawn description of this bizarre fish is needed to help the reader single it out from close relatives, for it has none. However, when we see the picture of so extraordinary a fish, we wish to know something of its peculiarities, and the uses for its fantastic fins.

This is in reality a fresh-water flying fish, the immense pectoral fins being even larger and more extended than a side illustration can show. The fish spends much time at the surface of the water, and is said to skim along it for at least 6 feet at a leap.

The fish is strictly a surface feeder and can be trained to take food from the fingers, such as strips of lean raw beef, meal worms, inch-long live fish or bigger earth worms.

Breeding Butterfly Fish is a rare achievement. Males are slimmer and have bigger "wings" in proportion, also longer anal fins. In the family group illustration the parent at the left is the female. Very large floating eggs hatch in a week at 75 degrees. Young look like little tadpoles. They remain at the surface; therefore must have newly-hatched mosquito larvae or else a sufficiently large supply of food like smallest sifted Daphnia so that many of them must be at the top of the water. Lowering the water level about 2 inches is a trick helping to bring the baby fish and the food together. The young can presently be weaned to taking some dry food that floats. The species is naturally long-lived, but often comes to an untimely end by leaping out when a forgetful aquarist fails to quickly replace cover on the tank (which should be 15-gallon size or larger). They snatch and swallow small surface fishes that come too close.

A FAMILY OF PANTODONS OF MIXED AGES

THE MORMYRIDS OR ELEPHANT-FISHES
FAMILY MORMYRIDAE
Pronounced Mor-my'ri-dee

These curious-looking fresh-water fishes are found only in tropical Africa. Some kinds have the jaws short and blunt, while in others a long, down-curved snout is present. Some have weak electric organs, perhaps used for communication. Finally, they have the largest brain for their size of any known fishes. Several species have been imported since 1954, of which perhaps the best known is the following.

Gnathonemus petersi (GUENTHER)
Pronounced Nay'tho-nee'mus   peters-eye
MEANING OF NAME: *Gnathonemus,* jaw-thread; *petersi,* for Dr. Wilhelm Peters, Berlin zoologist.

Niger River to Congo River   Western location map A56 to G61   Length, up to 9 inches

ALTHOUGH this odd-appearing fish has a rather stiff body and often remains still, it is nervous and is capable of rapid movement. Should be kept in a large, well-planted tank. While aggressive toward smaller fishes, it seems not to kill. The extension of the lower jaw is flexible and in Nature might be used in digging worms from soil. Brine shrimp, white worms or other live foods are needed. These are taken in the ordinary way. Breeding habits unknown. Temperature about 75 degrees. *(Photo by Wm. Harsell)*

127

THE FAMILY MAPS

$\mathcal{A}$S THE following is the first of our seven family maps, showing the world distribution of the principal groups of fresh-water aquarium fishes, a few comments may prove of interest.

What constitutes a family and its sub-divisions has already been explained. It will therefore be understood that the black areas indicate the distribution of all genera and species included in that family for which each map is made.

One of the first questions that naturally presents itself on viewing any of the maps showing a family which inhabits both the Old and the New Worlds is whether there are identical fresh-water species found on both sides of the Atlantic. The answer is that there are not any. Whether they have once been the same and then changed, owing to millions of generations under different environment is, and is likely to remain, an open question. There are scientists who believe that the Old and the New Worlds were once one, and then split apart, the Atlantic Ocean filling the vast intervening space. A glance at the map easily shows the basis for this theory. Push the Americas and Greenland eastward and the fit is not bad.

Various kinds of life, especially plants with fish eggs and microscopic organisms attached to them, have undoubtedly been introduced into new waters while clinging to the feet of aquatic birds. To span the Atlantic in its present size by this means would, of course, be out of the question on several counts, the one that would first occur to the aquarist being that the eggs would have dried long before their hatching period had been reached.

In some parts of the world, such as S. E. Asia, it is quite certain that man himself has increased distribution by carrying fishes from point to point.

The boundaries of distribution of many forms of life, including fishes, are now so well known that if a species is found far outside its natural family range, it would be taken for granted that it had been artificially introduced, the same as an Oregon Fir tree being found in England, or an African Lion discovered in the neighborhood of Hollywood, California!

Many of our aquarium fishes have been introduced into parts of the world to which they are not native. Some have prospered and are found wild in their new homes. Our maps, which were prepared by Dr. Myers, show only the original, or natural, distribution.

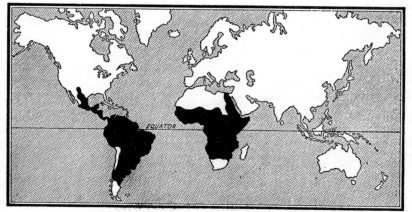

THE CHARACINS

FAMILY CHARACIDAE
Pronounced Ka-ra'si-dee

The Characins (pronounced kà ra sins) form one of the largest families of fishes in the world. They are all from Tropical America and Africa, as will be seen from the accompanying map. They belong to the great order Ostariophysi, together with the Carps and Catfishes. Many Characins look much like some species of Carps (Cyprinidae), but the aquarist seldom has trouble distinguishing members of the two families. No Carp ever has any teeth in the jaws, or any adipose fin. Most Characins possess both teeth and an adipose fin. Some lack one or the other, but few or no species lack both, and if aquarists will remember this "one-or-the-other" combination, they will seldom be puzzled. The presence of teeth in a small live fish is easily determined by running a pin or needle lightly along the upper jaw of a fish held gently but firmly in a wet cloth or net. (Some Characins have teeth only in the upper jaw.) Internally they differ from the Carps in the bones of the throat. All Characins have scales, excepting two very rare species from Argentina.

While there is considerable variation in members of the family as to size, shape and habits, ranging from the dainty water-skimming little *Carnegiella* to the blood-thirsty Piranha, there is usually a suggestion of uniformity that is not hard to discover.

Most of them are fairly hardy, considering that they come from tropical regions.

Generally speaking, they are not fighters, although any fish with good teeth is liable to use them. This sometimes results in a little sly nipping of fins. It takes place so seldom, and without any outward appearance of fighting, that it is hard to detect. On the whole they are peaceful and seldom kill.

In the matter of food most of them are easily pleased with an average fish diet. They appreciate variety, especially when it tends towards live foods and fleshy substance, such as minced fish or shellfish, either boiled or raw.

"Tetras" In those earlier days of the exotic fish hobby, a number of Characins were included in the genus *Tetragonopterus*, a generic name still used for a small genus, but under which many of our aquarium fishes used to be placed. It became the trade practice to apply "Tet" or "Tetra" as a blanket name to all Characins, especially the small ones, such as "Tet from Rio," "Lemon Tetra," "Black Tetra," "Neon Tetra"; also the "Silver Tetra," which is not small. The name "Tetra" has become well entrenched in popular usage, but has no present scientific standing.

Breeding and Care Very few of the species are easily bred. They offer an interesting challenge to the aquarist in that respect. A number of them yield to skillful handling, yet several of the most desirable species, such as *Hyphessobrycon heterorhabdus* (better known as *Hemigrammus ulreyi*), still oblige us to import native specimens in order to keep up our stocks.

With the few exceptions to be noted, Characins drop adhesive or semi-adhesive eggs, to which they pay no attention, except, perhaps, for the doubtful compliment of eating them. Failing this, they are likely to make up for the oversight by devouring the young. Not any or them fight in defense of their fry, as do the Cichlids and Bubble Nest-builders.

In general the Characins are not fishes requiring very "tropical" temperature. They do very well in water at from 70 to 75 degrees, although for breeding, it should, in some instances, be raised to 80. If kept at constantly high temperatures, the diminished oxygen content of the water seems to have a weakening effect on these and many other "tropical" fishes.

It has been found that some of the species spawn more readily in "soft" water. Indeed it may be hoped that this is the key to unlocking the difficulty of breeding this large and important family of fishes.

Breeding the Egg-scatterers

(Characins and Carps)

UNLIKE native fishes, most exotics have the advantage that they can be bred at any time of year if proper conditions are provided.

There are several classes of Egg-scatterers. Mainly, those which drop non-adhesive eggs (like *Brachydanio rerio*), those which scatter or drop adhesive eggs (like the Barbs), those placing eggs in bubble nests (described under "Labyrinth Bubble-nest Builders"), and those which carefully place adhesive eggs. The last are fully covered under the general heading, "The Cichlids."

We dwell here principally on that large and important class which scatters adhesive eggs, and particularly on the culture of all newly hatched fishes which are very small in size. That includes nearly all the classes of Egg-layers just referred to. It takes in most of the Characins, the Carps or Minnows, the Egg-laying Tooth-carps and others.

In general the requirements for breeders of this type are similar. The aquarium should have a reasonable amount of open space, but with thickets of plants having finely divided leaves, such as Myriophyllum.

For this purpose such plants can be added to an already established aquarium containing Sagittaria, Vallisneria, etc. Myriophyllum, in addition to its excellent form for egg-catching, also has the advantage of being easily removed, either with or without the eggs attached. Plenty of

Lyretails spawning in a green nylon mop, secured in a collar of cork. Mop may be dried and used repeatedly. Fishes accept it readily. Eggs are easily seen. An excellent substitute for egg-receiving plants like Myriophyllum. Easily made or purchased. Photographed at half size.

the floating plant, Riccia, is perfect for some of the species which like to spawn near the surface. Water Hyacinth is also good for catching and holding adhesive eggs spawned at or near the top. Reference to the chapter on plants will suggest other kinds.

Many fishes are more apt to spawn if previously separated a few days from their mates. "Absence makes the heart grow fonder." It is usually best to place the female in the breeding tank half a day in advance of the male. Feed rather often on the best foods obtainable, preferably live ones, or at least fresh ones, such as fine bits of raw fish, crab meat, shrimp, or chopped earthworms. Unless there is an abundance of room, aeration helps. A partial change of water sometimes stimulates spawning or delivery.

Remove breeders after spawning, or take out the plants bearing the eggs, and place them in seasoned water of equal temperature.

The greatest problem in fish culture is the first food.

Most fishes when hatched are more egg than fish. Some of them seem like a splinter attached sidewise to a ball. Gradually the fish enlarges and develops fins, while the ball contracts until it is a mere lump on the abdomen. It is the yolk sac. So long as it is visible it is Nature's reservoir of nourishment. Usually the babies are not much in evidence during this period. Being helpless to avoid enemies, they hover or hop about the bottom. Sac soon absorbed, the fish becomes more streamlined and takes to the open water. It is on its own.

The aquarist's problem right here, and for the next week or two, is to have enough of the right sizes and kinds of food ready. Standard directions say "feed infusoria." Sounds simple enough, and it *is,* if we are lucky. Infusoria covers a multitude of sizes and kinds of organisms. The predominating one in most prepared cultures is Paramecium, which happens to be only a fair food. It is mostly shell and not very fleshy. It is also too big for the smaller species of fry. On it the larger babies can usually bridge over this period. It is fortunate when the culture has enough of the smaller organisms to feed the tiniest youngsters. For them one of the best starts is a supply of green water. It feeds the very small animals that the fishes need. (See paragraphs under "Infusoria.")

Having passed the feeding point where infusorians are outgrown, something larger must be found. There are several choices. For fishes that have definitely grown, but are still small, the next perfect food is that rotifer, *Brachionus rubens,* previously described and pictured. Newly hatched Brine Shrimp, propagated in marine water from commercially supplied eggs, are a Godsend to breeders unable to secure the needed sizes of pond foods. They fill in nicely at this stage. Live sifted young Daphnia is a third choice, and of course a very good one. Naturally the next step is *adult* Daphnia, if obtainable. Chopped White Worms are substitutes. From this point they can, if necessary, be weaned to any foods they will take. With care they are now as good as raised.

Repeatedly it has been found that more youngsters can be brought through early infancy in an oversized, long-established tank. This is no doubt due to its containing more microscopic food of suitable sizes and quality. About the only way to bring through a large proportion of very small fry in a *small* tank is to feed them often on natural pond infusoria. As these organisms appear in usable quantity at unpredictable times, we have here an element of luck. It may be asked why scientific aquarists do not make continuous pure cultures of the best of the live micro-foods. This would indeed solve a problem and at least quadruple the output of fishes. It has been tried, but not successfully. However, it is the observation of experienced breeders that pond infusoria gives much better results than the cultured kinds.

Despite the difficulties considered here, the fact remains that most species of aquarium fishes *are* successfully reared.

How much infusoria to feed is an important question that cannot be answered in any exact way. *The bellies of the babies should bulge.* One soon learns to judge this. On the other hand, there ought *not* be *too much* live food present. It depletes oxygen and annoys the fishes. The amount of liquid to feed depends on the richness of the culture and the number of fry. It might be a spoonful or a cupful. A low-power microscope is important here. Examine the culture. It should be rich in life. Use with judgment. A test drop of water taken from the surface of the light side of the aquarium should show plenty of organisms.

Unfortunately it must be recognized that many, many ambitious aquarists are unable to secure even a few Daphnia, nor any good infusoria. By care they can succeed in a lesser degree. As has been mentioned elsewhere, there are fairly good substitutes for Daphnia, such as finely minced White Worms or grated raw shrimp. Some fishes have been reared on prepared dry foods, starting with flour size. Mashed yellow of egg, shaken in a bottle of water, sparingly fed, is an acceptable early food. It is almost impossible not to overfeed with prepared foods, so when using them it is well to have a number of small snails present to consume the surplus, but only *after* the eggs have hatched.

Inequality in the size of youngsters always puzzles the beginner. None can tell why it is any more than in human beings. Some fishes are no doubt born more vigorous than others. They get "the jump" by bolting the biggest and best food. Presently they become large enough to eat the smallest of their brethren. As these make the best of food, the disproportion increases. It is Nature's way. A plentiful early supply of the small live foods tends to equalize growth.

Ordinarily the young should not be placed with their parents or other fishes if there is enough difference in size so that they *might* be eaten!

Hyphessobrỳcon schòlzei AHL

Pronounced Hy-fess'o-bry"kon shol'ze-eye

MEANING OF NAME: *Hyphessobrycon*, little Brycon; *scholzei* in honor
of the aquarist Scholze.

Popular names, Black-line Tetra, and incorrectly African Tetra and *Aleta nigrans.*

Lower Amazon   Western Location Map G28   Length, 2½ inches

THROUGH no fault of its own, nor of Ahl, who correctly named it in
1937, this species was later introduced to aquarists as *Aleta nigrans,* a
name probably concocted by some dealer, who made "confusion twice con-
founded" by stating that it came from Africa, instead of South America,
confusing it with *Nannaethiops unitaeniatus,* the real "African Tetra."

Usually the white first rays on the anal fin are more pronounced in the
female, but this is not a dependable means of telling the sexes. In the
illustration the slightly deeper outline of the upper fish indicates the female. Her sides are slightly brassy.

These are among the few prolific, easily-bred Characins. Their adhesive eggs are deposited on feathery plants. An active, vigorous species
in all ways. Individuals are apt to develop bad "chasing" habits in a
community tank, and they are fatal to fishes small enough to be swallowed. Temperature, 65-80 degrees.

COLOR PLATE PAGE 546

Phenácográmmus interrúptus. (BOULENGER)

Pronounced Fee-nack"o-gram'mus in'ter-rup"tus   *Popular name,* Feathertail Tetra
MEANING OF NAME: *Phenacogrammus,* false line; *interruptus,* interrupted;
both names referring to the incomplete lateral line.

Congo River   Western Location Map G61   Length, 3 inches

HIS interesting tetra from Africa grows what look to be feathers on
the tail, hence the popular name. This happens only in the male,
as shown in our photo. The female, when adult, has shorter fins and
never grows quite as large as her mate.

This fish might be said to have many color phases, but more truly
they are prismatic effects according to how the light strikes their scales,
and the relative position of the observer. With a dark background and
the light coming from in back of the observer, brilliant prismatic colors
follow each other in endless variety, mostly blue, green and yellow,
inadequately hinted at in our color plate. Held in the air in net, under
flashlight the color effect is startlingly gaudy. Under ordinary aquarium
lighting, little or no color shows. The fish likes to hide, a tendency that
should not be encouraged. In other words, refuge should not be provided
for this timid fish if one wishes to enjoy its full beauty.

The Feathertail is one of the larger tetras and should not be kept
with much smaller species. It prefers soft, acid water.

Nematobrycon palmeri

Pronounced Ne-mat'-o-bry"kon palm-er"eye   *Popular name,* Emperor Tetra
Length, Male 2 inches; Female 1¼ inches
Colombia, S. A.   Western Location Map B-13

   HIS species was introduced to aquarists in the early 60's and because of its ethereal beauty, became a favorite as soon as it was made available. A black line running from the eye to the pedunclecaudal fades and picks up again to reach the center point of the three-tined tail. The edge of the tapered dorsal is accented along the upper edge, and the tines of the tail, anal and ventral fins are similarly outlined. These markings alone give the species a peculiar beauty but the blue and red shadings that follow the black body line are particularly exquisite, and the faintly yellow fins with edges finely terminating in black made this fish one of superb subtle beauty. The females carry the same distinguishing features but are less vividly colored.

   This is a relatively hardy fish, and its water requirements are not critical. A few days of live-food feedings seem to promote spawning activity, but for a successful group spawning, the males should be of equal size. One large male will have a tendency to herd the females away from the others. Mops or floating bunch plants such as *Nitella* of *Myriophyllum* may be used as a spawning medium. The male attracts the female by trembling movements, and here his graceful finnage comes into play. The actual spawning takes place when the male pursues the female into a mop or floating plant, and as the fish emerge, the eggs are expelled.

   The eggs are difficult to see but within three days after becoming free-swimming the young are ready to take brine shrimp. Growth is rapid and raising this delicately beautiful fish is particularly rewarding. Edited by H.S.

Hyphessobrỳcon bifasciàtus ELLIS

Pronounced Hy-fess′o-bry″kon by′fas-see-a″tus   *Popular name,* Yellow Tet

MEANING OF NAME: *Hyphessobrycon,* small Brycon; *bifasciatus,* two-banded

S. E. Brazil   Western Location Map U31 to Z26   Length, 2¼ inches

A FORMER favorite that of recent years has been outshone by its
more colorful relatives, and by its other self, the "Brass Tet."

It is a rather plain fish, overcast with dark yellow, yet not lacking in a
pleasant, variable iridescence. On the sides, just in back of the head, are
two vertical dark bars, of variable intensity, reminding one of well-known
markings on *Hyphessobrycon flammeus.* These show more plainly on the
fish to the left (the male).

In addition to being a good aquarium fish, suited to the community
tank, it is one of the few Characins that breeds readily. Formerly the
species was multiplied here in large numbers, so great was the demand
for it. Breeding conditions are the same as those described for its cousin,
Hyphessobrycon flammeus. The male has the broader anal fin.

A peculiarity of the young is that at the size of an inch or less, they
look like very fine Bloodfins, so fiery are their fin bases. A young one is
shown in the inset.

This species shares with other "Tets" in a lesser degree, the lengthen-
ing, with age, of points of the lower fins, especially the ventrals. The extra
growth begins at from one to two years of age, and continues throughout
the life of the fish. Temperature range, 68 to 85 degrees. Peaceful.

COLOR PLATE PAGE 546

Hyphéssobrỳcon flámmeus MYERS
Pronounced Hy-fess'o-bry"kon flam'me-us
MEANING OF NAME: *Hyphessobrycon,* little Brycon; *flammeus,* flame-like
Popular names, Tetra from Rio, Red Tet and Flame Fish
Vicinity, Rio de Janeiro   Western Location Map U31   Length, 1½ inches

*B*EAUTY has no relation to bulk. It only needs be large enough to be seen and appreciated. For that reason the smaller exotic fishes have gradually increased in popularity, because the little ones make small demands for space.

An inch-and-a-half size is, by many aquarists, regarded as ideal. The "Tet from Rio" is just that kind of a fish, and has all the other points of merit that could well be asked for. Its color pattern is brilliant and so simple that nothing is sacrificed to its small size; it is harmless, reasonably hardy, easily cared for and can be bred—but not so easily as to become uninteresting.

Professional breeders, especially in Europe, produce these fishes in such numbers that we are independent of direct importations for our new stock. The price is never in the dirt-cheap range.

Like many of our exotic fishes, *H. flammeus* needs favorable conditions in which to develop its best colors. Plenty of room in a well-planted aquarium, an occasional extra meal of Daphnia, or other live food, and a temperature of about 75 degrees will soon bring on "show condition."

The sexes may be told in several ways. The males have the Characin hooks on the end of the anal fin, which stick to a fine-mesh net when the fish is turned out. The anal fin of the male is fuller than that of the female. Its outline is more nearly straight. Hers is more concave, and pointed. In our illustration there are three males and two females, judged by this standard. It is said that the abdominal sac, when viewed *through* the light, is more pointed in the male than in the female. Color is not a dependable index.

This species is one that should be bred where at least a part of the aquarium has a thicket of finely divided leaves, such as Myriophyllum. After lively driving by the male, the fishes take a close parallel position among the plants. Accompanied by a little trembling, about 10 eggs are dropped and fertilized. This is repeated until 100 or more eggs are produced. They are small, nearly transparent and slightly adhesive. If not disturbed, they will remain fairly well on the plants, but those which fall may hatch. The young, at a temperature of 75 degrees, appear in three days. They are almost as transparent as the eggs. Green water is a good first food for them, but fine infusoria will do. Should no live food be available, a flour made of ordinary fishfood may serve the purpose. Considering the almost microscopic size of the young when hatched, it is surprising to find that when well fed they will be two-thirds grown in less than six months.

As a matter of practise, it is found that a higher percentage of eggs hatch when two males are used with a female.

The spawning fishes do not usually eat their eggs until the egg-laying is finished, at which time the breeders should be removed. As most fishes prefer eating Daphnia rather than their own eggs, it is a good plan to have a few Daphnia present during spawning, but not enough of them to create a problem after the young are hatched, for too many can crowd out and suffocate the baby fishes, and the infusoria, too.

The temperature range for the species is from 70 to 80 degrees.

For small fishes they are rather long-lived, attaining a ripe old age of from 3 to 4 years.

Dr. Myers found them not far from Rio de Janeiro in gorgeous color in brown, swampy waters at temperatures in the low seventies. He believes it would be well worth the attempt to breed them in the acid brown waters of the pine barrens and cedar swamps of New Jersey or elsewhere.

Hyphéssobrỳcon èos   **DURBIN**

Pronounced Hy-fess-o-bry'kon   e'os   *Popular name,* Dawn Tetra

MEANING OF NAME: *Eos,* Greek goddess of the dawn, from the rosy color

British Guiana   Western Location Map A21   Length, 1¾ inches

OUR subject here is one of the newer and not-so-well-known little Characins. To paint a word picture of its colors that would not mislead the reader, and yet do justice to the fish, is not easy. It has glowing tints and shades rather than clear-cut colors and markings, all variable according to how the light strikes. Taken from the shipping can and examined casually it has nothing that is outstanding. A more careful observation after the fish has become settled in sympathetic surroundings reveals a species of considerable charm. The body glows with a warm gold-to-copper, overtoned by an iridescent red and orange. Numerous small black spots on the body give a rather deep tone to the fish, contrasting with golden yellow in the fins, especially in the anal and the base of the tail fin, where the color deepens almost to red. Where the body joins the tail fin (the caudal peduncle) there is a strong oblong dark spot, barely visible in the illustration. Above this is a pale gold highlight. As in many fishes, the gill covers show a pleasing flash of blue-green. In its nature, habits, and general requirements, it is the same as other small Characins. It has been successfully bred.

COLOR PLATE PAGE 547

Hyphéssobrỳcon ínnesi MYERS

Pronounced Hy-fess'o-bry"kon in'nis-eye   *Popular name,* Neon Tetra

MEANING OF NAME: Named for the author, Wm. T. Innes

Brazilian-Peruvian border: far western Brazilian Amazon;
extreme eastern Peruvian Amazon

Western Location Map H14 to J11   Length, 1¼ inches

$\mathcal{A}$S THIS fish is generally regarded as the aristocrat of small aquarium personalities, some comments regarding its comparatively recent introduction and its peculiarities should be of interest.

Early in 1936 a young French banker, J. S. Neel, in the course of correspondence with the author, wrote that he had received from Brazil, through M. Rabaut, a French collector, "the most beautiful of aquarium fishes," and offered to prove his case by sending two pairs. The offer was accepted, but lightly, and with mental reservations born of former disappointments. They arrived in due course and made an instant hit; the universal acclaim with which they were greeted established history in our hobby.

Other larger importations followed, the second being of 10,000. As these were sold to a New York importer at an unheard-of high price for a whole-sale quantity, this probably constituted the largest single deal in the history of the trade. Dealers quickly exhausted the apparently inexhaustible supply and everybody was happy, except perhaps the breeders who hoped to cash in on young from this new, sensational fish.

Nothing would please us quite so much as to be able to give our readers a simple, sure-fire method of breeding this little beauty. Such a formula is not known. Enormous numbers have been imported since their introduction, and thousands of aquarists have tried. Very few have succeeded and still fewer have been able to repeat.

The old "law of compensation" seems to get in its stealthy work. Thus for its surpassing beauty, hardiness and perfect disposition it pays with two weak points. First, it is subject to a mysterious "Neon disease," causing body wasting and loss of color. The second is one with which we are particularly concerned here—the dissolving of the eggs, caused by penetration by bacteria. Overcoming that tendency is the most important and difficult step towards success. Spawning is frequent.

Select young breeders, domestic-raised, if available. Water should be slightly acid, soft and reasonably sterile. Distilled water, with 2 level teaspoons of salt to the gallon is one way of producing those conditions.

Sexes look alike, but the ripe females are easily told by their increased girth. Prepare breeders by separating them and feeding on live foods, such as Brine shrimp or on White Worms that have been kept in clean water for 24 hours. Breeding tank should be bare (no plants) and previously treated with salt brine or other germ deterrent that can easily be washed away with distilled water. Use light aeration. Place pair together in breeding tank in the evening. Arrange for very soft light next day. Spawn is difficult to detect. A flashlight helps. Eggs are non-adhesive and may be lifted by dip tube. Whether left where they fall or are transferred, they must be kept in virtual darkness until hatched (takes 2 days) and are free-swimming. Gradually increase light.

First food, yellow of hard-boiled egg strained through fine cloth, placed in a half-filled stoppered bottle of distilled water and shaken. Boil bottle and contents ten minutes; cool and place in refrigerator. It will keep for two weeks. To feed, shake the bottle and use single drops very sparingly. After a week, change to a floating flour-fine dry food, and in two weeks to newly-hatched Brine Shrimp. After that, sifted live Daphnia. From then on they are as good as raised.

Suitable temperature for Neons, between 72 and 76 degrees. For any further suggestions on hardness and pH of water, see the last chapter on General Information.

COLOR PLATE PAGE 547

Cheirodon axelrodi

Pronounced Ki'-ro-don   *Popular name,* Cardinal Tetra
Upper Rio Negro, Brazil   Western Location Map E16 to F18   Length, 1½ inches

U NTIL a decision made by the International Commission on Zoological Nomenclature, this fish was known as *Hyphessobrycon cardinalis* (Myers and Weitzman). The species appeared on the aquarium scene in the winter 1955-1956, and has since filled a similar position in the hobby as does *Hyphessobrycon innesi* which it resembles. The red is more pronounced in *Cheirodon axelrodi,* however, and runs up on the head. The blue line has a slightly more golden tinge, and the body is somewhat slimmer. According to Dr. Harold Sioli, who collected the fish on the Upper Rio Negro in 1952, the original discoverer was probably Mr. Praetorius, but it was not until Paramount's first importation of 1955 that the fish was seen in the United States.

The fish comes from brown, very soft, very acid water (pH 4.8 to 5.2, according to Dr. Sioli) and it is probably due to the lack of such water that most of the first shipment to the United States did not live.

The Cardinal Tetra has been successfully spawned and for this information see *Hyphessobrycon innesi.* Edited by H. S.

"Brass Tets"

JUST what the above name means to science is anybody's guess. To aquarists it conveys a fairly definite idea. In about 1929 a number of opaquely bright, slightly brassy, glistening "Tets" were imported. They were very distinctive and took fish fanciers by storm. None knew their scientific identity. The body seemed a little deeper than in the "Yellow Tet" (*Hyphessobrycon bifasciatus*), and the fins spread more saucily. Our photograph is from one of the characteristic early importations, and is approximately life size.

Now let it be said that the multitude of variations in closely similar plain "Tets" is a problem remaining to be unravelled. "Brass Tets" with other shaped bodies began to appear—four apparent kinds in all. It is now the settled conviction that the brassiness is purely an individual (and a rare) variation. It does not in any case seem to be a species, nor even a race, for of the thousands of them that have been bred in captivity we have not heard of one offspring that showed the peculiar color, even when bred from two first-class parents.

One of the peculiarities of this and many of the "Tets" is that with age they develop long, streaming points on the ventral fins.

(*Later:* Field observations by Dr. Myers prove that these "brass" fishes are individual "*sports.*")

COLOR PLATE PAGE 548

Hyphéssobrỳcon púlchripinnis AHL
Pronounced Hy-fess-o-brỳ'kon pul'kre-pin"niss   *Popular name,* Lemon Tetra
Incorrectly known as *H. erythrophthalmus*
MEANING OF NAME: *pulchripinnis,* pretty-fin
Amazon basin   Western Location Map H20 (approx.)   Length, about 1¾ inches

℘HE popular name of this rather new species seems to be well given. While the fish has a faint yellowish overtone, the color character is accentuated and brought out mostly by the intense yellow edging in the anal fin, and a little of it in the dorsal. Both those fins are usually well spread, giving the species a lively, saucy bearing. As indicated here, bodies are somewhat translucent, the only spot of warm color being the bright red in the upper half of the eye.

Eggs are quite small and the spawning fishes are very successful in gobbling them almost as fast as dropped, which is not surprising in this family of fishes. For this reason it is desirable to provide them with dense plant thickets, and with not too deep water — say about 6 to 7 inches. They have been known to spawn on the exposed roots of plants.

An average temperature of about 73-75 degrees suits them very well, but for breeding it should be raised to 78-80.

COLOR PLATE PAGE 548

Hyphessobrỳcon rosàceus DURBIN

Pronounced Hy-fess'o-bry"con   rose-ay'see-us   *Popular name,* Rosy Tetra
MEANING OF NAME: *Hyphessobrycon,* little Brycon; *rosaceus,* rosy
Sometimes known (in Germany) as *H. ornatus*

British Guiana and Brazil   Length, 1¾ inches
Western Location Map A21, G24 and P20

A FISH flying a black flag, but by no means a pirate. In fact it is one of the gentlest and best of aquarium species.

The handsome, over-arching dorsal fin with its great, black blotch, made more vivid by contrasting whites, is nearly always carried with military erectness as the fish darts about the aquarium in its busy way.

The fish is somewhat translucent; the color consequently varies according to whether it is viewed by transmitted or reflected light. At one time it is pale yellow; at others it is gently suffused with red. The red shown along the spinal column seems to be an internal color. Like other species of this type it appears best under strong overhead artificial light. Our photograph was so lighted.

The male (top fish in illustration) at maturity develops the longer dorsal fin, while the female shows a brighter red tip atop the white edging. Breeds the same as *H. flammeus.* Difficult to spawn. Temperature range, 72 to 82 degrees. Ahl identifies a similar fish as *H. ornatus.*

COLOR PLATE PAGE 549

Hyphessobrycon callistus BOULENGER

Pronounced Hy-fess'o-bry"con   cal-lis'tus   *Popular name,* Serpa Tetra
MEANING OF NAME: *Callistus,* pretty sail, in reference to the dorsal fin.
Formerly known as *H. serpae*
Parana-Paraguay System—Western Location Map S27 to W22 Length, 1½ inches

O NE of the most beautiful of small aquarium fishes, but not often seen. The large black spot on the dorsal fin suggests *Pristella riddlei,* but fins are a little shorter and more intensely red. For those who like their fishes quiet, and restful to contemplate, this species is perfect. They seem to prefer a level about ⅓ way up from the bottom, but are always on the alert to dash upward to catch falling food. Adipose fins are transparent.

They were first imported into Germany in 1931, and into the United States two years later. As they are hard to spawn they disappeared for some years, and we were without them until large fresh importations to U.S.A. in 1948. As they are now bred with fair success, it seems probable that we can look forward to the prospect of a fairly steady supply. They breed like *Hyphessobrycon flammeus,* but it seems that only a small proportion of females spawn. Mr. Roy Bast gives a detailed account of the action in "The Aquarium," for April, 1949. A charming species, neither timid nor aggressive, and an ornament to any collection of fishes of its own size. They live happily in a temperature between 70 and 80 degrees.

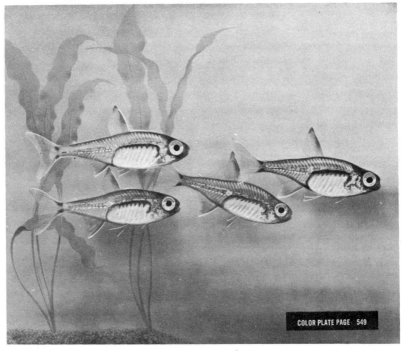

COLOR PLATE PAGE 549

Hemigrammus erythrozonus DURBIN

Pronounced Hem'i-gram"muss er'y-throw-zo"nus   *Popular name,* Glowlight Tetra

MEANING OF NAME: *Hemigrammus,* half-line, in reference to the incomplete
lateral line; *erythrozonus,* with a red zone (stripe)
Formerly known as *Hyphessobrycon gracilis*

Potaro and Mazaruni Rivers, British Guiana   Length, 1¾ inches

THE original importation was discovered by chance in a temporary
overflow pool bordering the Mazaruni River in Guiana. The fishes
proved to be both hardy and prolific, resulting in a firmly-established
and well-distributed breeding stock of this charming fish.

Their breeding action is a little different from most of the Characins,
in that they quickly lock fins, embrace and do a "barrel roll" while about
a dozen eggs are extruded and fertilized. This is repeated. Eggs are
slightly adhesive. A fairly large but loose bunch of Myriophyllum is an
ideal medium for catching them. They are being bred in fair quantities.

Although well suited to life among other fishes of about their size, they
make a beautiful picture as a small school of only their own kind, especially against a darkish background and a top electric light. Temperature, 70 to 80 degrees. Ordinary foods.

COLOR PLATE PAGE 550

Hyphéssobrỳcon heterorhábdus (ULREY)
Pronounced Hy-fess′o-bry″kon het′er-o-rab″dus
MEANING OF NAME: *Hyphessobrycon*, small Brycon; *heterorhabdus*, differently striped
Incorrectly known as *Hemigrammus ulreyi* (see the following)
The Amazon   Western Location Map F29 to G28   Length, 1¾ inches

G IVE this fish its proper setting, and its charm is hard to equal. Certainly it is one of the most attractive gems of all the beautiful cousins comprising the *Hyphessobrycon* group.

What it needs for setting off its fine points is a rather dark background and a strong overhead light, preferably artificial, shielded from the eyes of the observer. The red line almost disappears in an unfavorable light. Probably it is prismatic, and not dependent upon pigment. The difficulty of catching the fish in just the right light may be in part responsible for the author's feeling that this is perhaps his finest set of color plates, for it has caught the group at its best.

Unfortunately we are almost entirely dependent upon importations of native stock, because practically no results have come from the few recorded spawnings.

The males are easily told by the hooks on the anal fin, which cause the fish to stick when lifted from the water in a fine-mesh net. When the net is reversed it takes several light shakings to loosen the fish. As has been elsewhere remarked, these little hooks are imperceptible to the eye. It is something of a vexation that the sex is so easily told in a fish that is so difficult to breed.

The species is moderately hardy and does well in an aquarium containing the smaller sized fishes. Many a fish is not appreciated because it is cast into company out of scale with its own size.

Feedings of live Daphnia are not only much appreciated by them, but are also very beneficial. White worms or brine shrimp are the next-best substitutes.

This fish likes a temperature of about 75 degrees. A slow 5-degree variation either way does it no harm.

The purchaser of this species may need to exercise a bit of patience waiting for the fish to develop its full color. In being transferred from one water to another it is liable to take on a "washed out" appearance, but in a healthy, well-planted aquarium its original beauty will soon return.

Hemigrammus ulreyi (Boulenger), a vary similar species, is deeper in body and lacks the translucent quality of *H. heterorhabdus*, and has no black spot at the tail base. See the following.

Hemigrámmus úlreyi (BOULENGER)

Pronounced Hem'i-gram"muss   ul'ree-eye

MEANING OF NAME: *Hemigrammus,* half-lined, in reference to the incomplete lateral line; *ulreyi,* after the ichthyologist, A. B. Ulrey

Paraguay   Western Location Map Q21 to 22   Length, 1¾ inches

THIS fish is almost an exact duplicate of *Hyphessobrycon heterorhabdus* except that it is deeper bodied and less translucent. It is from Paraguay and only occasionally appears in our aquariums. Aquarists usually confuse the two. We give it a separate heading because many will look for the more slender fish of this name. Personally we have never seen the true *ulreyi* that we know of, and therefore have no photograph. For facts regarding the fish popularly known as *H. ulreyi,* see the illustration and description of the foregoing fish.

Hyphéssobrỳcon perúviànus LADIGES (?)
Pronounced Hy-fess'o-bry"con pe-roo'vee-ay"nus   *Popular name,* Loreto Tetra
MEANING OF NAME: *peruvianus,* Peruvian
Amazon River in Eastern Peru Western Location Map H14 to I11 Length, 1¾ inches

𝒯HIS introduction of 1955 has been imported in fair numbers. With its white-tipped dorsal and anal fins, its wide black stripe bordered above by a coppery line, and its pale red tail, it is a pleasing aquarium fish, offering contrast to the more brilliantly colored species. The dorsal fin is also pale reddish. The photo represents large adults, male to the right, female on the left.

The Loreto Tetra (pronounced Lo-ray'toe) is an active, gentle fish which minds its own business. Like the Neon, Cardinal, and in fact, most of the Amazon tetras, it prefers soft, acid (pH 5.0 to 6.0) water, in which alone it shows its true beauty. Temperature 72 to 76 degrees.

We are not yet certain of the identification of this fish. Some have called it *H. loretoensis* Ladiges but it seems to agree more closely with the technical description of *H. peruvianus.* Both species come from Loreto Province in Peru, as does the Neon.

COLOR PLATE PAGE 550

Hemigrámmus rhodóstomus AHL

Pronounced Hem'-i-gram'muss row-dos'to-muss   *Popular name,* Rummy Nose
MEANING OF NAME: *Hemigrammus,* half-line; *rhodostomus,* rosy-red-mouthed
Brazil   Western Location Map F to G on 28   Length, 2 inches

IRST imported to America in 1933, we included this interesting fish in our first 5 editions, but as no more were forthcoming, and as none had been bred, we dropped it, especially as our black-and-white photograph represented it poorly.

As the fish is again occasionally in stock, and seems likely to remain, we are glad to now include it, especially with this new color photograph, replacing a somewhat inaccurate color sketch recently used.

The reddish glow on the snout, extending over the top of the head, varies in intensity, sometimes barely showing. A small school of them in good color, preferably under a top light, makes a charming picture.

It is unaccountably strange that certain members of a family, outwardly similar, are so much more difficult to breed than some of their cousins. After years of the apparently happy domestication of this attractive species we have no record of its successful propagation. Temperature, 72-78.

Hemigrámmus nánus (LUETKEN)

Pronounced Hem'i-gram"muss nan'us   *Popular name,* Silver Tip Tetra
MEANING OF NAME: *Hemigrammus,* half-line; *nanus,* dwarf
Lagoa Santa, Minas Gerais, S. E. Brazil   Western Location Map S31
Length, 1¼ inches

HIS new little fish with silver-tipped fins is a species apt to be underrated unless seen against a dark background, and preferably under top lighting. Otherwise the effect of the fins is largely lost.

The species occurs both with and without an adipose fin. This has led to some confusion and caused one of Europe's leading ichthyologists to wrongly classify it as *Hasemania marginata,* a name known only in the European trade. It was brought to Germany just prior to World War II, and in 1949 Rakowicz of California made a direct importation.

The species has been freely bred by amateurs, as well as professional wholesalers, among the latter, Mr. O. C. Beldt, who gives an account of the action in "The Aquarium" for November, 1950. It is the same as for other small Characins. The male (upper) has somewhat brighter tips on fins.

Hemigrámmus unilineàtus GILL
Pronounced Hem'i-gram"muss un'i-lin'ee-ay"tus   *Popular name,* Feather Fin
MEANING OF NAME: *Hemigrammus,* half-line; *unilineatus,* one-lined
N. E. South America   Length, 2 inches
Western Location Map x between 18 and 19; y19 to A22; F29; O19

℘HIS Hemigrammus is easily distinguished from the others (and remembered) by the straight black-and-white line down the front edge of the anal fin. The word *unilineatus* meaning "one-line," makes one of those useful memory helps.

The tail fin is faintly suffused with brownish red. Otherwise the fish carries no color, other than the black-and-white shown in the illustration. It is, nevertheless, popular, and is one of the old-time favorites. The body is silver, shading upward to olive. Eye, warm silver. Breeds like *Hyphessobrycon flammeus,* but is much more easily spawned, and the young, being larger, do not require excessively small food at the start. The female is slightly larger than the male.

The fish has those cardinal virtues of being willing to eat practically anything, and of keeping at peace with its companions, whether they are of its own species or not.

This is one of the more hardy of the small Characins, and, owing to its lively ways and easy adaptation to the aquarium, it is in steady demand. It can be found in the stocks of most dealers. Temperature range, 68 to 85 degrees.

COLOR PLATE PAGE 551

Hemìgrámmus océllifer (STEINDACHNER)

Pronounced Hem'i-gram"muss o-sell'if-er *Popular name,* Head-and-tail-light Tetra
MEANING OF NAME: *Hemigrammus,* half-line; *ocellifer,* with eye-like spot
British Guiana and Amazon   Western Location Map A21, F29 to H13
Length, 1¾ inches

"HEAD-and Tail-Light" is one of the popular fishes in the trade, aptly named because the glitter in the eyes and at the base of the tail seems luminous. The three upper fish are males, identified by a faint white spot in the middle of the anal fin. Another similar species has added two white spots a little further down the tail, forming the base of a triangle with the luminous spot. In this species the sex white spot does not show in the anal fin of the male. We must here depend upon fullness of body to indicate the female.

These fishes are rather easily bred for Characins, following the method described at the beginning of this chapter. The result is that the market is usually well supplied with these very good and very attractive aquarium fishes. Their temperature range is about 67 to 84 degrees. They breed best at approximately 76. In the matter of food they are easily suited, but, like most fishes with teeth, they ought to have some meals of fresh animal substances.

COLOR PLATE PAGE 551

Hemigrámmus caudovittàtus AHL

Pronounced Hem'i-gram"muss cau'do-vi-tay"tus *Popular name,* Tet from Buenos Aires

MEANING OF NAME: *Hemigrammus,* half-line; *caudovittatus,* with tail stripe
(through middle)

Argentina   Western Location Map V22   Length, 3½ inches

THIS is the largest of the *Hemigrammus* known to aquarists. Although it has its defenders as a community tank fish, there are known cases where it has been convicted of fin-nipping, particularly after it becomes large. The fish is not so attractive in appearance after it exceeds the size shown in the illustration.

Breeds similarly to the Goldfish, the male chasing the female to thickets, where she drops rather adhesive eggs. Parents must be removed after spawning. Not difficult to spawn, but ought to have a tank of at least 15-gallon capacity. Breeding temperature should be in the neighborhood of 72 to 74 degrees. The species is easily fed and cared for, as may be surmised from its wide temperature range.

The female is slightly the larger and is fuller in outline. Except at the moment of spawning she is the aggressor in chasing the male, sometimes killing him. Temperature range, 60 to 85 degrees.

Hemigrámmus púlcher LADIGES
Pronounced Hem'i-gram"muss pul'ker
MEANING OF NAME: *Hemigrammus,* half-line, *pulcher,* pretty

Upper Amazon   Western Location Map H17   Length, 1¾ inches

*W*ITH so many small Characins looking nearly alike to the amateur, it is always a relief when a new introduction has at least one clear identifying characteristic. So far among aquarists' fishes, we have seen none with which this one might be confused. The illustration shows the tell-tale marking — a broad wedge of black on the posterior part of the body, extending about one-third its length. Body itself is also rather deep. The small light area in front of the black wedge is only a photographic highlight, due to the slight bulge of the belly. In back of the gill plate will be seen two small light spots; also a light area just above the black wedge. All these markings have a light golden metallic glow; lower fins lemon; dorsal flecked red. Illustration shows size at the time they were imported. After three years they have about doubled, which is probably the maximum growth. Unfortunately, with increasing size the brilliance of the black mark decreases. They breed like the other small Characins but do not spawn often. A grown female throws a large number of eggs.

Astỳanax fasciàtus mexicànus (FILIPPI)

Pronounced As-tỳ'an-ax fas'-see-ay"tus mex'i-kay'nus

MEANING OF NAME: *Astyanax*, son of Hector, a figure in Greek mythology, possibly because of resemblance of silvery scales to armor; *fasciatus*, banded; *mexicanus*. Mexican

Eastern Mexico to Southern Texas and S.E. New Mexico   Length, 3 inches
Western Location Map d-e, 8-10 to q20

HIS is the northernmost geographical race of the most widely distributed South American characin, and the only one found naturally in the United States.

In color it is silver, suffused light yellow. The anal and tail fins are apt to be thinly tinged with red.

There are two markings which do not show very well in the illustration, a backward-sloping darkish bar just behind the head, and a black, diamond-shaped spot at the tail base, extending into the tail fin. A suggestion of this is seen in the lower fish. The dark portions of the lobes of this fin are pale red.

Its hardy nature and free breeding quality are points that have made it popular in the past, but since the advent of so many of its more colorful cousins it is not seen as often as formerly. Breeding habits similar to those of *Hemigrammus caudovittatus*. The male is smaller than the female, to a greater degree than shown, the male being the lower fish.

Being of a peaceful nature and of lively movements, it is well suited to life in a community aquarium containing no plants. A terrific plant eater. Temperature range, 65 to 85 degrees.

COLOR PLATE PAGE 552

Pristélla ríddlei (MEEK)

Pronounced Pris-tell'a riddle-eye (not riddley-eye) *Popular name,* Pristella

MEANING OF NAME: *Pristella*, a little saw, referring to the teeth;
riddlei for Dr. Oscar Riddle, U.S. biologist, the collector

N. E. South America Western Location Map y19 to A22 Length, 1¾ inches

ORDINARILY this species does not show much warmth of color as
we have here, yet it is outstanding among small aquarium fishes. It
is because of its black-and-white contrasts in fins, particularly in the dorsal. As the fish nearly always bears itself well, like a miniature yacht with
sails spread, it can be depended upon to look its best. Without any loss
to itself, it sets off some of the more colorful species.

There are not many fishes in which white decorations in the fins form
such an outstanding feature. This comes out best when seen against a
dark background, such as is produced by plenty of foliage, like the leaves
of Sagittaria, Vallisneria or Cryptocoryne. The fish looks most attractive
when playing in and out of the shadows. When against lighter grounds
the *black* markings become prominent.

General comments regarding breeding habits, commercial supply, etc.,
are the same as for *Hemigrammus ocellifer*.

Astỳanax bimaculàtus (LINNAEUS)

Pronounced As-ty'an-ax by'mack-you-lay"tus

MEANING OF NAME: *Astyanax*, see under *A. mexicanus; bimaculatus,* two spotted
Formerly known as *Tetragonopterus maculatus*

Eastern S. America   Western Location Map z8 to J38 and V22
Length, about 4 inches

A RATHER robust species. In Nature it reaches a length of 6½ inches, but we aquarists have never seen it in such a size. It is a fine breeder and the young grow rapidly, even on prepared food, if fed small amounts frequently. As with all other species, however, good growth can only be had when the fishes have reasonable room and warmth.

Breeding habits the same as the other large Characins, such as *Ctenobrycon spilurus.*

The species, an active and graceful swimmer in the aquarium, is distinguished by the black spots on shoulder and tail. These, it should be added, are responsible for the specific name, *bimaculatus,* two spotted. Both sexes are silvery, with a decided yellow overcast. In the male (lower) the dorsal, anal and tail fins are yellow-to-red, according to the locality from which the stock was collected. He is smaller and slimmer than the female, even out of breeding season. Temperature range, 65 to 85 degrees. Breeds best at about 74 degrees. A peaceful fish.

Anoptichthys jòrdani HUBBS & INNES

Pronounced An-op-tick'thiss jor'dan-eye *Popular name,* Blind Cave Fish or
Blind Characin
MEANING OF NAME: *Anoptichthys,* fish-without-eyes; *jordani,* after C. B. Jordan
San Luis Potosi, Mexico   Western Location Map n13   Length, 3 inches

I N 1936 Mr. Basil Jordan, at Dallas, Texas, sent the author the eyeless
fish from which the above photographic illustration was made. It may
look like a preserved specimen, but it was much alive. Obviously it is a
Characin, the only blind one. With the aid of Professor Carl L. Hubbs,
the authority on cave fishes, it was found to be a new species, no doubt
descended from *Astyanax mexicanus.* It was found in a Mexican cave and
aroused such scientific interest that several expeditions were sent to study
it in its native habitat. Elaborate reports may be found in the publications of The New York Zoological Society or the New York Academy
of Sciences, the latter on April 5, 1943.

The fish is a whitish translucent, with an underglow of pink. It has
been commercially pushed as a "scavenger fish," and it really is one that
finds bits of food at the bottom of the tank, either lost or spurned by
other fishes. Gets along well in the aquarium, seldom bumps into anything
(never hard), is perfectly peaceful and hardy. Most aquarists at first feel
a needless pity for it, but they end by regarding it as a special pet.

Generations of influences which destroyed sight also changed breeding methods to an extent. They have trouble in keeping spawning contact, but in general they act like their prototype, *Astyanax mexicanus,*
with which they can be crossed, but with difficulty, for the actions of
each breeding partner seem to irritate the other. Young from the cross
have varying degrees of sight, seldom, if ever, perfect. Adult *A. jordani,*
by chance getting hold of an inch-long fish, will eat it.

Thayeria sanctae-mariae **LADIGES**

Pronounced Thay-er′ee-a   sank′tee-mar-ee″ee

MEANING OF NAME: *Thayeria* for Nathaniel Thayer; *sanctae mariae* for the town of Santa Maria, on the Tocantins River, where it was found.

Amazon Basin in Goyaz   Western Location Map K27   Length, 2¼ inches

OF fairly recent introduction in the United States, this rather odd and attractive fish has become moderately popular. While in motion it maintains a horizontal position, but when relaxed it assumes an oblique, head-up angle. The bold black stripe is edged above and below by iridescent pin-stripes. No other coloring. Sexes look identical.

The species accepts a variety of foods, spearing them as they sink. Peaceful, but expertly gobble baby fishes. Temperature, 70-78.

A breeding pair drifts about slowly in open water, then do a spirited love dance, nudging each other on the sides prior to the actual spawning. Very small fry hatch in 2 days, and require the smallest sizes of microscopic live foods, such as are found in green water.

Not closely related to *Hemiodus*, despite the color. We are not yet sure of the identification of this *Thayeria*. Dr. Boehlke has them under study. *Timmerman photo.*

Gýmnocorýmbus térnetzi BOULENGER
Pronounced Jim'no-ko-rim"bus ter'nets-eye *Popular names,* Black Tetra
and Blackamoor
MEANING OF NAME: *Gymnocorymbus,* naked (unscaled) nape;
ternetzi, after its collector, Carl Ternetz
Paraguay   Western Location Map P17 to W23   Length, up to 3 inches

WHILE preserved specimens from Nature come as long as 3 inches, fortunately aquarium specimens rarely reach 2 inches. After the fish attains a length of 1½ inches, its chic black markings progressively pale as the fish gets bigger. At the size shown in the illustration they really look their snappy best. In action they look like little black fans moving about, for the tail fin is so translucent that it is barely seen.

They have been bred at this size, but the 2-inch ones are more apt to produce. We receive frequent inquiries as to how this species may be bred. Their habits conform to standard method described in the paragraphs of the introduction to Characins.

At time of this writing the species has been introduced several years, and most of the present fairly large stock is descended from early importations, indicating that breeding has met with success.

This pert-looking fish is in good contrast with other members of a community tank, where without being aggressive, it is able to take care of itself.

Moenkhausia oligolèpis   (GUENTHER)

Pronounced Monk-house'e-a ol'ee-go-lee"pis   (ol'ee-gol"ee-pis is allowable)

MEANING OF NAME: *Moenkhausia,* after W. J. Moenkhaus; *oligolepis,* with few scales

Brazil and Guiana   Western Location Map G14 to I28 and A21   Length, 4 inches

A FLASHING red upper half of the eye, contrasting with a leaden gray body gives this fish an individuality easily remembered. It has other features, too. The large, black spot at the tail root and the black edging of the scales, presenting a laced effect, are pleasing points. The front ray of the anal fin, as with so many of the Characins, is white. There is a small golden spot in back of the adipose fin (just above the tail).

The market is mostly supplied by foreign breeders, who send quantities of them here at a size of about 1½ inches. Purchasers are usually surprised to find how large and how rapidly they grow.

In 2-inch size it makes a fairly good community-tank occupant, but as it reaches maturity it is not to be trusted among other fishes.

The species is not easily spawned, but when it does breed, large numbers of fertile eggs are produced. Breeding habits similar to those of *Hemigrammus caudovittatus.* Temperature range, 70 to 85 degrees. Breeds best at about 75 degrees. Should often have chopped worms or minced raw fish, but will take any food.

Moenkhausia píttieri EIGENMANN

Pronounced Monk-house'ee-a pit"tee-air-eye

MEANING OF NAME: *Moenkhausia,* for Dr. W. J. Moenkhaus, Indiana University; *pittieri,* for H. Pittier, a botanist of Venezuela

Venezuela (Lake Valencia)   Length, 2½ inches

Western Location Map 15 between x and y

PROBABLY color is the first thing that is looked at in an aquarium fish, but of almost equal importance is the size and shape of the fins. In particular a characteristic dorsal fin makes a quick and lasting impression. The accompanying illustration demonstrates the point. The dorsal is bold, striking and different from that on any other aquarium fish that we are able to recall. The magnificent anal fin matches it.

Otherwise the fish is a beautiful glistening silver, with iridescent small sparkles of green. The ventral area of the body, in certain lights, displays a light shade of blue. Contrasting with these generally cold colors is an eye of fiery red, especially in the upper half of the iris. Altogether we would say that this is a fish of distinction.

In adult specimens the sexes may be distinguished by the males having longer and more pointed dorsal and anal fins. The lower fish in the illustration is the female. The species has been bred by European aquarists, and the habits are the same as for similar Characins. It is a good community tank fish. Temperature range, 70-82 degrees.

Ctenobr̀ycon spil̀rus   (CUVIER AND VALENCIENNES)

Pronounced Ten'o-bry"kon spy-lew'rus   *Popular name,* Silver Tetra from Guiana

MEANING OF NAME: *Ctenobrycon,* rough-scaled Brycon; *spilurus,* with tail spot
(at base)

Guiana			Western Location Map y19 to B24			Length, 3¼ inches

cA FLASHING, silvery fish of flattened shape, very much as shown in the illustration. The only relieving bit of bright color is a glow of red in the rear portion of the anal fin in the *female.* She is the larger.

This is a hardy, peaceful fish, and is one of the stand-bys in a community tank of larger species. It is one of the most easily bred of the Characins. Writers have described "circular and spiral dances" during the mating season, but the author and local breeders of experience have not observed anything different from the ordinary breeding habits similar to those of *Hemigrammus caudovittatus.* However, we must always keep open minds as to the actions of the fishes. They have an interesting way of doing the unexpected. Incidentally, notice the above correct pronunciation. Unnecessary effort is sometimes made to pronounce the *C.*

The deserved popularity of this species is due not only to its glittering appearance in the aquarium, but largely to its hardiness. Eats anything, and *nibbles plants,* especially Vallisneria. Temperature, 65 to 80 deg.

Glandulocauda inequälis EIGENMANN

Pronounced Gland'u-lo-caw"da in'e-qual"iss

MEANING OF NAME: *Glandulocauda*, with a gland on the tail (base, in the male);
inequalis, unequal, with reference to the male's tail fin

S. E. Brazil   Western Location Map ★26   Length, 2½ inches

GUN-METAL blue is a very fair color description of this interesting and rather tender fish. The dark portions seen in all the fins are yellow to dark greenish. The dorsal, tail and anal fins are tipped white. Shoulder spot just back of gill plate is black or dark blue. Eye, red in upper part, silver below. A chunky but graceful, nicely rounded fish.

This is one of a number of species having some modification of the gills in order to hold atmospheric air. It is not as developed in this respect as is the Betta, for instance, but it often comes to the surface for a bubble of air, making a little clicking noise each time. Meinken describes a noise they sometimes make at the surface of the water as being like that of a fly caught in a spider's web.

Although this fish has been successfully bred a number of times, there remains some question as to just how fertilization takes place. The fishes do a side-by-side love dance, but no eggs seem to appear at the time. Reliable observers claim that the female several hours later deposits fertile eggs without the presence of the male. Possibly she draws into her egg duct water that has been charged with the sperm of the male. The author has never proved the process and there is not sufficient confirming evidence for him to make positive statements regarding it. The male may be distinguished by a more bulging outline of the inner edges of the tail fin, particularly of the lower lobe.

The species has a kindly disposition, is easily fed and does well in a temperature range from 70 to 80 degrees.

Mimagonìates microlèpis　(STEINDACHNER)

Pronounced Mim′a-gon-eye′a-tees mike′ro-leep″iss　　　　*Popular name,* Blue Tetra

MEANING OF NAME: *Mimagoniates,* similar to *Agoniates,* a genus of Characins;
microlepis, with small scales

Incorrectly known as *Paragoniates microlepis,* and *Coelurichthys microlepis*

S. E. Brazil　　　　　Western Location Map V30 to U31　　　　　Length, 2¼ inches

THERE are some fishes which aquarists know to be difficult to keep alive, yet they repeatedly accept the challenge because the charm of the species justifies it. Such is the "Blue Tet," the hope and despair of many a fancier.

Let us hasten to correct any idea that the fish is bright blue. It gives an impression of dark bluishness, produced mainly by a broad, dark blue lateral band, some blue on the rear part of the body and in the margins of the dorsal and anal fins. The lines pictured through the dorsal are yellow to orange. Fins otherwise clear, with a yellow-green hue. A fine line of gold tops the broad blue band along the body. A peculiarity of the species is a fullness of the *upper* edge of the *lower* half of the male's tail fin.

This fish has been bred in the aquarium, but neither the author nor his associates have ever been fortunate enough to witness the act; nor do we know of a strictly authentic account of what happens. Rumors place it in the same breeding category as *Glandulocauda inequalis.*

With these egg-layers that are supposed to produce internal fertilization, we know of no physiological peculiarity making this possible.

Their weakness is a tendency to contract "Ick" as a result of a slight chilling of the water. They should be kept between 75 and 80 degrees.

Pseudocòrynopòma dòriæ PERUGIA

Pronounced Soo'do-ko'ree-no-po"ma do'ry-ee   *Popular name,* Dragon Fin

MEANING OF NAME: *Pseudocorynopoma,* false *Corynopoma; doriæ,* after the
Marquis G. Doria, the collector

Paraguay, S. E. Brazil   Western Location Map Z26 to V22   Length, 3½ inches

A VERY outstanding fish on account of the spectacular dorsal and anal fins of the male. The scales are silvery to blue and green. The tail fin of the male is split to the root. A jumper.

The male in breeding encircles the female with spasmodic, trembling movements in which he assumes the queerest positions. Presently both fishes dart off abruptly and about 20 eggs the size of millet seed are dropped. This is repeated at intervals for half a day. They should be bred in a large aquarium, not too deep—say 8 inches. An inch layer of marbles or large pebbles, as for Brachydanios, will save most of the eggs from the devouring parents. Hatching time, 2 days at 75 degrees. The aquarium should be free of algae, as the young become entangled in it. The young look like splinters of glass, and may be raised as per directions for egg-droppers.

There have been claims made that this is one of the species where a form of internal fertilization takes place, but this is doubtful. Temperature range, 70 to 85 degrees. They are peaceful.

COLOR PLATE PAGE 552

Aphyochàrax rubripínnis PAPPENHEIM

Pronounced Af'ee-o-kay"rax rub'ri-pin"niss   *Popular name,* Bloodfin

MEANING OF NAME: *Aphyocharax,* small Charax; *rubripinnis,* with red fins; formerly well known as *Tetragonopterus rubropictus*

Argentina   Western Location Map ‡21   Length, 1¾ inches

IT seems that few of our more showy aquarium fishes either come from or can endure cold water. The popular "Bloodfin" from Argentina is an outstanding exception. In situations where a temperature below 60 degrees is liable to occur, this is one of our safest fishes. Singly, or especially in a group, they always make a pleasing picture. They are well-mannered, easily-fed, active and long-lived.

Although they breed like the other Characins, they seem to do best in certain districts. In Chicago, for instance, where the water is alkaline, they are produced in quantity. Here some of the breeders successfully use the large breeding trap with screen bottom, described under "Wholesale Breeding." Eggs are non-adhesive. The sexes are hard to distinguish except by the fuller body of the female prior to spawning. The red in the fins of the male averages a little deeper, but as this is variable from time to time in both sexes, it is not a dependable guide.

Corynopòma riisei GILL

Pronounced Ko'ree-no-po"ma rees'ee-eye   *Popular name,* Swordtail Characin

MEANING OF NAME: *Corynopoma,* with a spatula attached to gill plate; *riisei,* after A. H. Riise, the Danish zoologist of St. Thomas, West Indies. Also known as *Stevardia albipinnis*

Trinidad, Venezuela and E. Colombia   Length (exclusive of tail), 2 inches

Western Location Map A12 to x20

SIMPLY a silvery fish, but a pleasing one with several marked peculiarities. A long, tough, thread-like extension of the gill plate, ending below the dorsal in a little paddle (see illustration), is one of three ways of identifying the male. All of his fins are much the longer and the lower lobe of his tail fin ends in a spike or sword, which gives it the popular name, "Swordtail Characin."

Although often bred, its mating action is not clearly known. The male while actively circling the female occasionally extends his gill plate paddles at a wide angle to his body. At the same time his long anal fin is curved towards, but not in contact with, the female. In some mysterious way she seems to get the sperm in her mouth. She prepares spawning spots and presses her eggs on them much after the manner of the *Corydoras,* but she continues to care for them and to move them from place to place. Hatching period, 26 hours at 75 degrees. Parents do not eat either eggs or young.

The babies are quite small, but are not difficult to raise by the methods described for egg-droppers. Breeding should be in a well-established and planted tank of 10 to 15-gallon capacity. Adults are easily fed, but should have live Daphnia prior to breeding. A fish of gentle habits, whose temperature range is 68 to 85 degrees.

Prionobràma filigera (COPE)

Pronounced Pry'o-no-bray"ma fill'idge"er-a   *Popular name,* Translucent Bloodfin

MEANING OF NAME: *Prion,* saw tooth; *brama,* bream (a fish); *filgera,* bearing a
filament (on anal fin)

Formerly but incorrectly known as *Aphyocharax analialbis*

Amazon Basin   Western Location Map H14 to G20 and M17   Length, 2 inches

TO THE careless observer this fish might easily be mistaken for the
much better-known *Aphyocharax rubripinnis.* A closer examination
will show it to have distinct, beautiful characteristics of its own. The
body has a very beautiful translucent quality that is almost glass-like.
The anal fin in adults is long and pointed, the first ray being opaque
white. The red in the fins is confined to the base of the tail fin in the
female, the coloration in the male extending well into the lower and
partially into the upper lobe. The red color is not as vivid as in the fins
of *A. rubripinnis,* and the fish is a little longer. At the end of the spinal
column will be seen a little heart-shaped design which can be noticed in
many fishes having bodies that are partially transparent. This is the
fan-shaped end of the backbone, called technically the hypural fan.

Probably the breeding habits of both species are similar, but at this
time no spawning of this fish has been recorded.

Temperature range, 66 to 85 degrees.

Phoxinópsis týpicus   REGAN

Pronounced Fox'in-op"siss tip'i-cuss

MEANING OF NAME: *Phoxinopsis*, similar to Phoxinus, the European minnow; *typicus*, typical. Also known as *Spintherobolus broccæ*

Vicinity of Rio de Janeiro   Western Location Map U31   Length, 1½ inches

A BOUT the only part of the illustration needing any interpretation is the light marking just at the tail base. This is an encircling golden ring and gives somewhat the same luminous effect as the spot on *Hemigrammus ocellifer*. There is no adipose fin. One authority describes the first as having light red fins. Those we have observed were colorless. The horizontal band extending into the tail fin is dark brown. The body is quite translucent. This is perhaps its most interesting quality. While the majority of aquarists prefer fishes having showy colors, there are some who are equally impressed by more subdued characteristics. To such, this species will prove interesting.

Dr. Myers, who has collected this fish in its natural habitat near the city of Rio de Janeiro, says that it loves deep brown, strongly acid water. In such places, it takes on a golden brown, translucent color, the midside stripe and the one along the lower part of the caudal peduncle being black. In such color, the fish is a real ornament to the aquarium.

To the average eye it is a meek little fish for which one is apt to feel sorry, yet in company of approximately its own size it seems to get along very well. The aquarist should always keep in mind the fact that fishes with small mouths ought to be supplied with sizes of food that they can easily swallow. Otherwise they are liable to decline and die.

The species has not been bred. Temperature, about 74 degrees.

Crenùchus spilùrus GUENTHER

Pronounced Kren-oo'kus spy-lew'rus

MEANING OF NAME: *Crenuchus*, with a notch on the nape of the neck; *spilurus*, with a spot on tail (root)

Amazon   Length—male, 4 inches; female, 3 inches

Western Location Map B21 to F26 and G20

IT IS quite a common thing for fishes to undergo great changes in appearance between infancy and adulthood. This is one of them. Ichthyologists have been acquainted only with immature fish.

When the male, in its second or third year, passes the 2½-inch length, his dorsal and anal fins, which previously had been only a little fuller than on the average fish, suddenly sprout into luxurious elegance, so that he is scarcely recognizable as the same individual. The beautiful mosaic-like markings in the fins are of a rich, deep orange.

They have been spawned a few times, but none was reared and we know nothing of their breeding habits, beyond the fact that their behavior seems to be about the same as that of the usual Characin. They have been successfully maintained for several years at a temperature of about 75 degrees. Easily fed. Not a good community tank fish.

The Hatchet Fishes

STRANGE little creatures, these Hatchet Fishes, with their bulging bellies, yet so thin from the front view. They seem to be built on some highly specialized plan, not unrelated to the principles employed in airplane construction. They are indeed known as Dwarf Freshwater Flying Fishes, for in their native waters, when alarmed, they skim lightly over the surface for considerable distances. Although in the aquarium they will eat Daphnia and even prepared food that floats, it seems to be their nature to catch insects on or near the surface of the water. They do not like to pick food from the bottom.

It has been found rather difficult to keep most of the few species we aquarists have had, probably because the wild-caught fish are easily frightened and, in trying to fly, dash themselves to death against the cover-glass or sides of the aquarium. Specimens once well acclimatized often live rather long when fed only on dry prepared foods that float on the surface. Few have been bred in captivity, and importations surviving over a year are considered to have done well. This review does not sound very encouraging, but they are attractive novelties, well worth a place in a mixed aquarium, provided one does not hope to breed them nor to be their host for a very long visit.

They are not related to a well-known genus of marine Hatchet Fishes, nor to the famous Flying Fishes of the seas.

It has been pretty well established after centuries of argument that marine Flying Fishes, despite their amazing performances, do not voluntarily move their wing-like fins while sailing through the air. Our little Hatchet Fishes, however, are equipped with a deep, thin breast keel of bone, supporting relatively huge muscles attached to the "wings." It is known that this equipment enables them to vibrate their plane-like pectoral fins when in flight.

In the matter of temperature they seem, on the average, to prefer water in the neighborhood of 75 degrees. Like must fishes that hang about the surface of the water, they are not very active, but can move fast enough when occasion demands.

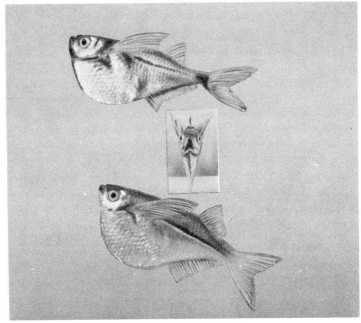

Gásteropelecus lèvis   (EIGENMANN)

Pronounced Gas'ter-o-pel"e-kus   lee'viss

MEANING OF NAME: *Gasteropelecus*, axe-belly; *levis*, smooth.
Formerly known as *Pterodiscus levis*

Known in the trade as *Gasteropelecus sternicla*, which is a different species

Amazon   Western Location Map G28   Length, 2¼ inches

⟲ HIS is the commonest of our Hatchet Fish importations. The lower
part of the body is mirrored silver, while the top is olive. These
colors are separated by a pleasing blue-black stripe, which itself is
enclosed between two narrow, pale silver lines. All fins are clear, including the long, arching graceful pectorals or "wings."

These fishes like clear water and a temperature of about 75 degrees.

There is a similar species, *Gasteropelecus sternicla*, which is so similar
that a count of fin-rays, teeth and scales is needed to detect the difference—a job for an ichthyologist. The aquarist may regard them as one.

Like many of the fishes with marked ability at leaping, it spends much
of its time near the surface of the water, probably looking for small
insects, either that have fallen on the surface, or that are flying near it.
The species tends to die off in a few months in the aquarium but occasionally last for two years or more. Frightening them often results in
death.

Carnegiélla märthœ MYERS

Pronounced Kar-nay'gee-ell'a mar'thee   *Popular name,* Black-winged Hatchet Fish
MEANING OF NAME: *Carnegiella,* for Miss Margaret Carnegie; *marthœ,* for
Martha Ruth Myers
Amazon and Orinoco Rivers   Western Location Map A15; G20   Length, 1¼ inches

THIS is the smallest of the Hatchet Fishes so far known to aquarists and is often quite hardy if not frightened by sudden movements. One of the photographed specimens successfully got over the effects of a dash to a dry concrete floor. Also the species readily takes dried, prepared food. Minds its own business, but this can also be said of its near relatives (as well as of the ladies for whom the species was named).

The "Black-Wing" part of the popular name is due to the fact that at night the centres of the long pectoral fins are black. The silver sides of the belly and up towards the head are heavily sprinkled with small black markings. The halftone plate loses the clearness of these, but they may be distinguished in the upper fish. Adipose fin (behind the dorsal) is absent. It will be noticed that the lower body black outline is much stronger than in *Gasteropelecus levis*. *Carnegiella strigata* has no marginal edging at all. Its dark parts are only portions of its patterns and its long lower stripe does not come to the edge of the body.

C. marthœ seems to have a temperature range of 65 to 85 degrees, but it appears to be happiest at about 75. Owing to its quaintness, this little fish has become a fairly popular aquarium species.

Carnegiélla strigàta (GUENTHER)

Pronounced Kar-nay'gee-ell'a stry-gay'ta

MEANING OF NAME: *Carnegiella,* named for Miss Margaret Carnegie; *strigata,* streaked

N.E. South America Western Location Map A21 to H12 and G28 Length, 1¾ inches

*C*ONSIDERABLY smaller, more wisp-like and colorful than *Gastero-pelecus.* Highlights seen about the head are metallic, olive green, while the one traversing the broad belly (lower fish) is translucent gold. The dark parallel markings decorating the belly are brown or black. It will be noticed that no adipose fin is present. While not hardy, it is often more durable than *Gasteropelecus levis.* Requirements the same.

One breeder reports several large spawnings. These took place at a temperature of 83 to 87 degrees. Courtship of the male consisted in circling the female and dashing closely past her. The pair did much leaping out of the water, but the actual spawning took place in a side-to-side, head-to-tail position, the small transparent eggs being scattered among floating plants, such as Riccia. The species takes a variety of dry and living fishfoods.

The sexes can be told only by the broader body of the female (taking a top view).

Chàrax gibbòsus (LINNAEUS)

Pronounced Kay'rax gib-bo'sus

MEANING OF NAME: *Charax*, an old Greek name of some fish; *gibbosus*, gibbous, with
reference to the projecting nape

Amazon Guiana   Western Location Map A21 to K10 and G25   Length, 4 inches

A NUMBER of South American genera seem to have a natural
balance in which the head is down and the tail up. This is one of
them, but with an added peculiarity. The head itself, taking a line
through the nose, eye and gill plate, is about horizontal, while the body
from this point shoots oddly upward.

The color is an interesting, translucent brownish amber. In the right
light, fine scales scatter an assortment of opalescent colors.

The fish takes kindly to captivity, and is easily fed, but has never
shown the slightest intention of breeding. It is not very active. There
are a number of very similar species in the genus *Charax*. The genus
Roeboides, with several species, is also much the same.

The similarity of related fishes sometimes gives rise to the belief that
the owner has a pair, whereas he has only single fish of two species,
possibly both being of the same sex. A count of fin rays by the aid of a
good photograph will often establish a difference in species, for in most
instances males and females of a kind have the same number of rays in
the fins, especially in those of the dorsal and anal.

This and similar fishes seem to be quite harmless. One might say they
are harmless to the point of dullness. They are easily fed and seem to be
contented in any temperature between 72 and 82 degrees. Since first
appearing on the market in 1932, they have been in fairly continuous
supply, although there is no prospect of their ever becoming popular.

COLOR PLATE PAGE 553

Serrasálmus spilopleùra KNER
Pronounced Ser′ra-sal″mus spy-low-plu′ra
MEANING OF NAME: *Serrasalmus,* salmon-like; *spilopleura,* with spots on sides
Popular name, Piranha (pronounced pee-ron′ya)
Amazon and La Plata Basins   Western Location Map z17 to M25   Length, 10 inches

ALES of how swarms of bloodthirsty Piranhas skeletonize large
wading or swimming animals in a matter of minutes have created
a rather morbid public interest in them as aquarium fishes. Aquarists with
nipped fingers are jestingly members of the mythical "Piranha Club!"

These fishes have razor-sharp triangular teeth that interlock between
lower and upper jaws. They bite out chunks of flesh that are swallowed
whole. Wound is said to be painless. They can cut nets and fishing lines.

There are several species, varying in ferocity, some even being harmless. The most savage are those with the shortest, bulldog-like muzzles.

They sometimes attack each other. In the aquarium they are fond of
Tubifex worms, but may be fed on raw meat, liver or fish. Color varies
with species, from lemon trimmings on silver, to some with bright red
bellies. *S. spilopleura* is characterized by black edge on the tail fin.

Occasionally stocked. Not yet bred. Temperature about 75 degrees.

Exodon paradóxus MUELLER AND TROSCHEL

Pronounced Ex'o-don pa'ra-dox"us

MEANING OF NAME: *Exodon,* with teeth projecting outward; *paradoxus,* paradoxical

Amazon   Western Location Map B21 to G22 and N29   Length, 3 inches

*H*ERE we momentarily depart from our avowed principle of listing only such fishes as have become fairly well established in aquaria, and which aquarists may reasonably expect to secure, at least from time to time. Although this fish has been known to science since it was named by Mueller and Troschel in 1845, only a few living specimens have reached our shores. The first shipment was in 1932 and a few other small lots have since arrived, selling at high prices. The species is not difficult to transport nor maintain, but is said to be very elusive. By its graceful, rapid swimming in the aquarium this can easily be believed.

From the general appearance and the presence of the little adipose fin near the tail, together with the knowledge that it is a South American fish, the aquarist will easily perceive that it is a Characin. Obviously the huge, intense black spot on the silver sides and the smaller one at the tail are the outstanding characteristics. The larger spot covers over 30 scales. As no other known fish closely resembles this one, the lucky aquarist who obtains specimens will have no trouble in identifying them. The male has a warm, pink glow in the tail fin.

Single specimens are satisfactory in a community tank, but they fight their own kind almost continuously.

Some of the original imports lived for 10 years, but remained "childless." There are now occasional fair importations, from which we may hope for better things.

Mylóssoma aureum   (SPIX)

Pronounced My-loss'so-ma aw're-um   Popularly and incorrectly, *schreitmuelleri*
MEANING OF NAME: *Mylossoma*, body shaped like a millstone; aureum, golden.
Amazon   Western Location Map z16 to F26   Length, 3½ inches

ONE of the most attractive and enduring of the disc-like, or "pancake" Characins. It is so flat that it seems emaciated. The fact that it keeps living happily in what appears to be a thin condition reminds one of the old saying, "a lean horse for a long race."

The dark portion of the anal fin is a rich, golden brown. Note that the broadest part is in an exceptional place—up towards the tail. In life, and even more so in the photograph, it is difficult to tell just where the body edge ends and the anal fin begins. An imaginary continuation of the curve of the lower belly line approximates it. The scales are very small and very silvery. The soft vertical bars are gray, and the back is light olive. A speck of color will be noted in the adipose fin, the little projection just above the tail. The dark portion is reddish. Eye, warm golden.

The ventral fins are unbelievably small. They are indicated by the white spot on the lower part of the body. Sex differences not known.

A good community fish, especially when kept with companions that are not diminutive. Comfortable between 72 and 85 degrees. Easily fed. Never been bred.

Colóssoma species

Pronounced Co-los'so-ma

Amazon Basin

Length, 4½ inches

*I*F THE reader, in looking at the photograph, will bear in mind that the dark portions about the head and gills and the entire ventral and pectoral fins, as well as the markings in the anal fin, are deep red, it will be readily realized what a striking fish personality is pictured. The rest of the lower half of the body is delicately suffused orange. Tail edging, gray to black. Note the fine scales for a large fish.

The pectoral fins are nearly obscured because of their deep red color, matching the body color in their vicinity. Aquarists will recall that, regardless of how brilliantly a fish may be colored, its pectoral (breast) fins are nearly always transparent. Possibly this is a matter of protection, for these fins are usually in motion, and, if bright, would attract the attention of enemies. "See but don't be seen" is a good motto in a cannibalistic world. This fish is so well able to take care of itself that it can afford to flaunt an extra bit of color. Never bred. Canned shrimp is taken eagerly. Temperature needed, about 75 degrees. As earlier stated, "spec." is an abbreviation for "species." When "spec." or "species" is used it commonly means that the species has not yet been identified, or that the complete name is unknown to the writer.

Metýnnis species
Pronounced Me-tin′niss
MEANING OF NAME: *Metynnis,* with a plough
Amazon   Western Location Map G between 20 and 24   Length, 4 inches

METYNNIS is a genus distinguished from *Colossoma* and *Mylos-soma* by the *long, low* adipose fin (see photo). At least three species have been imported, usually under the name *M. maculatus, M. roosevelti,* or *M. schreitmulleri.* The two latter names are not valid, *M. roosevelti* being the same as *M. maculatus* and *M. schreitmulleri* equalling *M. hypsauchen.* The different species are impossible to tell apart in an aquarium except for *hypsauchen,* which has an adipose fin much longer and lower than the one shown here (which may be *M. maculatus*). Males of all seem to possess the rounded extension at or near the front of the anal fin shown in our photo. Females lack this.

All *Metynnis* are silvery in color, sometimes with dark spots or bars which disappear with age. There is usually some orange or yellow in the tail and anal fin. All will take prepared foods but in nature they feed on aquatic plants and fallen fruit and will create havoc with aquarium plants. Peaceful, attractive and hardy. Almost never bred. They are said to scatter non-adhesive eggs. 72 to 82 degrees.

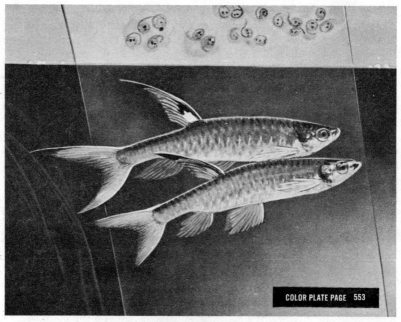

COLOR PLATE PAGE 553

Copeina arnoldi REGAN   (Showing eggs above water on sanded glass)

Pronounced Ko-pie'na ar'nold-eye

MEANING OF NAME: The generic name *Copeina* after E. D. Cope, the Philadelphia scientist; *arnoldi* after Johann Paul Arnold, of Germany; formerly known by aquarists as *Pyrrhulina filamentosa*

Brazil   Western Location Map G24   Length—Male, 3 inches; female, 2½ inches

THIS is one of the most extraordinary of all aquarium fishes, and one of the most desirable, for in addition to its unbelievable breeding habits, it is of attractive appearance, is peaceful and easily kept.

As people like to be shown in their best raiment, we assume that if fishes have any preference, it is the same with them. So we try to extend them that courtesy, as has been done here. Even when much less colorful there is a suffused red in the anal and ventral fins and a red tip on the lower lobe of the tail fin. The male (upper) can always be distinguished by his longer fins and the white spot at the base of his dorsal.

The perpetuation of all animal life is obviously dependent upon the preservation of the young. This preservation is accomplished in three principal ways. First, we have parents which are so prolific that the fraction of their young which escape their natural enemies is sufficient to carry on the species. Such young receive no parental protection. Second, we have parents, not so prolific, which fight in defense of their young. Third, we have parents which are neither prolific nor fighters, but which depend upon clever ways of protecting their offspring. Of this class *Copeina arnoldi* is a perfect example, and all the more outstanding for being an animal in water, where cannibalism is more prevalent than on land.

Mating them is a simple matter. Place a pair together in a covered aquarium of about 10-gallon capacity, using water which is neutral or slightly acid, and at a temperature of about 73 to 75 degrees. Feed well on live Daphnia, chopped earthworms or mosquito larvae. Presently love play and tremblings will begin, and soon we may look for results. The water should be about 7 inches deep. Into this stand a sheet of sanded glass, large enough to stand several inches out of the water. Lean this at a moderate angle against the end of the aquarium which is nearest the light. It is on this glass, about two inches *above the water line,* that the spawn should be deposited. When the female is ripe she not only shows fullness, but the yellowish eggs can be seen through the abdominal walls.

The male soon busies himself looking for the most favorable place for the spawning and then drives the female to it. Here, in a sudden action they partially lock fins (her right side to his left) and leap together out of the water to the chosen spot. By fin suction they adhere to the glass and remain in this position for about 10 seconds, depositing a jelly-like mass containing about 10 eggs. This is repeated at intervals for perhaps an hour, until approximately 100 eggs are laid. None are placed over the others and usually the whole is evenly joined into a solid, flat mass about the size of a silver half dollar. Notwithstanding the difficult gymnastics involved in the act of spawning, every egg is fertilized.

Now begins the second stage of this remarkable procedure. With the eggs placed well out of the reach of other fishes, the problem of keeping them moist arises. The male ingeniously supplies the answer. In order to attract as little attention as possible to the eggs or maturing embryos, he stations himself a distance away. Every 15 to 20 minutes he rushes to a position below the eggs and splashes them by several rapid lashings of his tail. He then retreats to the other end of the aquarium, where he likes to have a few floating plants in which to hide. The embryos can be seen in 24 hours and hatch in about 72 hours, when they burst their thin egg shells and fall into the water, where, for nearly a week, they seek shelter at the bottom, after which they rise in a school and swim about. Use infusoria and the regular feeding program for egg-layers.

There is no object in keeping the parents present after the young have hatched, but it has been done successfully as an experiment.

The pairs in spawning are able to leap at least 4 inches out of water and deposit their eggs on the cover glass. Unless this is roughed they cannot adhere, and will not hatch if they fall into the water.

The young have a peculiarity common to several species. A narrow fin develops above the top edge of the tail fin, which appears as though the main fin were split, and that the split section had grown longer. This is known in science as the urostyle, and is present in this species between the ages of 2 and 5 weeks. The appendage is rounded (not flat like a fin).

It would be difficult to imagine, much less find, a fish to equal *Copeina arnoldi* in its interesting and resourceful life habits, yet there is nothing about the appearance of the fish to lead one to expect the unusual.

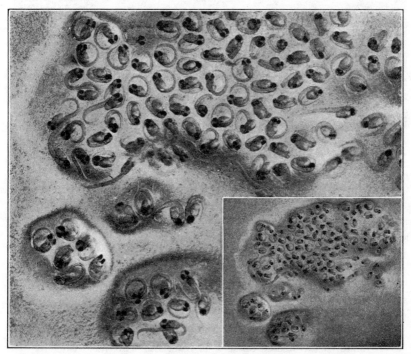

Masses of Embryos of *Copeina arnoldi*

The insert in the lower right-hand corner is from the original photograph, and is a little larger than life size. The larger picture will be recognized as a further magnified section from the same negative.

The eggs were on a sheet of sanded glass, and were above the water line, where they were placed by the fish. A few embryos had burst their shells and were ready to drop into the water. Within an hour after the photograph was taken, every one had plunged to its native element.

COLOR PLATE PAGE 554

Copeìna guttàta (STEINDACHNER)

Pronounced Ko-pie'na gut-tay'ta

MEANING OF NAME: The generic name is for the Philadelphia scientist, E. D. Cope; the word *guttata* means spotted, as with rain drops; also known as *Pyrrhulina guttata*

Amazon   Western Location Map I9 to G24   Length, 3 to 4 inches

ITH many species of aquarium fishes we never get them quite as large as they grow in their native waters. An extreme instance is the case of *Osphronemus goramy*. In aquarium specimens we seldom see one over 5 inches long, yet in Nature they arrive at the magnificently impossible size of 24 inches.

Copeina guttata reverses all this, in moderate degree. We grow it to 4 inches, yet collected specimens from the wild have thus far not exceeded 3 inches. The difference may not be great, but the exception is notable.

The fish is a long-established one in the fish fancy, and always has a few good friends, but for some reason has never become popular. In outline it is not particularly pleasing, and for periods the colors become pale, but when at full color and viewed in the right light, it is really a show-piece.

The reader will have little trouble in selecting the upper fish as the male, although he does not show the orange dots clearly when cool or out of condition. The female has few, if any red dots; her fins are paler, but she has a much more intense black mark in her dorsal fin.

Breeding habits are quite simple. Spawns are large and the young are easily raised. The pair fans a depression in the sand, often in the fore part of the aquarium. Into this the eggs are deposited and fertilized. Very few other Characins pay any attention to eggs or young, except to eat them. In this instance the male drives the female away and fans the eggs with his pectoral fins. It is common practise to remove the female after spawning. The eggs, at 75 degrees, hatch in about two days. Ordinarily the male does not eat the young, but it is safer to remove him when they are a few days old. They should have the regular feeding previously prescribed for the medium-sized egg-layers.

The fish is apt to be just a little sluggish in its movements, which perhaps in part accounts for its lack of general popularity.

This species has a wide range of temperature tolerance. Anything between 60 and 90 degrees. Quite peaceable. Easily fed. Not timid. A good egg-laying fish for the beginner who is willing to give it a space of not less than five gallons to the pair. They have been known to breed and rear young in a community aquarium, although survival under those circumstances would depend largely on the natures (and appetites!) of the other fishes present.

Pyrrhulìna rachoviàna MYERS
Pronounced Pir'rew-lie"na rak-ko'vi-ay"na
MEANING OF NAME: *Pyrrhulina,* little red; *rachoviana* for Rachow, the German
aquarist and author

| Rosario, Argentina | Western Location Map ‡21 | Length, 1¾ inches |

𝓗ANDSOME as this little fish is, the meaning of the name might mislead. "Little red" originally referred to the red spot in the dorsal fin of *P. filamentosa.* Anal and ventrals of the species are edged orange. While this color is lacking in the female, she has an orange tip on the anal fin. The dark spot at the tip of the dorsal fin in the male is black. It will be noticed that a similar spot is on the female, more towards the centre of the fin. The general color of the back is brown to olive. Belly white. A rather clear saw-tooth band of blue-black traverses the entire length of the body, about the middle, dividing the back and belly colors. Red dots appear in the male in the V spaces in the upper half of this line. The fins are slightly yellow, being a trifle deeper shade in the male. Also his anal and ventrals are lightly edged with orange. The fish to the right is the male.

This species likes to spawn on the leaves of broad aquatic plants, such as Giant Sagittaria. The male guards and fans the eggs, which hatch in about 24 hours at a temperature of 75. The young sink to the bottom for a few days. The leaf bearing the spawn may be removed and hatched independently, as described for hatching the eggs of *P. scalare.* Otherwise apply described standard culture for the young of egg-layers.

The commonest species in our aquaria in 1954 was *P. filamentosa,* larger and slightly more long-finned than this species.

Abramites microcéphalus NORMAN

Pronounced A-bray-my'tees mike'row-sef"al-us *Popular name,* Norman's Headstander
MEANING OF NAME: *Abramites,* like Abramis, the bream; *microcephalus,* small headed
Lower Amazon   Western Location Map F26   Length, 3 inches

ISTINCTLY a novelty, and with its assortment of markings, ranging from white, through shades of gray and into heavy black, it
catches and holds the eye as being something unusual. The crescent in
the tail fin is white. The other parts are mostly grays and blacks, pretty
much as the photograph shows. Too few have yet been imported for us
to know much about them, but from familiarity with its relatives, we
could hardly expect to learn a great deal, even though their numbers
were greater.

While this fish is not a member of the genus *Leporinus,* it is closely
related, and, no doubt, has many of the same characteristics. Going
about with the fore part of the body tilted downward is one of them.
From this peculiarity one would expect them to be bottom feeders, but
from their manner of taking food in the aquarium, this does not appear
to be the case.

The fish has been kept with other species and no harm was done on
either side. At an exhibition in Brooklyn this species took a prize for
being "the rarest" fish shown.

Judging by its near relatives it should be happy in an average temperature of 75 degrees.

COLOR PLATE PAGE 554

Anóstomus anóstomus (LINNAEUS)

Pronounced An-os'to-mus an-os'to-mus   MEANING OF NAME: Turned-up mouth

Common in Guiana, rare in Amazon   Length, 4 inches

Western Location Map z21 to G23

*W*HEN one is used to seeing *Nannostomus trifasciatus* this fish seems like a large and rather sluggish cousin to it. The dark portions of the forked tail root are deep blood-red. Also the dark parts in the dorsal, the adipose and the beginnings (at the body) of the ventrals and anal are red. Aside from these strongly characteristic markings the broad black stripe along the body is very striking. There are two narrower dark stripes on the sides and one down the middle of the back which do not show in the illustration. These dark stripes are set off by being placed against a background of metallic gold.

The fish is related to the genus *Leporinus* and swims in somewhat the same head-down fashion. Although this species was described by one of our earliest great naturalists, it was not imported for aquarists until 1933. As yet we know nothing of its breeding habits. Generally peaceful.

In the matter of food it will take either prepared dry food, boiled shrimp, white worms or the unfailing Daphnia. It frequently scrapes at algae-covered rocks in a "headstanding" position. Temperature 75.

Leporìnus fasciàtus (BLOCH)

Pronounced Le-po-rye'nus fas-see-a'tus

MEANING OF NAME: *Leporinus,* with a snout like a rabbit; *fasciatus,* banded

Amazon and Guiana   Western Location Map z15 to B24 and H33

Length, 4 to 6 inches

*A*LTHOUGH this very striking fish has long been kept by aquarists, it has never become commonplace. This is for two reasons; it is extremely difficult for collectors to gather, and it has not been bred in captivity. It is an enormous leaper and jumps over the nets of the natives. Just to give an idea both of its acrobatics and its toughness, an incident in the Battery Park Aquarium in New York will demonstrate both. One of them jumped obliquely upward a distance of 5 feet, landing in a marine aquarium of a different temperature. After several hours it was returned undamaged to its own tropical fresh-water aquarium.

As the fish is rather sluggish in its movements, the aquarist is apt to become careless about keeping the aquarium covered. Reflection, however, will recall that the worst jumpers, such as Pantodon and Blue Gularis, are apparently slow movers.

The light bands in the photograph represent ivory yellow, while the dark bars are black. The fish has and needs no other colors. An interesting feature is that with age the number of bands increases. The young have 5, while fully grown adults show 10. In the upper fish it can be seen where 2 bands are beginning to split so as to add 2 more. The species usually maintains a slightly head-down angle, common in the family. Eats anything. Harmless. Temperature, 70-80 degrees.

Prochilòdus insignis SCHOMBURGK

Pronounced Pro'ki-low"dus   in-sig'nis

MEANING OF NAME: *Prochilodus,* with teeth on the forward-projecting lips;
insignis, distinguished

Amazon Basin   Length—Aquarium, 5 inches; Nature, 11 inches

Western Location Map C20 to G24

THE particular feature of this fish which captures the eye is, of
course, the flag-striped tail. A visitor at an exhibition dubbed it the
"Flag Fish," but as this name has already been preempted for the
Jordanella floridœ, we can hardly bestow it on both. Thus the advocates
of popular names for fishes may get some idea of the importance of having an organized naming system.

Prochilodus insignis has no bright colors, but the belly is rose-tinted
and the lighter parts of the tail fin between the dark stripes are opaque
ivory. Dorsal and darker portions shown on the lower fins are yellow.

The mouth is peculiar and can be used as a sort of sucking disc, with
which it digs in the soil. Likes algae and boiled spinach. Quite peaceful.

It is necessary that this fish be carefully covered, as it can leap high
out of the water. Fortunately for the author and his readers, this one
landed back at the same spot where it left the photographing aquarium
on an aerial excursion. The owner of the fish reported a similar experience, without the photography.

Chilòdus punctàtus MUELLER AND TROSCHEL

Pronounced Ky-low′dus   punk-tay′tus

MEANING: *Chilodus,* with teeth on lips; *punctatus,* spotted   *Popular name,* Headstander

Guiana   Western Location Map A21 to B25   Length, 3 inches

THERE are those fishes which, without possessing any actual bright-
ness of color, are nevertheless brilliant. An arrangement of contrasts
or of designs in blacks, grays, olive or brown tints, combined with
sparkles of silver can be very effective. Such a fish is *Chilodus punctatus.*
The middle band is clear black, while the spots on the scales and the
markings in the dorsal fin are brownish. This is one of those species that
maintains an oblique balance most of the time, head downward. Whether
absorbed in thought or merely looking on the bottom for food is a question any aquarist can answer for himself, without fear of contradiction.

The species, to the best of our knowledge, has never been bred in
captivity. It seems, however, to be content with aquarium life at a
temperature of about 75 degrees and is readily fed. The mouth is rather
small, so when dried prepared food is used it is advisable to select something composed of small grains. Peaceful and not very lively.

Hemiòdus semitœniàtus KNER

Pronounced Hem'ee-o"dus sem'ee-tee'nee-a"tus

MEANING OF NAME: *Hemiodus,* half-toothed (as there are teeth only in the upper jaw); *semitaeniatus,* half striped, referring to the short body stripe

Guiana and Amazon Basin   Western Location Map A21 to P17
Length, 4 to 5 inches

𝒯HE sharp, black spot on the side of this silvery fish, followed by the dark line extending without interruption to the tip of the lower lobe of the tail is something unique among aquarium fishes. Below the black line, and also faintly above it, is a stripe of ivory tint. The upper tip of the tail fin is touched with black, a point our camera missed, likewise a bit of white on the first anal ray. The only suggestion of color in the fish is an iridescent green along the spinal line. There are a number of similar species in which the color pattern differs in details. All are slender, with smaller scales than the usual "tetras."

Not a species commonly obtainable, but well worth securing when occasion offers. While not appearing to be a particularly active genus, most of the species are very difficult to catch in a net. Not only are they elusive, but they are liable to leap out of the water when pursued, or to jump from any small container in which they have just been placed. It is even difficult holding them in a net. The fish is something to add to a miscellaneous collection, rather than to acquire enough of them to make a "school." Some fishes appear best in numbers, but this is not one of them. It is what might be called a "contrast fish."

It lives well but we have never heard of its being bred in captivity. Suggested temperature, 75 degrees. Varied diet.

Characidium fasciàtum RHEINHARDT

Pronounced Ka'ra-sid"e-um   fas'see-a"tum

MEANING OF NAME: *Characidium*, a little Charax; *fasciatum*, banded.

E. Central Brazil, Orinoco, Amazon, Paraguay, Rio Sao Francisco

Western Location Map A15 to ‡21 and L36   Length, 2½ inches

THIS fish comes from cooler water than do most of our exotics, and is comfortable at 65 to 73 degrees.

There are no very distinctive colors. A dark stripe decorates the sides, while a number of vertical bars cross it at times. The male has longer anal and tail fins, as well as a higher, broader dorsal. In the illustration he is the fish to the left. The species is rather carnivorous, although it will eat prepared foods containing a large percentage of animal substance.

Spawning takes place in the lower part of the aquarium. Fontinalis is a very good receiving plant for the eggs. The young must have small live food. Not commonly for sale, as it has no outstanding appeal to the eye. It is a fish for those desiring a comprehensive collection.

A dozen or more species of *Characidium* have been imported from various parts of South America. Many have a more pointed head than the one illustrated, and all sit on the bottom a good deal. In fact these fishes, in their South American habitat, take the place of the little Johnny Darters in our North American streams.

COLOR PLATE PAGE 555

Nannóstomus margìnàtus EIGENMANN
Pronounced Nan-os′to-mus mar′jin-ay″tus
MEANING OF NAME: *marginatus*, margined

N. E. South America   Western Location Map A21; G28   Length, 1½ inches

CONSIDERABLY smaller, and more blocky than *N. trifasciatus,* this
fish can easily be distinguished by a broader black body horizontal
stripe. They are subject to the same quick appearance and disappearance of the dark areas shown on the plate of *N. trifasciatus.* Other minor
color differences will be noticed.

Although *N. trifasciatus* is ordinarily a peaceful fish, we have found
it to delight in persecuting *N. marginatus,* when the two species are kept
together. *N. marginatus* is exceptionally long-lived.

Oddly enough, the smaller species is much more easily bred. Eggs are
deposited in plants like Riccia. Youngsters, for some weeks, have
rounded, not forked, tail fins. Temperature 70-78 degrees.

Showing big fishes in a reduced size is sometimes unavoidable, but we
always aim to illustrate smaller specimens at life size. In this instance,
however, they are slightly enlarged.

COLOR PLATE PAGE 555

Nannóstomus trifasciàtus STEINDACHNER

Pronounced Nan-os'to-mus try'fas-see-ay"tus

MEANING OF NAME: *Nannostomus*, little-mouth; *trifasciatus*, with 3 bands

Amazon   Western Location Map H13 to G28   Length, 1¾ inches

IT is one of the most satisfactory and beautiful of fishes. Our illustration depicts the colors correctly, but obtainable stock is usually a little smaller than shown here. Some specimens are more slender than these and may be a different species. The large dark blotches on the bodies of two fishes are temporary, and mean nothing as to sex, which is indicated in males by the broken line of red dots on the stripe of gold. The female is at the lower right.

The species has an ideal aquarium temperament and lives well on a variety of ordinary foods, but it should not be crowded.

Spawning, which is rather rare, usually takes place among loose Riccia. The eggs are adhesive and are sometimes placed on Sagittaria leaves or even on the glass of the aquarium. They hatch in 3 days at a temperature of 75 degrees. The babies are long and narrow and do not resemble the parents for several weeks. They poise themselves at odd angles.

Unless very hungry the parents do not eat the eggs. With good feeding and plenty of room the young become adults in 7 months. Temperature range, 70 to 80 degrees.

The species went through a period of scarcity following its first introduction, but new importations have been made since World War II. It continues to be stubborn about spawning.

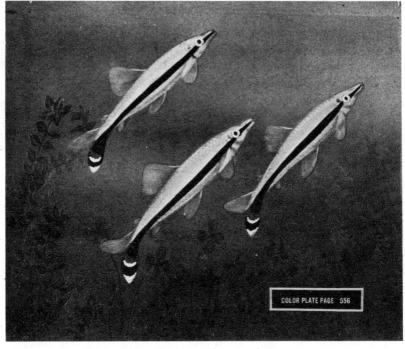

COLOR PLATE PAGE 556

Nannobrỳcon unifasciatus   (STEINDACHNER)

Pronounced Nan'o-bry"con u'ni-fas'see-ay"tus   *Popular name,* Spot-tail Pencilfish
MEANING OF NAME: *Nannobrycon,* little Brycon; *unifasciatus,* one-banded ·
Amazon   Western Location Map G17 to G20   Length, 2 inches

J UST before World War I a friend in France sent us a water color
sketch, from which we made the above plate. Unsuccessful efforts
were made to learn the name of the artist, who probably was lost in
battle. The posing is a little stiff, but gives a good idea of the fish,
except that the black line should continue through the eye.

Breeding is the same as for *N. auratus* (following), but they rarely
spawn. A peaceful fish liking a temperature range of 68-80 degrees.

Nannóstomus anómalus STEINDACIINER

Pronounced Nan-os′to-mus   an-om′al-us

MEANING OF NAME: *Nannostomus,* little mouth *anomalus,* abnormal, referring to lack of adipose fin; also known as *N. beckfordi,* a Guiana species which may be identical with this one

Amazon and Rio Negro   Western Location Map G20 to G24   Length, 1½ inches

ONE might be justified in recording two separate color descriptions of this fish, one made by day and the other by night when a light has suddenly been turned on. The latter would be the more alluring, for the colors seem to be brightest at night when there is no one to appreciate them, like the violets that blush unseen.

Our photograph was taken against a dark background with the idea of bringing out on the male the blue-white tips on the ventrals and a tiny tip of it on the anal. This was secured at the cost of losing the effect of red ornamentations in the dorsal, tail and anal fins, which would have shown against a lighter background. The long, dark body band is intense black, bordered above by gold, which glistens vividly. The eye is light gold, divided by the black line which extends to the tip of mouth. The back is "fish olive." Belly, bright white. It is sprightly in its movements, standing still momentarily and then moving forward briskly.

Difficult to induce to spawn. Their procedure is like the average egg-dropper, depositing spawn among rootlets and plant thickets. The babies adhere to plants and glass sides rather longer than do most fish babies, taking about 5 days before they become free-swimming. The temperature at which they do best ranges from 73 to 80 degrees. Any food for this species, living or prepared, shall be small, for they have tiny mouths.

Nannobrỳcon èques (EIGENMANN)

Pronounced Nan'o-bry"con ek'wees   *Popular name,* Pencilfish
MEANING OF NAME: *eques,* a horseman or rider
Formerly known as *Poecilobrycon auratus*
Guiana and Amazon   Western Location Map A21 to G28   Length, 1¾ inches

THE Nannobrycons are very similar to the genus *Nannostomus,* but they tend to go about with their bodies tipped up at an angle. Hence the name Pencilfishes.

This species has a golden brown color with several narrow brown stripes and one broad black one traversing the length of the body, ending in a splendid spread over the entire lower half of the tail fin. The light line seen just above this is metallic gold, and the dots below are dark. Anal fin, brown with a red spot next to body.

As breeders the Nannobrycons are not much of a success in the aquarium. They deposit about 40 scattered single eggs on the under side of such leaves as Sagittaria or Cryptocoryne. These are guarded to some extent and are not eaten. The young appear in about two days at a hatching temperature of 80 to 84 degrees. The species does not at other times require so high a temperature to remain in health. It is best to remove the parents after spawning, as their services to the young seem to be principally sentimental. Ordinarily this fish does not swim rapidly, but when alarmed darts with lightning speed.

Nannaèthiops ansòrgei (BOULENGER)
Pronounced Nan-ee'thee-ops an-sorge'e-eye

Named for W. J. Ansorge, of England.   Formerly: *Neolebias ansorgii*
West Coast, Africa   Western Location Map H60   Length, 1¾ inches

IT will be seen that the form of both sexes is quite similar, and, so far as we know, their characteristics are the same. In life they may easily be told apart, as the broad line down the body of the male is, in this species, a metallic green when seen in a favorable light. There is a good, though slightly exaggerated, color picture of it in the National Geographic Magazine for January, 1934.

This fish and its close relatives used to be placed in the genus *Neolebias* but the latter is now merged with *Nannaethiops*. Note absence of adipose fin in this fish.

Very little is known about the fish, except what may be inferred by its family connections. It has been said that a man is known by the company he keeps. A shrewd guess may be made about a fish if we know its family. Although this idea may at times lead us astray, it is at least a good starting point.

Nannaèthiops unitœniàtus   GUENTHER

Pronounced Nan-ee'thee-ops u'ni-tee'nee-a"tus

MEANING OF NAME: *Nannaethiops,* small African; *unitaeniatus,* single-lined

Nile, Congo, Niger   Length—Male, 2½ inches; female, 3 inches

Western Location Map B56; B53; C58; w69

*A*FTER viewing this fish closely, one is aware of a body shape that is different from that of our other aquarium fishes. It has a sort of rounded plumpness, seeming to denote a good supply of vitality. The fins are always erect and well spread, which gives an appearance of well-being to any fish.

The lateral stripe shows an attractive golden line just above it. As this proceeds towards the tail, it becomes coppery. Continuing into the upper half of the tail fin it spreads into a reddish area. The centre of the lower half of the tail fin is a subdued red. This, however, along with the brighter red in the central lower portion of the dorsal fin, becomes very bright at times, especially at the breeding season. The forward part of the dorsal is edged black.

A 15-gallon aquarium planted closely with Myriophyllum is ideal for breeding. Any plant thicket will do. Eggs are numerous and hatch in 2 days at a temperature of 78 to 82 degrees. Parents should be removed when spawning is completed. Follow standard directions for rearing young of egg-layers.

A hardy, peaceful, attractive aquarium fish. Temperature range, 70 to 85 degrees. Eats anything.

THE GYMNOTID EELS
FAMILY GYMNOTIDAE
Pronounced Gym-n'o ti-dee

*T*HE Knife Fishes, as aquarists call the Gymnotid Eels, are not Eels at all, but close relatives of the Characins, as has been determined by anatomical studies. From the Characins, and, in fact, most other fishes, they differ in having the vent placed at the throat, rather than immediately in front of the anal fin, and by their elongate body and long anal fin. All of them are from South America or southern Central America. Most aquarists confuse the Gymnotids with the African and Asiatic "Knife Fishes" (*Notopterus* and relatives) which are occasionally brought in as aquarium fishes. The Notopterids have the vent in the normal position and do not even belong to the same order as the Gymnotids.

The two Gymnotids pictured on following pages have no tail fin, but others have tiny bunches of rays at the tip of the tail, representing that fin in ordinary fishes.

These Knife Fishes, so-called on account of their blade-like appearance, are, in some species, entirely too large for the household aquarium, the adult size in Nature being 2 feet or more. It is therefore only the smaller sorts we aquarists occasionally possess.

There are many species looking closely alike, so that positive identification is not easy. However, they are so similar in their ways that, so far as the aquarist is concerned, they may be treated as a group.

The most interesting thing about them is their ability to swim forwards or backwards, seemingly with equal ease. A graceful rippling of the long anal fin propels them in either direction, slowly or rapidly as occasion requires. The way in which they instantly reverse themselves in the aquarium when pursued by a net is most interesting.

All of the species are cannibalistic and had best be kept by themselves. They have sharp teeth.

Nothing is known of their breeding habits. We do know that they are tough and can live in pretty bad conditions. They seldom die. The great trouble is that even despite the stunting influence of a small aquarium, they presently become larger than aquarists like.

The best known member of the family is the "electric eel" (*Electrophorus electricus*) of South America, often seen in public aquaria but too large (up to six feet) for a home aquarium. The family Gymnotidae is sometimes split up into several families by ichthyologists, but we prefer to keep it intact in this book.

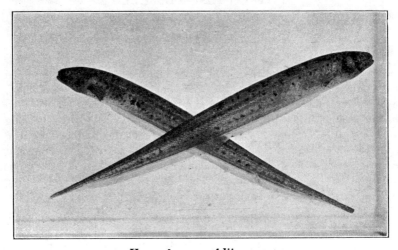

Hypopòmus artédii KAUP
Pronounced High' po-po"mus ar'ted"ee-eye
MEANING OF NAME: *Hypopomus,* with the (gill) cover underneath; *artedii,* after
　　　　Peter Artedi, the father of ichthyology
Guiana　　　　　　　　　　　Western Location Map A22 to G24 and X22

ONE of the several peculiarities of many of the Knife Fishes is that
some have no dorsals nor tail fins. Both representatives of the type
shown have those deficiencies, but this is apparently no handicap. In
fact, considering the described gift these fishes have for swimming backwards, and possessing no eyes in the rear to guide them in avoiding
collisions, it would seem better to have a plain stump, such as we see
here, rather than a fragile fin.

The body of this species is gray-green, dotted black, and with a thin
dark line parallel with the spinal column. Fins clear.

Gymnòtus carapó LINNAEUS
Pronounced Jim-no'tus sar-a-po'　　　　　　　*Popular name,* Sarapó
MEANING OF NAME: *Gymnotus,* with naked back; *carapo,* the native name (see below)
N. South America　　　　　　　　　　　Length, up to 12 inches
　　　　Western Location Map t19 to s21; z8 to v22 and F29

THIS brown fish is fairly well distinguished by the approximately 20
backward-sloping bars, the centres of which are gray and the edges
black. In life, these markings give the impression of being slightly
s-shaped. The pectoral fins are clear, with a dark spot where they join
the body. Temperature, 65 to 85 degrees.

The scientific name of the species, *carapo,* is of some interest. The
Brazilian Indian name for gymnotids (save the electric eel) is "Sarapo,"
but is frequently spelled with a French "ç" which has the soft pronunciation, like an "s". The accent is on the final "o"

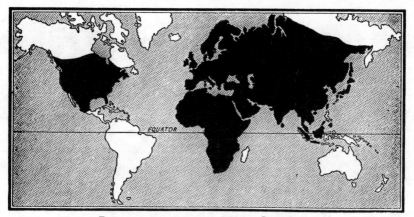

THE CARPS OR MINNOWS

FAMILY CYPRINIDAE
Pronounced Sy-prin'i-dee

The Carps form the largest family of fishes known. Nearly all have scales, but none has teeth in the jaws. In place of jaw teeth, they have curved pharyngeal bones in the throat which bear grinding teeth. Many Carps have barbels (whisker-like structures about the mouth) but only a few rare ones have more than 2 pairs. No carp has an adipose fin, and no Carp ever occurs naturally in South America or Australia.

The Carps vary in size from the giant Mahseer of India, which grows to 6 feet in length, to such tiny creatures as our little *Rasbora maculata*, of scarcely more than an inch. By far the greater number of species are small and minnow-like, and among these we find many of our best small aquarium fishes. The genera and species are most numerous and varied in Southeastern Asia, tropical Africa, and the United States, in the order given. Towards the north the species are much fewer in number.

Some of the minnow-like ones are among the most brilliantly colored of all fishes. This is particularly true of the minnows of the Southern Appalachians, the gorgeous colors of which, at times, equal or surpass the showiest of the exotics. Unfortunately most of the more gaudy American minnows live in swift-running water and would not be well suited to the ordinary still-water aquarium.

General breeding directions are given previously under the title "Breeding the Egg Scatterers."

(Photo by Paul Unger)

Rhòdeus sericeus PALLAS

Pronounced Roe'de-us ser-iss'see-us   *Popular name,* Bitterling, so named on
                                                account of the bitter taste of the flesh

MEANING OF NAME: *Rhodeus,* rosy red; *sericeus,* silky sheen

Central Europe   Western Location Map 59c-59f   Length, 3 inches

NO FISH of its own intelligence is really resourceful, but many fishes, along with other animals, do wonderful things that reflect the accumulated experience of countless ancestors. For convenience we call the process "instinct," which a friend of the author once described as *inherited memory.* Whatever it may be, its highest, most surprising developments are often utilized in the preservation of the young.

One of the most ingenious and seemingly intelligent plans for protecting the eggs and the young of a fish is that employed by this fish, known as the Bitterling. As breeding time approaches the female develops from her vent a long ovipositor tube. This she inserts in the gills of a living freshwater mussel, and deposits her eggs, where they are about as safe from robbers as treasure in a bank vault. The young emerge at their leisure after they have absorbed their own yolk sacs. Some writers have thought that the young live for a time on the juices of the mussel, but this is probably not the case. They take free lodging, but no table board.

As is later observed about the Cichlids, it is remarkable with what accuracy the female can control her ovipositor so as to accurately place the eggs on a spot that she cannot possibly see at the moment. It is even more mystifying how the female Bitterling, with her extremely long ovipositor (shown in the illustration), can unerringly locate the small opening in a mussel.

Another vital part of the breeding scheme requires a seeming act of intelligence on the part of the male fish. Mussels live by extracting microscopic life from the water that they constantly draw in at the gills and discharge at the siphon. Immediately after the eggs are deposited in the recesses of the mussel, the male fish charges the surrounding water with his sperm. The mussel obligingly draws this in and so fertilizes the eggs.

It has been thought that the mussel is tickled by the ovipositor of the female and shuts on it, thus forcing out the eggs. As we know that the fish deposits her eggs a few at a time in a number of mussels, this theory seems improbable, for the severe clamping of which the mussel is capable would be likely to injure or even cut off the tube. A complete spawning takes several days.

The Bitterling has long been known to European aquarists and has several times been bred in captivity. It prefers a temperature not over 70 degrees.

In color it is silvery, with light rosy fins. The body of the males during breeding becomes golden, flushed red.

This fish, along with an oriental species, aroused a scientific furore in America in 1936 as a cheap medium for determining human pregnancy. Urine of a pregnant woman when placed in the water with a female fish was supposed to cause the ovipositor to develop. This proved unreliable, but not before the American market had been raided of its then limited stock.

The fish is a minnow, belonging to the sub-family Rhodeinae, of which there are about half a dozen members, all characterized by the physiological peculiarity here described.

There are a number of close relatives of the Bitterling found in Japan and China. All have similar breeding habits. Occasionally some of them have been imported and sold as "Asiatic Bitterling."

COLOR PLATE PAGE 558

Upper left, *Brachydanio rerio;* upper right, *Brachydanio nigrofasciatus;*
lower, *Brachydanio albolineatus.*

Bráchydànio rèrio　(HAMILTON-BUCHANAN)

Pronounced Brack′i-day″ne-o ree′re-o　　　*Popular names,* Zebra Fish, Zebra Danio
MEANING OF NAME: *Brachydanio,* short Danio; *rerio,* a native name; also known
as *Danio rerio*
Bengal, India　　　Eastern Location Map w22 to p28 and p33　　　Length, 1¾ inches

OF THE various small egg-layers this fish is, no doubt, the most
permanently popular, and with good reason. In an exceptional
degree it has all the points which make an ideal aquarium occupant.
It is unusually active without being nervously annoying, and as a fish
to show to advantage moving in schools, it scarcely has an equal, for its
beautiful horizontal stripes, repeated in each fish, give a "stream-line
effect" that might be the envy of our best automobile designers.

The sexes can be distinguished, but not at a glance. As is usual in
many species, the females are noticeably fuller as spawning time
approaches, and this is particularly true of all of the Brachydanios, but
it is possible to tell the sexes of adult *rerios* by the fact that there is a
more bluish cast over the female, and particularly in the tail fin.

The spawning of the Brachydanios is interesting because it challenges our ingenuity and resourcefulness in overcoming the strong tendency of these active fishes to eat their own eggs as they fall.

The scheme is to have the water so shallow that the fishes have no chance to spear them as they sink, and to then have the eggs fall into a trap where the fishes cannot follow. The trap consists simply of small marbles or pebbles to a depth of about an inch. The eggs are non-adhesive and drop between the marbles to the bottom. One danger with marbles is that the fishes in fright are liable to wriggle among them and be unable to get out. In that respect, quarter-inch rounded stones are

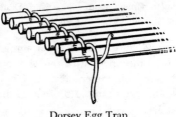

Dorsey Egg Trap

better. A mat of glass bars, such as illustrated, serves the purpose well. This is fastened together with 16-gauge soft aluminum or solder wire. It is raised off the bottom by resting on 2 bars laid at right angles to those in the mat. The water should not be higher than 4 inches above the pebbles or glass bars.

As spawning time approaches it is well to separate any promising-looking female and feed her for a week on choice food. Have the trapped aquarium prepared and seasoned, ready for her and 2 or 3 lively males. Place the aquarium where it will get good light, introduce the female a day ahead of the males, and if there is no spawn in 3 or 4 days, separate and try again. The spawning action is easily recognized. It is a wild chase, similar to that indulged in by Goldfish. The business-man does not need to stay home to save the eggs, for with the arrange-ment described he can be assured that few will be lost. If a glass-bottom tank is used, the aquarist can look up through the base to see whether eggs are scattered among the marbles. To a practised eye the shape of the female is sufficient indication as to whether there has been a spawning.

The fishes, of course, are removed after spawning, and at this time an Infusoria culture should be started as directed under "Egg-layers," for the young will hatch in about 2 days. They at first adhere in odd positions in their first efforts at moving about, but in 2 more days they act like fish and have appetites. As the spawns average about 200 eggs, it is desirable to give the babies plenty of room. They should be continuously pushed in growth. It is the only way in which to produce fine, large specimens, and they are well worth the pleasant effort. While it is possible to raise them entirely on prepared foods, graded according to size, the result does not produce a robust fish. They are apt to be small, and even deformed. Live food is better. The best age for breeders is about one year. At two years they are old. They seldom live beyond an age of three years. "Zebra Danio" is a misfit name, since the stripes on Zebras are mainly vertical. The fish has extraordinary temperature tolerance, from a low of 60 to a high of 110 degrees, but is sensitive to changes of water. Breeds at 72-77. Takes any food.

Brachydànio nigrofasciàtus   (DAY)

Pronounced Brack'i-day"ne-o   ny'grow-fa'see-ay"tus
MEANING OF NAME: *nigrofasciatus*, black-lined

Also known as *B. analipunctatus*   *Popular names,* Spotted or Dwarf Danio
Burma   Eastern Location Map v between 32 and 33.   Length, 1½ inches

HIS species is a little smaller than *rerio,* and while it has a similar horizontal golden line, edged by two blue ones, all three of them passing through the tail fin, its distinguishing characteristic is a group of rows of blue dots along the light belly, and extending into the anal fin.

It is indeed a beautiful little fish, but has never been as popular as *rerio,* nor is it as easily bred, although the method of collecting the spawn is the same. The females seem more liable to become egg-bound. After much chasing the sexes assume a vertical position towards each other, the eggs being dropped during a partial embrace. Temperature for the species should be 70 or above, and 80 for breeding.

Brachydànio albolineàtus   (BLYTH)

Pronounced Brack'i-day"ne-o   al'bo-lin'ee-a"tus   *Popular name,* Pearl Danio
MEANING OF NAME: *albolineatus,* white lined, an erroneous designation
due to description from a preserved specimen which had
changed color; also known as *Danio albolineatus*
Burma   Eastern Location Map v33, w35 and D34   Length, 2½ inches

ANY fishes in order to be seen at their best should be viewed by reflected light. That is, with the light coming from the observer towards the fish. This is especially true of *Danio albolineatus,* whose exquisite mother-of-pearl colors can only be appreciated under those conditions. This is particularly true of the interesting colors in the anal fin, which ordinarily pass unnoticed. It has been claimed that this fin shows colors in the male only, but this is not in accordance with the observations of the writer, who finds that both sexes possess it. Possibly it is a little stronger in the male. Also the ruddy glow about the lower rear part of the body is deeper in the male. There is now in commercial supply a strain with golden bodies in which the markings are faint.

Brachydanio Hybrids
B. rerio x B. nigrofasciatus

HE Brachydanios offer some possibilities in hybridizing, but the progeny are sterile. Crosses have been made between *rerio* and *albolineatus*, and *rerio* and *nigrofasciatus* (*analipunctatus*). The young from the latter cross, illustrated above, are longer and more slender than either parent. In life the resemblance to both parents is a little more apparent than is shown in the photograph. A few of the *nigrofasciatus* (*analipunctatus*) spots may be seen on the central fish. In the *rerio* x *albolineatus* the resulting progeny are more like *rerios*, but with the warm, purplish glow of *albolineatus*.

These hybridizations have been produced both by natural and artificial spawnings, the latter being brought about by what professional culturists of food fishes call "stripping." This consists in gently expelling, or "expressing" the eggs from the ripe female by a stroking pressure down her sides. After they are secured, the spermatic fluid of the male is forced in the same manner, and is stirred up with the eggs, thus fertilizing them. With tiny aquarium fishes it is almost impossible, even with the most delicate touch, to bring about this fertilization without killing the fishes.

The experiment is chiefly one of scientific interests, as there is nothing about these species that would be likely to be improved by crossing.

*COLOR PLATE PAGE 557

Dànio malabáricus   (JERDON)

Pronounced Dan'e-o   mal'a-bar"i-cus   *Popular name,* Giant Danio
MEANING OF NAME: *Danio,* after a native name Dhani; *malabaricus,* from Malabar
India   Eastern Location Map x18 to A20; C22   Length, 4 inches

HIS is in many ways an admirable fish. Always on the move, easily fed and bred, rather long lived and ordinarily peaceful, this species is considered to be one of the standard members of a "happy family" tank. We have heard of their eating much smaller fishes, but this is liable to occur with many species when the difference in size is great.

Brachydanios were formerly known as Danios. On this basis it will be seen that this species is entitled to be called a giant.

Distinguishing the sexes is not easy except at breeding time, when the female is fuller in belly outline. The ruddy hue shown in the fins and anal region is a breeding color, and ordinarily does not appear. It is stronger in the male. On the sides of mature fish the golden vertical and horizontal bars and stripes are more broken in the female. Also the lower jaw of the male protrudes slightly. The illustration shows all three of these points, the lower fish being the male. The size of the sexes, however, should be reversed, the adult female being slightly larger than the male. They have *adhesive* eggs and breed like Barbs. Temperature, 68 to 80 degrees.

COLOR PLATE PAGE 557

Tanichthys albonùbes LIN

Pronounced Tan-ick'thiss al-bo-new'bees
Popular name, White Cloud Mountain Fish or White Cloud
MEANING OF NAME: Named for Tan, a Chinese boy scout who found the fish;
ichthys, fish (Tan's fish); *albonubes*, White Cloud

White Cloud Mountain   Eastern Location Map p44   Length, 1¼ inches
near Canton, China

SELDOM has a fish so many good points. In addition to being attractive, peaceful, active, and easily bred, it also stands a great range of temperature (40-90). Eats anything, but prefers small food given often. Breeds best at 68-75 degrees. Male chases female, who scatters eggs freely. They have been successfully bred both with and without the presence of plants, but it is safer to use them and remove breeders after spawning. At ages from two to ten weeks the babies are extremely beautiful, looking like young Neon Tetras (*Hyphessobrycon innesi*) with a dazzling streak of electric blue-green from the eye to the tail. Professionals breed them in quantity over glass bars as earlier described for *Brachydanio rerio*. Also in wire cages mentioned under "Breeding the Livebearers." An apparent color variation has red at the tips of the fins instead of the base. Males are distinguished by longer dorsal fins.

THE RASBORAS

(O)F THE approximately 45 species of *Rasbora* known to science, about 10 have been tried in aquariums. Those listed here are the only ones that have become established in any degree of popularity. They have only been bred semi-occasionally and more or less accidentally, for there has been no secret discovered that can be depended upon to consistently produce results. Those who were fortunate enough to propagate them can seldom repeat.

Wing Commander Marsack, an experienced aquarist, has made personal field studies of the Malayan region and the conditions under which most Rasboras live and breed. The waters are generally acid, going as low as 5.5 on the pH scale. This is very likely produced by humic acid, generated by the decomposition of leaves and dead wood as the streams pass through dense jungles before emerging into the open where these fishes mostly live.

Broad-leaved Cryptocorynes grow in such profusion that their roots creep out of the soil and form mats over the bottom, making a perfect refuge for newly-hatched fishes. Eggs of *Rasbora heteromorpha* (and probably others) are spawned against the underside of the leaves, where they adhere until hatched.

The fact that most of the species are, in Nature, observed in large schools, leads the author to suspect that they are what are known as "community breeders" in which large numbers take part, and the action requires liberal space. In aquariums we get them into seemingly perfect condition, loaded with spawn, yet nothing happens. The same theory applies to the hard-to-spawn Characins. Certainly we have missed some trick, for in natural conditions both of them are tremendous breeders. What makes it all the more puzzling is that they both take kindly to aquarium life and live for-years in splendid health.

Except for a very few little-known species from Africa, all the Rasboras are native to southeastern Asia, from India to Borneo.

Rasbòra danicònius (HAMILTON-BUCHANAN)

Pronounced Raz-bo'ra dan'e-cone"e-us

MEANING OF NAME: *Rasbora*, a native name; *daniconius*, from a native name

India, Ceylon   Eastern Location Map W19 to Q29   Length, 3 inches

*R*ECORDS of size of this fish, a very common one in all sorts of pools, ditches and streams in India and Ceylon, run as high as 5 inches, but no aquarium specimens give any hint of such length.

It is not a particularly outstanding species as to color. The central body stripe is blue-black, delicately edged, above and below, by a thin, metallic golden line. Back olive, belly white, fins tinged with yellow. It will be noted that a narrow stripe on the body, just above the anal fin, is dark. The lower fish is the female. There are no exterior signs of sex, except shape. They spawn on fine plants, much the same as *R. taeniata*. Temperature range, 72 to 85 degrees. Active and peaceful.

Rasbòra dòrsiocellàta   (DUNCKER)

Pronounced Raz-bo'ra dor'see-o-sel-lay"ta

MEANING OF NAME: *dorsiocellata* refers to ocellated spot in dorsal fin

South Malay Peninsula and Sumatra   Length, 1¾ inches

Eastern Location Map D38 to H39

*A*PPEARING briefly in choice German collections in 1934, nothing more was heard of this distinctive little fish until Mr. Rakowicz of California imported a number of specimens from Singapore in 1947. These were well distributed in the tanks of American aquarists from the Pacific to the Atlantic States, and have done well, except that as yet we have no account of a successful breeding. As the fresh waters of the Malay Peninsula flowing through jungles are largely acid in character, we do not hesitate to suggest acidified water in any attempt to breed them. This could have a pH reading as low as 5.5. Such water might be secured in cedar, sphagnum or pine swamps, lakes and streams.

As the fish has no bright colors, the only interpretation our illustration needs is to say that the large black spot in the dorsal fin is set off by a whitish or iridescent surrounding circle.

We found this species to be a pleasant little fish in a community tank, but one of our associates caught it nipping the long fins of a Veiltail Guppy. This can happen with individuals of peaceful species. It does well at about 75 degrees.

Rasbòra einthòveni (BLEEKER)
Pronounced Raz-bo′ra eint-ho′ven-eye
MEANING OF NAME: *Rasbora,* a native name; *einthoveni,* for Dr. J. Einthoven,
the collector
For a time erroneously known by aquarists as *R. daniconius*
Malay Peninsula and Archipelago   Length, 3½ inches
Eastern Location Map x36 to F39; I40; I42; E47

A BLACK stripe running from the *lower half* of the tail-root to the tip of the lower jaw, characterizes this species. It divides the golden eye in equal upper and lower halves. The stripe is wider in the male, which in the illustration is the upper fish.

The general color is yellowish brown, the scales, with darker edges. The male is slightly suffused purple, while the female is more greenish. There is also a difference in the fins, the male having reddish ribs in the tail fin, as well as a touch of warmth in the dorsal. All fins in female are clear, except for a tinge of yellow in her tail fin.

An attractive, vigorous, fairly well-known aquarium fish. Although this fish has large spawns, many of the eggs fall to the bottom, and are attacked by fungus. The eggs had best be moved to shallow, clear water. The young vary greatly in size, and should be sorted to prevent cannibalism.

Like practically all of the Rasboras, they are fishes easy to get along with and mind their own business. Temperature range, 72-82 degrees.

Rasbòra élegans VOLZ
Pronounced Raz-bo'ra el'e-gans
MEANING OF NAME: *Rasbora*, a native name; *elegans*, elegant
Sumatra and Malay Peninsula Eastern Location Map F39; J40; H46 Length, 5 inches

*c*A CENTRAL black body spot below the first dorsal ray, more or less oblong in shape, and varying in intensity, roughly distinguishes this species. Besides the ocellated dot at the tail base, there is a horizontal narrow dark line just above the anal fin. This mark and a dark nick in the upper part of the silvery iris, for some reason, fail to show in our illustration. The fish does not have the glittering appearance of burnished silver common to such individuals as *Ctenobrycon spilurus*. It is more of a leaden gray. There is just a touch of warmth to it, as in the interesting shade called French gray. The dorsal fin is light brown.

In the female the central body spot is paler, and she is the more aggressive. Anal yellow in male, clear in female. Seldom breeds. Spawns on fine plants. The species is in fairly good commercial supply.

As will be seen from the length given, this species grows to be a rather large fish, the illustration representing it at just about half size. While it is always a pleasing fish to see, it makes an especially attractive show fish when fully grown. The rather large scales, edged dark gray, show like a sleek coat of armor, which, of course, is what they are.

In the small streams of Sumatra, Singapore, Malacca and Borneo, where it is generally found, it occurs in large numbers.

The species enjoys a mixed diet, will live at peace in a community tank and will do well in any ordinary temperature of from 70 to 80 degrees.

Female (lower fish) in upside-down position, rubbing leaf preparatory to spawning.

Rasbòra heteromòrpha DUNCKER

Pronounced Raz-bo'ra   het'er-o-morf"a   *Popular name,* Rasbora, or Red Rasbora

MEANING OF NAME: *Rasbora,* a native name; *heteromorpha,* differing in shape
(from most members of the genus)

Malay Peninsula and Sumatra   Length, 1¾ inches

Eastern Location Map F39; D34; x38

ALTHOUGH until recently an expensive and rather rare fish, *R. heteromorpha* has for many years occupied a prominent place in the minds of all advanced fish fanciers. It has been the open or secret ambition of many a one to own this little beauty, so individual in its appearance. It ships well, and is a leader in sales volume.

So outstanding is this species among its cousins that the popular and trade name, "Rasbora," takes it for granted that R. *heteromorpha* is meant, just as though no other species existed!

The lure of financial returns has spurred collectors and importers to such elaborate efforts in bringing them alive from far Asia that they now arrive by thousands, where before dozens were considered an event. This state of affairs has its disadvantages as well as advantages, so that one is not certain whether to be glad or sorry about it.

Many an expert has set himself to the task of breeding them. A few have had partial success. Reports of spawnings vary somewhat in detail, but in the main they agree. The successful temperature is from 78 to 82 degrees, and the action takes place within a day or two after a ripe pair has been placed in a planted tank containing water that has aged only a few days. The male swims over the female for a time. She often assumes an upside-down position, contacting her belly with the underside of leaves, such as Cryptocoryne or large Sagittaria, apparently searching a suitable place on which to spawn. Possibly she is doing something to prepare a place so that the eggs may adhere. Our photograph gives a true picture of this action. She may be coaxing the male, for presently, but not immediately, he joins her under a leaf and quickly clasps her in the crescent he makes of his body, the female continuing in an upside-down position. During the momentary, trembling embrace several small crystal-clear eggs appear. These are attached to the underside of the leaf. The action is repeated at intervals under different leaves for a period of about two hours, at the end of which time there are from 30 to 80 eggs. It is probable that clean, new leaves best serve the purpose. If they are coated with algae the eggs are apt to fall and be eaten. At a temperature of 80 degrees they hatch in 18 hours. One successful breeder uses water at pH 6.5, has Bacopa as a spawning plant, and conditions his breeders on white worms and brine shrimp.

The surest method of telling the sex in breeding size fish is by the golden line along the top edge of the black triangle. It is more brilliant and deeply colored in the male, especially by overhead artificial light. This is partially shown in our natural color photograph (frontispiece), the lower fish being the male. He also happens to show another sex indication, this one not being regarded as dependable. That is the forward-pointing of the bottom of the vertical side of the triangle.

Rasbora heteromorpha moves about the aquarium easily but not nervously. It is adaptable both as to food and temperature, a range from 68 to 88 degrees producing no ill effects. Lives about 5 years.

Rasbora pauciperforata   **WEBER & DE BEAUFORT**

Formerly *Rasbora leptosoma*

Pronounced Raz-bo'ra paw'si-per'for-ay"ta

MEANING OF NAME: *Rasbora*, a native name; *pauciperforata*, "few perforations" refers to the incomplete lateral line

Malay Peninsula, Sumatra   Eastern Location Map H39   Length, 2½ inches

*A*S IN many other fishes, the horizontal body stripe divides an olive back from a more or less white belly. The line itself frequently has interesting character, such as in this instance. It is a pretty band composed (from bottom to top) of red, gold and black, and runs through the eye to the tip of the nose. The top of the eye is red gold. Fins all clear. Breeding habits not known. An attractive fish in a quiet way, and one not often seen in collections.

The lower fish is the female. They are quite playful in chasing each other about, but no damage seems to get done, nor does the fish population seem to be increased as a result of playful pursuits.

They are adaptable as to food, but, as with other members of this family, they are much benefited by an occasional meal of live food, such as Daphnia or mosquito larvae. In the absence of these an occasional bit of minced earthworm or scraped fish is acceptable. Temperature range, 72 to 80 degrees.

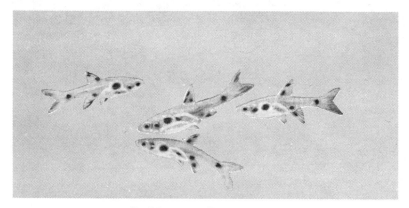

Rasbòra maculàta DUNCKER

Pronounced Raz-bo'ra mac'you-lay"ta   Known incorrectly as *R. kalochroma*
MEANING OF NAME: *Rasbora,* a native name; *maculata,* spotted
Malay Peninsula   Eastern Location Map F39   Length, 1 inch

THIS rare and dainty little fish at first glance reminds one of a male Guppy, partly on account of its size, but more especially owing to the large, rainbow-edged spot on the fore part of the side. The bearing of the fish, however, is more perky, with the fins always well spread. It is also more slender, and the fins are differently shaped.

The general color is reddish, but the abdominal area is a greenish white, separated from the color of the upper body by an arching line of gold. The dark portions of the fins are red and there is a smaller ocellated spot at the tail base. Males may be distinguished by their whiter bellies, and the large spot on the side is more distinct. Also they have one small black spot above the anal fin, while the females have two. The central figure in the illustration is a female, the others being males.

In breeding season, both sexes become a deeper red on the body. For breeding, and for the best color, this fish must be kept in a very soft water of pH 6.0 to 6.5.

The species has been bred a few times in small numbers. The eggs are deposited on the underside of a leaf, much the same as with *R. heteromorpha,* but there is no embrace, the male fertilizing the eggs immediately after they are attached. Being extremely small, the young must be fed on the finer sizes of Infusoria and rotifers.

The adult fishes will eat anything, but should be given a liberal proportion of live food of suitable size. Temperature range, 73 to 80 degrees.

Rasbòra meìnkeni   DE BEAUFORT

Pronounced Raz-bo'ra   mine'ken-eye

MEANING OF NAME: *Rasbora*, a native name; *meinkeni*, after Herman Meinken,
German aquarist and ichthyologist

East Indies   Sumatra, exact location unknown   Length, 3 inches

$\mathcal{E}$XCEPT for this fish having a marked yellow-brown cast all over, the
same remarks apply as to *R. daniconius*, only that it is not so common. The difference in color and the less clear side stripe in this fish are
the two main points by which the aquarist may tell the two species
apart. In this illustration it is the upper fish that is the female.

The dark line near the vent in the illustration is characteristic of the
species.

This is one of the more easily-bred Rasboras.

Rasbòra taeniàta AHL

Pronounced Raz-bo′ra tee-nee-a′ta

MEANING OF NAMES: *Rasbora,* a native name; *taeniata,* with narrow stripe

Malay Peninsula　　　　Sumatra, exact locality not known　　　　Length, 2¼ inches

A RATHER plain fish, light olive to brown in color, with the scales edged black. The dark body stripe is edged above with dull gold. Fins clear except tail fin. There is a dark edging on the lips.

A moderately lively fish and one of the few Rasboras that is not so difficult to breed. They spawn much in the manner of the Barbs, on the finely divided leaves of plants, depositing about 250 eggs.

The fuller body of the lower fish correctly suggests the female. The male shows orange in the base of the tail fin. He is not usually smaller, as here shown. Subject to the parasitic disease, Ichthyophthirius, at any temperature below 70 degrees.

On the whole we would say that the species is better looking and more lively than the photographic illustration seems to indicate.

Dr. Martin Brittan, who has recently made a careful study of *Rasbora* classification, thinks our photo may represent *Rasbora bankanensis* instead of *R. taeniata,* but is not sure.

Rasbòra trilineàta STEINDACHNER

Pronounced Raz-bo′ra   try′lin-ee′-a″ta   *Popular name,* Scissors-Tail Rasbora

MEANING OF NAME: *Rasbora,* a native name; *trilineata,* three-lined

Johore in Malay Peninsula Eastern Location Map F39 to C37 Length, up to 8 inches

A NUMBER of the Rasboras are difficult for the amateur ichthyologist to identify, but fortunately most of our aquarium species are quite individual. Mr. M.W.F. Tweedie, Curator of the Raffles Museum at Singapore, who has personally collected many Rasboras, assures us in THE AQUARIUM, January, 1940, that this species cannot be confused with any other of the genus, the markings on the tail fin being distinctive. Each lobe is orange towards the outer part, then tipped black. The body is somewhat translucent. Although the fishes in Nature become more than twice as long as our aquarium specimens, we find that they will breed at a length of about 3 inches. The actual spawning has not, to our knowledge, been observed, but pairs kept at 70 degrees in a well-planted tank have several times produced young, indicating that when well fed they do not eat eggs nor fry. Many fishes partially close the tail fin when starting to move, but with this species the markings render it very apparent, making a sort of clipping action. Hence the popular name, "Scissors-tail."

Esòmus danrìcus   (HAMILTON-BUCHANAN)

Pronounced Ee-so'mus dan-ree'cus   *Popular name,* Flying Barb

MEANING OF NAME: *Esomus,* slender body; *danricus,* after native name; also known as
Nuria danrica

Northern India and Burma   Length, 4 to 5 inches

Eastern Location Map 119 to p29 and y21

A GRACEFUL, active fish, spending much of its time at the surface.
It has a wide spread of pectoral fins, as indicated in the figure to the
right. These fins enable it to make sizable leaps from the water, giving
rise to the popular name, Flying Barb. There are two pairs of barbels,
or "whiskers," the lower pair being extremely long, reaching to the
middle of the body. The line along the body is black, with an upper
ribbon of gold, dividing an olive back from silver sides. The line goes
faintly into the tail fin. At breeding time the male develops a reddish
hue towards the end of his body, and the triangular red speck at the base
of his tail stands out more clearly.

They breed prolifically, somewhat in the manner of the Barbs. They
should be provided with a large, thickly planted aquarium, with water
not over 6 inches deep. A layer of natural settlings, or of large pebbles,
should be on the bottom, in order to conceal such eggs as fall, for they

are only partially adhesive and do not hold very well on the plants. The spawning situation should be a sunny one, and the temperature about 78 degrees. The breeding action has an unusual variation from most of the egg-droppers. The male strikes against the sides of the female to induce her to spawn and then she returns in kind and pokes him so as to assist him in fertilizing the eggs with his sperm. Remove breeders after spawning.

The small, pale yellow eggs hatch in 2 days and Infusoria should be supplied the fry 2 days later. The young are not easily raised.

Owing to the ability of Esomus to leap, it is important to keep their tanks well covered. An interesting characteristic of the species is that each fish seems to have a sense of property rights, patrolling back and forth over a selected spot, attempting to keep away any intruders that do not look too formidable.

This sounds rather unfavorable if the fish were a candidate for a community aquarium; but, as a matter of fact, these threats result in no damage.

Temperature range, 70-84 degrees.

Esòmus malayénsis   (MANDEE)

Pronounced E-so'muss may'lay-en"sis

MEANING OF NAME: *Esomus,* slender; *malayensis,* from the Malayan region

Malayan Region   Location not exactly known   Length, 3 to 3½ inches

V IRTUALLY all that has been said about the general habits of the foregoing species also applies to this one. The only further instruction the reader needs is to be able to distinguish one kind from the other. *Malayensis* is about an inch smaller, it has not such a clear side stripe, but the decorative spot at the base of the tail is larger and prettier. Also it has a small black spot at the base of the anal, not well shown here.

Both of the *Esomus* shown are popular and are in fairly good supply, especially *malayensis,* which is a very pretty little aquarium fish, waving its dark tail-spot through the water.

Notròpis hypselópterus (GUENTHER)

Pronounced No-tro'pis hip'sel-op"ter-us

MEANING OF NAME: *Notropis,* with keel-shaped back; *hypselopterus,* deep, or
long-finned. Generally known as *Notropis metallicus*

Georgia and Florida   Western Location Map e to g on 25

ONE of our beautiful American minnows. It has more than once been
used as the medium of a practical joke on some seasoned fancier
of exotic fishes. When it is shown him as a "new importation from
Timbuktu," or elsewhere, he is thrilled by its beauty, and must have
some at any price. His ardor soon cools when informed that it is a
home product. However, the fish is. never what might be called "dirt
cheap," for it is not found in large quantities, and is not easily captured.

The former specific name, *metallicus,* gives some hint of its general
color. It is a coppery, warm-brown with yellow in the fins. The base
of the dorsal is red, shading to black. These colors make a fine setting
for the broad, golden-topped, blue-black band extending the entire
length of the body.

This is really a most attractive fish, and is easily domesticated, but
it can hardly receive full approval as a "tropical." It should be kept
in a well-planted aquarium of not less than 10-gallon capacity, and at
a temperature of 65 to 70 degrees. The males have all the color and
much the larger fins. Never bred in close confinement. Aeration desirable.

THE BARBS

𝒯HE Barbs give gaiety and grace to an aquarium. Their large, mirror-like scales constantly catch the light and flash it back from many angles, for they are seldom still.

A sparkling appearance is only one of their merits. They are peaceful, playful, most of them are easily bred and they prosper at moderate temperatures, being quite happy within a range of 68 to 76 degrees. It might be added that most of them are of popular aquarium sizes. Despite their general similarity, it is not difficult to detect the interesting differences in the many species known to the aquarist.

Nearly but not quite all of them have short whiskers or barbels about the mouth, a characteristic for which the genus is named.

In some books it will be noticed that our small Barbs, for which we use the generic name *Barbus,* are placed in the genus *Puntius* (*Puntius conchonius* instead of *Barbus conchonius,* for example). Dr. George Myers, who helps us with nomenclature, says this is an unimportant matter, and that aquarists are justified in sticking to *Barbus.* The reasons are several, partly ichthyological and partly a matter of convenience.

A sunny situation not only suits them, but shows them off best. Old water and plenty of plants should be provided.

As to breeding *Barbus,* this is a simple matter. The female, naturally a little bigger than the male in many species, becomes noticeably larger as she fills with spawn. When this evidence is apparent, she should be placed with one or two males in a thickly-planted aquarium as described under "Breeding the Egg-Scatterers." The breeding is similar to that of the Goldfish, to which it is related. The males chase the female and when she becomes sufficiently excited, she scatters or sprays adhesive eggs on the plants or wherever they may fall. As both sexes soon eat what eggs they can find, it is well to have the plants densely arranged so as to defeat this destruction. Naturally, with that thought in mind, the aquarist will promptly remove the fish when spawning is finished. The eggs hatch quite quickly, requiring only about 38 to 40 hours. The young are easily reared by the described formula for egg droppers.

They are rather long-lived, 4 to 8 years under favorable conditions.

So simple are the temperature requirements of the Barbs that they are included among exotic fishes which may be bred in outdoor pools in the summer climate of our states where the nights are not cold. If placed in a large, well-planted space and constantly supplied with live food, they will prosper and breed without further attention.

They will accept any kind of food. Another point of value is that they are not "scary" fishes.

Bärbus binotàtus   CUVIER AND VALENCIENNES
Pronounced Bar'bus by'no-tay"tus

MEANING OF NAME: *Barbus*, from the barbels present in some, but not all species; *binotatus*, two spotted

Malayan region   Length, 5 inches

Eastern Location Map w37 to F39; D35 to K41; L42 to N49; I45 to B50; and y52

THE size of the dark markings on fishes must not always be taken too seriously in the matter of identification. This fact is mentioned here because this fish is a case in point. Apparently all of the foreign books show quite a large black spot at the base of the dorsal fin, comparable with that of *B. dunckeri*. The species is fairly common among American collections, and almost always the spot is small—sometimes smaller than shown here. This fish is known to be particularly variable in that characteristic. The spots become less distinct with age. Except for dull-gold-to-brown eyes, the color is confined to silver and black.

Inset in illustration shows characteristic markings on young.

The sexes are much alike, but breeding is not difficult. A large aquarium at 70 to 80 degrees is advised, and standard treatment for Barbs. A fairly popular species.

COLOR PLATE PAGE 55b

Bärbus conchònius   HAMILTON-BUCHANAN

Pronounced Bar'bus   kon-cho'nee-us   *Popular name,* Rosy Barb

MEANING OF NAME: *conchonius,* after a native name

India   Eastern Location Map 119 to q31   Length, 3½ inches

AKEN over a period of years, the Rosy Barb is easily the best known and most popular of the genus, as far as aquarists are concerned. In selecting it as a color subject, we do so because it is familiar to many, and is brilliant when breeding.

Anyone with just a little experience will identify the lower fish as the male, but from the colors shown it should not be assumed that the sex is always so easily distinguished, for when love-making is over, he lays aside his gay courting costume. Even outside breeding season the tops of those fins shown dark here have a tendency to be darker than those of the female. On the average, he is also a little smaller.

The dark spot on the body is slightly ocellated, a point which our color plate has failed to pick up. That is to say, it should be edged with a lighter color, gold—in this species.

Usually in good supply and is one of the hardiest of the Barbs.

COLOR PLATE PAGE 558

Bärbus cummingi GUENTHER

Pronounced Bar'bus cum'ming-eye (not cum-ming'-eye)

MEANING OF NAME: Named for Cumming, probably the collector

Ceylon   Eastern Location Map B22   Recorded length, 2 inches

THIS fish is among the most recent acquisitions of exotic fishes, and let us add, one of the best. The species has been successfully bred by one of our largest producers, as well as by a number of amateurs. We hope it will be with us permanently.

We aquarists know only too well that the best colors of some of our fishes come and go. This is true of most of the Barbs, but a male *cummingi* in good condition and not recently moved consistently retains its red fins. Probably *B. tetrazona* is its only Barb rival in color consistency.

A peculiarity of the species is an unusual variation in size among the males. Specimens smaller than shown in the illustration display full color. It seems difficult to bring these little individuals up to bigger size. The largest adults we have seen are 1¼ inches long. The usually pale fins of the female are sometimes flushed light rose.

They breed like the other Barbs, and are apt to frequent the lower water levels, feeding at the bottom. Very peaceful.

Bärbus chòla   (HAMILTON-BUCHANAN)

Pronounced Bar'bus cho'la   *Popular name,* Chola Barb

MEANING OF NAME: *Barbus,* with barbels; *chola,* after a native name

India   Eastern Location Map z19 to p29 and w36   Length, 4 inches

THERE is a strong family resemblance between this species and the better-known *B. conchonius.* It is slightly more slender and the dark spot is nearer the base of the tail. This species has a small pair of barbels, whereas *B. conchonius* has none. A further point of identification is a rosy spot on the gill plate. This is suggested in the illustration, a little in back of the eye, and almost in a line with it.

The sexes are distinguished by the orange-tinted anal and ventral fins of the male. All fins in the female are quite clear. While she is slightly the larger, the difference is not usually as great as shown here. The species does not breed so freely as its neighbor in Nature, *B. conchonius,* but requires the same treatment in all respects.

This is one of those species which, while not rare, can only be obtained from time to time. Those who own it like it very much, and find that with moderately good treatment it enjoys robust health and lives for years. Experimental efforts have been made to cross the species with *B. conchonius,* but without results.

Bärbus dúnckeri AHL

Pronounced Bar'bus doonk'er-eye

Named for Georg Duncker, the German ichthyologist

Malay region, Malayan rivers   Eastern Location Map about D37   Length, 4½ inches

NOT many aquarists keep this species, for the reason that it has no outstanding beauty to offset the disadvantage of its large size, such, for instance, as that possessed by *B. everetti.*

The one feature which will help the amateur ichthyologist identify the species is the large spot on the body, just below and nearly the size of the dorsal fin. This spot becomes rather indistinct at maturity. In color the fish is olive silver, with a yellow undertone. The dorsal is dirty yellow. The other fins have a yellow cast, and, in the case of the anal, it shades to a reddish-brown at the end. Eye, silver with a dark ring outside. There are 2 pairs of barbels, the lower pair being long.

Breeding and care conform to instructions for *Barbus.* They are quite hardy, but are seldom bred. Not easy to spawn.

The female (upper fish) is apt to be just a little the larger, about in the proportion shown in the illustration. There are no other known sex indications.

COLOR PLATE PAGE 559

Bärbus éveretti BOULENGER

Pronounced Bar'bus ev'er-et-eye   *Popular name,* Clown Barb
Named for the collector, Everett
Also widely, but incorrectly, known as *Barbus lateristriga*
Malay Peninsula and Borneo   Eastern Location Map F39 and F45   Length, 5 inches

HIS fish is a good proof of the importance of introducing a species under its correct scientific name, or of promptly changing it when we discover a mistake. For quite a while the beautiful *B. everetti* was known as *B. lateristriga,* but when the true *B. lateristriga* was brought on the scene, and in its own right turned out to be a fish of importance, something had to be done about the awkward situation. By a study that could have been made earlier we would have found that what we were calling *B. lateristriga* is really *B. everetti.* After a bit of mental adjustment, we are now giving each of the two species its correct name.

The "Clown Barb," as it has been called on account of its characteristic, conspicuous spots, is one of the bigger Barbs and one of the more difficult to spawn. Aeration, a little fresh water and plenty of live food help put it in breeding condition.

The colors develop when the fish is about 2 inches long, and at that size, or a little larger, the big blue-black spots are more clearly defined than in the fully mature fish. They have 2 pairs of barbels. A large, well planted aquarium should be given them, and a temperature range of 72 to 78 degrees.

On account of its rather robust size and striking markings, *Barbus everetti* makes one of the best of exhibition fishes.

Bärbus lateristrìga   CUVIER AND VALENCIENNES

Pronounced Bar'bus lat'er-iss-tri'ga

MEANING OF NAME: *lateristriga,* with lateral stripes

Popular name, T-Barb or Spanner Barb

Malay Peninsula and East Indies   Length, 5½ inches
Eastern Location Map F39; I40; L43; I45

T O aquarists this species was a new introduction in 1932. The first ones we saw were about the size of our illustration, and were very interesting, with their shield-like arrangement of vertical and horizontal stripes. Since then they have grown apace and now rank with the largest of our Barbs in the aquarium. There are no bright colors to be seen, and as the fish becomes large, it loses that crispness of the black pattern which makes them more interesting in their smaller sizes.

See the foregoing (*B. everetti*) as to requirements, and also regarding confusion of the two names.

Bärbus fasciàtus (BLEEKER)

Pronounced Bar'bus fa'see-a"tus

MEANING OF NAME: *fasciatus*, striped

Borneo, Sumatra, Malay Peninsula

Popular name, Striped Barb

Length, up to 5 inches

Eastern Location Map G45, J40, H41 and F39

*I*T IS quite evident that we have by no means come to the end of the species of *Barbus* suited to life in the aquarium. The main difficulty is in securing the kinds which are naturally small or that can be kept from growing too large. So far as attractiveness and good disposition are concerned, it seems that no Barb is a bad Barb.

The species shown here was first brought to the attention of American aquarists in 1935. It is a brilliant, silvery fish, and as the well-defined blue-black stripes run horizontally, in contrast with the vertical slashes we are more used to in Barbs, they have made a deeply favorable impression. There is a stripe along the middle of the back, which can not be shown in a side-view illustration. Thus far the fish has been held down to a size not much larger than shown in the illustration.

They have not as yet been bred here, but the sexes are easily told, both by the fuller form of the female, and the fact that her stripes are not quite as clear. Her middle stripe is broader. Temperature, 70-80 degrees.

Bärbus gélius (HAMILTON-BUCHANAN)

Pronounced Bar'bus g-el'ee-us

MEANING OF NAME: *gelius,* after a native name   *Popular name,* Geli Barb

India Eastern Location Map r27 to p30 Length—male, 1¼ inches; female, 1¾ inches

A RATHER rare and odd Barb is shown here. It is characterized by three features; its diminutive size, its slim shape and its oddly sprinkled black spots. A fourth point is that it is expensive, but that means nothing, for tomorrow it may be cheap. In this instance we doubt that possibility, for it is a difficult little fish to breed, and imports have to come from a great distance. Furthermore, being without bright color spots anywhere, it can hardly be expected to attain popularity. The broad dark stripe along the body is brownish, while the nearly translucent fins have a tinge of yellow. Barbels are present.

The sexes appear very much alike, the black markings in the male (at left) appearing to be just a little more brilliant.

This species is particularly adept at eating its own eggs, so that those who hope to breed it must be clever enough to outwit the fish. Breeding temperature, about 75 degrees, which is also their top for comfortable living. They may go down to 65 degrees without distress, being one of those exotics which is not necessarily a "tropical."

The illustration represents the maximum size, which they seldom attain. Ordinarily aquarium size is about 2/3 as large as shown here.

A special effort should be made to keep up the strength of small fishes by occasional feedings of live foods, such as Daphnia, white worms and tubifex worms. *B. gelius* is included among the small fishes.

Bärbus hexazòna WEBER AND DE BEAUFORT
Pronounced Bar'bus hex'a-zo"na
MEANING OF NAME: six banded or zoned   *Popular name,* Six-banded Barb
Sumatra, Malay Peninsula Eastern Location Map F39 and I41 Length, 2½ inches

*I*T SEEMS that no matter how many Barbs are introduced, each has some individual characteristic by which the aquarist can recognize it, once he has learned the identification. In this they have a marked advantage over some of the nearly-alike Characins, which puzzle not only our leading aquarists, but our trained ichthyologists as well.

To account for the six characteristic dark bars on this species, we must notice one which traverses the eyes and one at the other extreme—the base of the tail. These clear-cut vertical slashes are nearly black, but have a suggestion of a blue-green overlay.

The fish does not show its full beauty until well-grown. The male then has a pleasing orange-red in the bases of the anal and vertical fins, and in the central area of the dorsal. He also shows a few flecks of red on his upper sides, the ground color in both sexes being a warm, brownish yellow. The female shows the color only in her dorsal fin.

This attractive Barb is one of the more recent importations, and while the breedings have been few, it is to be hoped that it will become permanently established. It breeds in the customary Barb manner, and enjoys a temperature between 70 and 80 degrees. Perfectly peaceful.

COLOR PLATE PAGE 559

Bärbus nìgrofasciàtus GUNTHER

Pronounced Bar'bus ny'grow-fas'see-ay"tus *Popular* name, Black Ruby Barb

MEANING OF NAME: Black-banded *Barbus*

Ceylon   Eastern Location Map C22   Length, 2¼ inches

*A*LTHOUGH collectors of this interesting fish tell us of having to endure sultry equatorial heat, the fishes themselves do not seem to like it either, for they are captured while taking refuge under shady banks. When naturalized in the aquarium they are happy in comfortable room temperatures, although breeding is most successful at between 75 and 80 degrees. They breed like the other Barbs, as already described.

If this species would appear at all times in its best color, we would not hesitate to rate it as the most beautiful Barb now known to aquarists. The rich glow of strawberry red in the forward part of the body, seeming to force itself through a stubborn film of near-black, is simply stunning. Only the males assume this color, and not for long. A partial change of water or other stimulation may start the magic. The contrasting blackness of the fins and body accompanies the glowing dark cherry red; when one goes, the other vanishes, and we have only a rather drab, barred Barb.

COLOR PLATE PAGE 560

Bärbus oligolèpis   (BLEEKER)

Pronounced Bar'bus ol'i-go-lee"pis (ol'i-gol"ee-pis is allowable)
MEANING OF NAME: *oligolepis*, having few scales   *Popular name*, Checkerboard Barb
Sumatra   Eastern Location Map E35 to J40   Length, 2 inches

THE beautiful black-bordered orange dorsal identifies this fish instantly. No other known Barb is even slightly similar.

The lower fish is the female of the trio. Usually the double dark line showing on the side of the males does not appear so strongly on the female as it does here. In addition, the sexes are easily distinguished by the differences in color. The species has a small pair of barbels.

At breeding time the orange in the dorsal of the male is intensified and he becomes suffused with black, through which sparkles many a scale of blue and green. Breeding as per other Barbs. There are about 200 eggs to a spawning, and the young, which hatch in 60 hours at 78 degrees, are very small and translucent, requiring the finest sizes of live food, in addition to green water.

It has been found that where several females are ripe at the same time they may be bred together with an equal or a greater number of males.

The species sometimes, but seldom, reaches the size shown.

Bärbus semifasciolàtus GUENTHER

Pronounced Bar'bus sem'ee-fa'see-o-lay"tus

MEANING OF NAME: *semifasciolatus*, half-banded   *Popular name,* China Barb

S. China   Eastern Location Map p45; s43   Length, 2½ inches

*I*N OUR own lives we often find ourselves agreeably attached, not so much to persons of brilliance, as to those having good dispositions; those who endure much and ask little. So it is with *B. semifasciolatus,* a fish without any striking beauty, and which has for many years maintained a degree of popularity among aquarists.

Its half-dozen partly broken bands give the fish its outward identity. These cross a green-golden lateral stripe and a field of large, iridescent scales. The fins are tinted yellow. At mating time the belly of the male is moderately flushed with red. Barbels (2) very small.

They breed freely in the *Barbus* manner and may be kept with other exotic fishes without danger, at any reasonable temperature.

Mr. Thomas Schubert, of Camden, N. J., has developed a handsome golden strain of this species which breeds true. The young are light yellow but develop a deeper, richer tone as adults. Faintness of the usual markings makes it hard to recognize them as *B. semifasciolatus.* In the trade they are known as "Schuberti." *Barbus fasciolatus* is a very similar species from West Africa, having about twice as many bars and exactly twice as many barbels, one pair of which is large.

Bärbus tetrazòna BLEEKER (incorrectly *B. sumatranus*)

Pronounced bar' bus tet'ra-zoe' na

MEANING OF NAME: four-banded   *Popular name*, Damsel Barb

Malay to Borneo   Eastern Location Map D38 to G46   Length, 2 inches

W̶E meet here a fish of unusually high spirits. As might be expected, it possesses both the merits and the faults of that characteristic. Very lively and stimulating to the other fishes in an aquarium, this exuberance is sometimes carried too far, especially when it comes to nipping the flowing fins of slower-moving fishes, such as Bettas. This colorful fish, according to our observation, is best kept only with its own kind. Even then the tank should be a rather large one, say 10 or preferably 15 gallons. One of the prettiest sights imaginable is a 25-gallon tank containing about 50 of these lively beauties.

Females can usually be picked by their fuller outline, as indicated by the top figure in the color plate. Also she shows less red in the ventral fins, unfortunately partly covered here.

Breeding is typical as described under "The Barbs," but they are keen spawn-eaters. Males liable to nip anal fins of females prior to spawning, even to the extent of killing them.

Bärbus tèrio   (HAMILTON-BUCHANAN)

Pronounced Bar'bus tee'ree-o

MEANING OF NAME: *terio,* after a native name   *Popular name,* Teri Barb

India   Eastern Location Map 119 to q29   Length, 2½ inches

ALTHOUGH this species looks a good deal like *B. conchonius,* there are several differences to be noted by the close observer. One is a reddish orange spot on the gill plate. Another is a faint dark line between the body spot and the base of the tail. Also the dorsal fin is more pointed.

The male may be identified by the fact that he is yellowish all over, and his anal and ventrals are touched with orange. The female is silver with clear fins. Breeding and care are the same as for *B. conchonius,* but the species does not spawn so readily. The male instead of turning crushed-strawberry red at mating time becomes a beautiful orange.

The personal name following any scientific name (as above) is that of the "authority" who made the first description and established the name. Sometimes two persons working together are responsible. It has been taken for granted by some that Hamilton-Buchanan, who named many fishes now used in the aquarium, represents such a partnership. This is not the case. It is the compound name of a Scottish scientist who had a colorful career in the Orient.

COLOR PLATE PAGE 561

Bärbus ticto   (HAMILTON-BUCHANAN)

Pronounced Bar'bus tick'toe

MEANING OF NAME: *ticto,* after a native name   *Popular name,* Ticto Barb

India   Eastern Location Map q17 to r29 and A20   Length, 3½ inches

A POPULAR Barb favorite, this fish. The arching reddish area in the
dorsal fin of the male easily distinguishes the species. It becomes
vivid in breeding season, and as he moves briskly about it reminds one of
a spray of scarlet sage swaying in a September breeze. The color is reasonably permanent, but at times is reduced to a mere blush. There is
always enough color present to tell the sexes, as the dorsal of the female
is pale, except for a faint rose at breeding time.

The males do not rival the occasional body brilliance of their same-sized
cousins, the Rosy Barbs, but their banners of color are carried more consistently. Of both species it may be said that they are Barbs without
barbels or "whiskers." Both are active, especially the male *ticto.* He is
seldom at rest, busily hustling about the aquarium and occasionally
nudging some slower fish as if to say "Come on, let's play." These high-
spirited doings result in no damage.

A durable species, easily bred. See standard directions for Barbs.

Bärbus partipentazòna   FOWLER
Pronounced Bar'bus par'tee-pen'ta-zo"na
MEANING OF NAME: *partipentazona*, partly five-zoned
First known to aquarists as *Barbus sumatranus* (incorrectly)
Siam and Malay Peninsula   Eastern Location Map x36 to F39   Length, 1¾ inches

THIS is one of those fishes whose misfortune (or is it the aquarist's?) it was to be introduced under the name of another species, *B. tetrazona*. The error was one that was easily made, as the two fishes are fairly similar, but such mistakes are always difficult to correct, even when the error has been rooted but a short time. The genuine *B. tetrazona* had not then been imported. It has since been marketed in great numbers, almost to the exclusion of *B. partipentazona*, for it is more brilliant, and shows red in the anal fin.

B. *partipentazona* is a very pleasing Barb of small size. It has a silver body, slashed vertically with black bars as shown in the illustration. One feature the plate cannot show without the aid of colors is the very pretty streak of red in the dorsal fin, just in back of the black. This begins to show at a fairly early age, but does not reach its full depth and brilliance until maturity, which is in about a year. It is slightly brighter in the males, and, except for the shape, is the only outward indication of sex.

Like many of their Barb cousins, they do not seem to be at all "scary," and early learn to regard their owner as their friend.

They breed like other Barbs, but so far have not proved prolific. Temperature for them should average about 75 degrees.

Bärbus phutùnio   (HAMILTON-BUCHANAN)
Pronounced Bar′bus foo-too′nee-o   *Popular name,* Dwarf Barb or Phutuni Barb
MEANING OF NAME: *phutunio,* after a native name, pungti phutuni
India   Eastern Location Map r28 to v33   Length, 1¼ inches

℘RESENTING one of the most charming of diminutive fishes, and one that ideally qualifies for those aquarists who like small pets in small aquaria.

The species has in marked degree that silvery sparkle which characterizes so many of the Barbs. Photographs show something which the unaided eye scarcely detects. The sparkle for the most part is confined to vertical lines from the *centre* of the scales. In contrast with silvery sheen, the body dots of the photograph are black. The dark spot on the gill plate is not black, but translucent, exposing the pink of the gills. Fins, pale orange, slightly darker in the male. Sexes difficult to recognize, except by the time-honored method of noting the fuller body of the female, especially as breeding time approaches.

The species does not require a high temperature. Eggs hatch in 2 days at 75 degrees. Although small, they are not as difficult to rear as might be imagined. With these, as well as with other small fish babies, it is well to avoid the introduction of Cyclops among the living food.

The species is a very easy one to feed, and makes a good community fish, if not overshadowed by disproportionately large companions. Not especially difficult to spawn.

Our photograph is made just a little larger than life size, a fault we usually strive to avoid.

COLOR PLATE PAGE 561

Bärbus tittèya   DERANIYAGALA

Pronounced Bar'bus tit-tay'a   *Popular name,* Cherry Barb
        MEANING OF NAME: *titteya,* native name in Ceylon
Ceylon   Eastern Location Map B22   Length, 1⅞ inches

HIS is one of the instances in which no single picture of the fish is completely satisfactory, for the reason that while color variation is not rapid, it is considerable. It is not unusual for the males to give the impression of being entirely suffused or overcast with a blush of deep red. Our illustration, correctly portraying one phase, altogether misses that effect. Some strains of the fish show more color intensity than others.

The species is best bred in pairs in the usual Barb manner, but they are avid egg-eaters. Shallow water and plenty of plants help prevent this. The young are very small, but in a large, established tank they get enough natural infusoria to give them a good start, the parents, of course, having been promptly removed after spawning. To rear fifty is considered good. A school of about that number is a pleasant sight.

This species in spawning sometimes jumps out of the water, or even out of an uncovered aquarium.

Bärbus vittàtus   (DAY)

Pronounced Bar'bus vi-tay'tus

MEANING OF NAME: *vittatus,* striped   *Popular name,* Kooli Barb

India, Ceylon   Eastern Location Map q17 to A20, and C22   Length, 2 inches

ONE of the smaller Barbs is shown here. It is difficult to see where *vittatus* or "striped" applies, but it is too late to dispute with the namer, Dr. Day, about that. The body is warm silver, yellowish towards the rear, and in addition to the single black spots in the anal, caudal and dorsal regions, shown in the photograph, the sides are also peppered with small dark dots. Other writers find the fins to be yellow, but those photographed were clear, except the dorsal which we agree has an oblique, dark band as shown, producing a triangle with the front edge of the fin, and enclosing an area of orange. No barbels. Silver eye.

As a rule dealers do not carry this fish in stock, but it is not to be considered a rarity.

Mr. Holbein, a prominent New York aquarist, has one of the species which is over 10 years old.

This is a hardy little fish and a good breeder. It is quite inoffensive. Temperature range, 65 to 85 degrees. See standard breeding directions.

Osteocheìlus vittàtus (CUVIER AND VALENCIENNES)

Pronounced Os′tee-o-kile″us vi-tay′tus

MEANING OF NAME: *Osteocheilus,* bony lips; *vittatus,* striped

Malay Peninsula, Siam, Indo-China   Length, 2½ inches

Eastern Location Map G37 to J41; F39; s39; L42 to M48; I45 to B50

ONE is reminded by this fish of our own Black-nosed Dace (*Rhinich-thys atronasus*), but the black line in this species is, if possible, even more intense. From the scientific standpoint the resemblance is superficial only. The fins are differently located, while the fin ray and scale counts do not match at all with those of our pleasant little native fish.

Osteocheilus vittatus is another of those comparatively rare importations of which we know little, but would like to see more. It shows itself to be an active, good-natured aquarium fish with sides and belly of bright silver, the back being tinted olive. Close inspection will reveal small barbels, or "whiskers." The fins are all quite clear, except where the little spur of black enters the tail fin. Takes almost any kind of food. Never bred. No differences in sex characteristics have been observed. A suitable temperature is about 75 degrees.

Labeo (morulius) chrysophekadion **BLEEKER**

Pronounced Lay'be-o (mo-ru'li-us) kry'so-fe-kay"dee-on　*Popular name,* Black Shark

Meaning of name: *Labeo*—lips; (*morulius*—black)
chrysophekadion—chryso—golden

Sumatra, Java, Borneo　　Eastern Location Map L4°, G44, M46　　Length, 12 inches

*T*HIS species when first introduced to the aquarium scene caused considerable excitement. Its black shark-like appearance set it apart and its high price indicated rarity. As it became more available, the price became less formidable and when the Red-tailed Shark (*Labeo bicolor*) was introduced sometime later, *L. chrysophekadion* lost in popularity. It is an excellent species, however, for a large aquarium and its hardiness and willingness to accept all types of aquarium fare make it a fish worthy of consideration. It is a bottom feeder and is somewhat shy. Although it feeds on algae, it does not remove it from leaves. We have found no reports of its breeding in captivity. It is apt to be aggressive with its own kind. See *Labeo bicolor* for water temperature, etc.　Edited by H. S.

Labeo bicolor **SMITH**   (Photo by Gene Wolfsheimer)
Pronounced Lay'be-o bi'col'or   *Popular name,* Red-tailed Shark
MEANING OF NAME: *Labeo*—lips; *bicolor*—two colors
Thailand   Eastern Location Map X36   Length, 4¾ inches

*T*HE position of the rather triangular dorsal fin occurring anteriorly
to the ventral fins and the ventral mouth have led aquarists to dub
this fish, as well as *Labeo chrysophekadion*, shark. Nothing in the disposition or personality of either species warrants the designation. The
body of *L. bicolor* (elongate and compressed to some degree) is black
as well as the fins. The forked tail is a contrasting bright red. A velvet
black and brilliant red are indications that the fish is in good condition.
Inferior color occurs when conditions are faulty. The point of the dorsal
fin is edged in white. The female's red tail is slightly less vivid than the
male's and when mature her body is somewhat heavier. The protruding
lips (labeo) indicate the sucker mouth characteristic. There are two
sets of barbels.

The fish likes slightly alkaline water (pH 7.1 - 7.3) and prefers a temperature in the high 70's F. Hiding places should be provided such as
inverted flower pots or thickly planted areas in the aquarium. Algae that
have grown on leaves or aquarium walls are good news to this species
and if such growth is missing in the aquarium, water soaked lettuce will
be accepted. Live food and the usual aquarium fare are adequate. This
species has bred in captivity but details are not available. These fish
play rather roughly among themselves but apparently do not harm one
another seriously. Edited by H. S.

THE LOACHES
FAMILY COBITIDAE
Pronounced Co by' ti dee

The Loaches are much like the Carps, but they differ from them in having 3 or more pairs of barbels. They never have jaw teeth. The Loaches are all from the Old World.

Acanthophthalmus semicinctus   FRASER-BRUNNER
Pronounced A-kan'thof-thal"muss   sem'ee-sink"tus
MEANING OF NAME: *Acanthophthalmus,* with spine near eyes; *semicinctus,* Half-banded. *Popular name,* Coolie Loach
Malay Peninsula and Archipelago   Length, 2¾ inches
Eastern Location Map x36 to F39; G38; L43; G44 to D48

*A*N odd little Loach, and rather pretty. Active, too. The body is a sort of salmon-pink. Markings across the back and sides, dark gray to black, being darker on the edges. The eye, occurring on one of the dark spots, is not easily seen. A rather comical set of bushy barbels adorns the mouth, looking like an obstinate little moustache.

The fish is a fair scavenger of rather limited capacity. Although nocturnal by nature, it readily learns to eat in daytime. On the other hand, it has an advantage over most of the other Loaches of the aquarium, inasmuch as it never grows too large. This fish was formerly known as *A. kuhlii,* actually a species in which the bands reach from top to bottom of the body. In "The Aquarium" for November, 1947, Fraser-Brunner illustrates the true *A. kuhlii* and another species which has been imported. Examination reveals distinct differences in markings. However, for aquarists' purposes the popular name of "Coolie" may be applied to all of them. A few spawnings are recorded, but none observed. They almost certainly breed in the mulm at the bottom. This is a durable fish. See the following.

Cobìtis taènia LINNAEUS

Pronounced Ko-by'tiss tee'ne-a   *Popular name,* Spotted Weatherfish

MEANING OF NAME: *Cobitis,* meaning not certain; *taenia,* striped

Western Location Map k51 and b56 Eastward and Northward to edges of map

Eastern Location Map from h1 and a1 through Siberia to b51   Length, 4 inches

THIS fish, like *Acanthophthalmus,* has a movable spine below the eye. There are 3 pairs of barbels on the upper jaw. It is one of our best scavengers, and has the advantage that it does not grow over 4 inches in length. The dark markings are variable, and appear on a buff-colored background.

We were once asked whether the dark leaf, just above the tail, is a part of the fish! It is because of such possible confusions that we seldom use any plants in our black-and-white photographs.

Like many of the Loaches, this fish is long-lived and can endure pretty bad conditions, as well as extremes of temperature.

The details of its breeding habits are not known with certainty, but we have reasons to believe that they are similar to those of the European *Cobitis fossilis.* We know of an authentic instance in which they bred in a lily pool during the late summer. The young wriggled out of the mud the next May, much to the surprise of the owner, especially as the winter had been a severe one.

COLOR PLATE PAGE 562

Bòtia mácracántha BLEEKER

Pronounced Bo'-tee-a mac'ra-can"tha   *Popular name,* Clown Loach
MEANING OF NAME: *macracantha,* big spine; from the spine on the face below the eye
Borneo   Eastern Location Map 148   Length, 5 inches or more

L OACHES are usually thought of as long and eel-like, such as Weatherfish, but there are others of more usual fish form, like our present subject.

Our color plate gives a good general idea, but is lacking in two details, mainly in failure to show a broad dark line in the dorsal fin, extending obliquely from near the front top to the lower rear end. Also the dark marking on the head should continue down through the eye to the jaw.

The hinged spine, which lies in a groove beneath the eye, is a vicious weapon which makes other fishes keep their distance.

By nature a shy fish, largely nocturnal, but by association with other sorts it can be "reformed," as it were, especially if not given places where it can completely hide. The fish has a quaint habit, alarming when first seen. When any fish lies on its side at the bottom it usually means *finis.* Clown Loaches love to rest this way, and do so frequently, especially under the shallow shelter of an overhanging stone. Lives 8 years or more.

Eats anything and is a good, long-lived "scavenger." Efforts to breed it have all met with failure. Temperature range, 68-82.

Misgúrnus angùillicaudàtus (CANTOR)

Pronounced Mis-gur'nuss an-gwill'ee-caw-day"tus *Popular name,* Japanese Weatherfish

MEANING OF NAME: *Misgurnus,* from Misgurn, old English name for Loach;
anguillicaudatus, with an eel-like tail

Japan, China, etc.   Eastern Location Map e58   Length, up to 8 inches

THIS fish differs from *Cobitis* and *Acanthophthalmus* in the absence of the movable spine below the eye. It is light gray with irregular blotches of darker gray, while the European form, *Cobitis fossilis,* is light brown with several dark stripes along the body. They are virtually the same fish, both from the scientific and the aquarist's standpoints.

Before the merits of *Corydoras* as aquarium scavengers were so well known, the "Weatherfish," as well as other forms of Loaches, were much used for the purpose. Some aquarists still utilize them, but seldom in sizes over 4 inches in length. Their movements are wild and unpredictable, somewhat "like a chicken with its head off." When size is added to the fish, these strange, lashing actions become unendurable to the aquarist, for the sediment is whipped into a state of suspension and sand is shifted without regard to scenic effect. It would not be correct to give the impression that this fish is always on the rampage. It is quiet for periods, often buried in the sand with its head looking out cutely. Then it will emerge and begin a peculiar, interesting action of "combing" the sand surface, in search of food. Sand and dirt are taken into the mouth and rapidly expelled through the gills.

Will stand temperature from 40 to 80 degrees and has seldom been bred. They spawn on the bottom and the young bury themselves for a long period, no doubt feeding on microscopic life and vegetal decomposition.

THE CATFISHES

The Catfishes or Siluroids used to be placed in a single family, Siluridae, which is nowadays split up into several. We have used these newer family designations, but wish at this place to point out the distinguishing features of Catfishes as a whole. No Catfish ever has scales, though some of them are more or less completely covered with bony plates. The chief differences from the other families of the order Ostariophysi are internal, but there are not many Catfishes which are not immediately recognizable as such. All but a few obscure ones have conspicuous barbels and most have a broad, rather flattened head. They form the suborder Nematognathi or Siluroidea (sometimes recognized as an order by itself).

Most catfishes are more or less strictly nocturnal fishes. They hide or are quiet during the daytime but move about very actively at night. This often terrorizes the other fishes in an aquarium, who like to rest or sleep at night. The Smooth Armored Catfishes, such as *Corydoras*, seem to be an exception to this rule.

THE DORADID CATFISHES
Family Doradidae
Pronounced Doh-ra'di-dee

The Doradids are heavy-bodied Catfishes which can easily be placed by the single row of bony plates, each bearing a spine, which runs along the middle of each side of the fish. In some species which we have had in our aquaria (such as *Acanthodoras spinosissimus*) there are smaller spiny supplementary plates, both above and below the main series. Such species might be confused with the Armored Cats, treated further on, but the Doradids never have a spine supporting the front of the adipose fin, as do the true Armored Cats. All the Doradids are from South America.

A number of different species of this family have been imported and sold very widely, usually without careful identification. Most of these have been rather similar in appearance, and the differences which do exist are seldom easily visible because most of the species burrow in the sand at the bottom of the aquarium during the daytime and come out only at night. Some of the species feed on snails, swallowing and digesting shell and all.

The doradids are sometimes known as "talking catfishes" for many of them make the grunting noise mentioned on the next page. This noise is probably produced by the airbladder of the fish. Members of some other catfish families also "talk", especially while being transferred from one tank to another in a net.

THE MOCHOKID CATFISHES
Family Mochokidae
Pronounced Mo-ko'ki-dee

The Mochokid catfishes form a small family confined to the fresh waters of tropical Africa. Most of them have the barbels on the lower lip fringed or branched, like some (but not all) of the South American Doradidae. Many Mochokids swim upside down.

Synodontis nigriventris (DAVID)

Pronounced Sy'no-don"tis ny'gree-ven"tris   *Popular name,* Upside-down Catfish
MEANING OF NAME: *Synodontis,* with fused tooth plates; *nigriventris,* black belly
Lower Congo River, Africa   Recorded length, 3¾ inches
Western Location Map H60 to G61

THIS entertaining little character, completely unconcerned as to whether it swims top-up or top-down, or even spirally, was introduced to aquarists in 1950. As will be seen in the illustration, its pupils are extremely large, which would lead an ichthyologist to suspect that it is the young of a larger species. However, after nearly three years of being well fed in various aquaria, we have learned of no specimens over 3¾ inches long, or about twice the importation size. Markings are in shades of gray and black on a changing background, ranging from olive to light yellow.

They have proved peaceful and interesting. Few died (and none bred).

As with many catfishes, they tend to be nocturnal. They have a keen sense of ownership of a favorite location, usually in the vertical angle-frame of the aquarium. The underside of an elevated flat stone, if provided, is a favorite perching spot. In the illustration the fish at the top is in the upside-down position at the surface of the water. Easily fed. Temperature, 74-80.

THE SILURID CATFISHES
Family Siluridae
Pronounced Si lu'ri dee

These Catfishes are easily identified by the *very* long anal fin and by the fact that the dorsal fin is either very small and far forward, or absent. All the Silurids are from Europe or Asia.

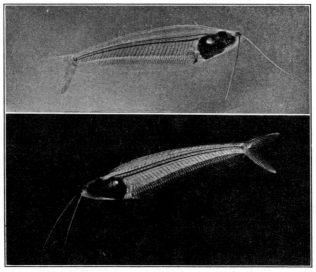

Kryptópterus bicírrhus (CUVIER AND VALENCIENNES)
Pronounced Krip-top'te-rus by-si'rus
Popular name, Glass Catfish   *Native name,* "Limpok"
MEANING OF NAME: *Kryptopterus,* hidden fin, an allusion to the almost invisible one-rayed dorsal fin; *bicirrhus,* with two hairs (whiskers)
Java, Borneo, Sumatra, Siam   Eastern Location Map, G38, etc.   Aquarium size, 2½ in.

*C*HIS is one of the most nearly transparent fish kept by aquarists. Were it not for the opaque, silvery sac containing the internal organs, it would really be difficult to see the fish at all. Its skeleton is fairly visible, but the flesh, from the intestines to the tail, is truly glass-like. When a light is held so as to shine *through* the body, it displays a wealth of prismatic colors. The lower illustration was lighted in that way. The fish maintains a constant rippling motion of the lower fin.

One is impressed on examining the photograph by the fact that the internal organs (dark area in back of head) are set forward about as far as it is possible for them to be. Also note forward position of hair-like dorsal fin.

Daphnia, tubifex, glassworms, enchytraeids are eagerly (although at first shyly) eaten. Harmless. Not bred. Temperature, 72-82 degrees.

THE BAGRID CATFISHES
Family Bagridae
Pronounced Bag'ri dee

The Bagrids are "ordinary" looking Catfishes, with dorsal fin present and of usual place and size, anal fin of moderate length, no "armor" on the body, and the "whiskers" usually long. All are from Africa or Asia. The differences between the Bagrids and the South American Pimelodids are small, and internal, so that, for the aquarist, the best distinguishing feature is the habitat.

Mystus tengàra (HAMILTON-BUCHANAN)
Pronounced Miss-tus ten-ga-rah'

MEANING OF NAME: *Mystus* derived from *mystax*, meaning whiskers; *tengara*, the native name in the Punjab is "ting ga rah"

Usually known to aquarists as *Macrones vittatus* (another species)

N. India, the Punjab and Assam Eastern Location Map, p. 27, etc. Length, 4 inches

THIS species, to be correct, should have 8 barbels, 2 of them nasal. Our photograph does not show that many, but otherwise the fish looks very much like correct figures of the species as listed above. It is not impossible that some of the barbels were out of view when the photograph was taken. At any rate, this illustration will serve to indicate the fish now being sold under the name. If not *Macrones vittatus*, it may even be a species of South American origin. In any case it is an interesting, attractive aquarium fish. Easily fed and cared for. Harmless. Seems happy at a temperature ranging at about 72-80 degrees.

Photo by Braz Walker

Leiocassis siamensis **REGAN**

Pronounced Lee-o'ca-sis sia-men'sis   *Popular name,* Bumble-bee Catfish
Thailand and Cambodia Eastern Location Map U38 to Z49 Length, Reaches 6 inches

☞ HE popular name of this attractive catfish was inspired by its striking pattern of bands of off-white on black. The small head (small in comparison to the depth and length of the body of the fish) carries off-white patches below and just posterior to the bright little eyes. A collar of white encircles the body about midway between the nape and the dorsal fin. A broken girdle of white appears anterior to the dorsal and is interrupted by black to be picked up again as an irregular white area anterior to the ventral fin. Another white girdle appears posterior to the ventral and slants up over the sides of the fish and continues on the base of the dorsal. A white band encircles the anterior part of the peduncle. The area where the peduncle meets the forked tail is black, but the tines of the fork are white. All in all, this is a strikingly marked fish and a photograph does it far more justice than a written description can. The barbles of the chin sweep back from below the corners of the mouth and give the fish character as well as a somewhat humorous appearance. Older specimens tend to lose the distinguishing coloration, the white no longer sharply contrasted against the black.

This fish does very well in a community tank and will not harm fishes smaller than itself. It is a hardy eater and although nocturnal in nature, it seems to be quite willing to go on a day shift. Its temperature tolerance is broad but probably is most comfortable in the mid-seventies. Water quality is no problem either but in that the fish comes from soft, acid water, this should be considered if breeding the fish becomes a target. Incidentally, this is one of the "talking fishes" in that when removed from water, it makes an audible protest. Regular aquarium fare seems to be highly acceptable to this exotic. Edited by H. S.

THE PIMELODID CATFISHES
Family Pimelodidae
Pronounced Pim e lò di dee

The Pimelodids are Catfishes very similar in most features to the last family (Bagridae) but come from South and Central America.

Pimelòdus clàrias (BLOCH)

Pronounced Pim'el-o"dus klar'ee-as

MEANING OF NAME: *Pimelodus*, fat toothed; *clarias*, like the Indian catfish, Clarias

All of South America East of the Andes from Panama to Buenos Aires

Aquarium size, 4 inches and over

THIS is one of those fishes which is most attractive in its smaller sizes, but which when fully grown is neither good looking nor suited to the aquarium. Adults not only lose those stunning big spots, but reach a length of 10 to 12 inches. Varieties from different places are spotted differently. Only smaller specimens are imported and, in an ordinary sized aquarium, they retain both their dimensions and their dots. These decorative spots are dark brown, placed on a golden ground. Harmless, moderately active aquarium fishes having the novel qualities of the South American Catfishes, including that of being difficult to breed. We know nothing of its reproductive methods. It is a species which has for years been brought in only occasionally, and is, therefore, not often to be found in the stocks of dealers.

The temperature of the average warm-water aquarium suits it very well. Easily fed. Some varieties are differently spotted, or even un-spotted.

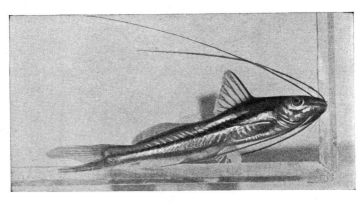

Pímelodélla grácilis (VALENCIENNES)

Pronounced Pim'el-o-del"la gray'sil-iss

MEANING OF NAME: *Pimelodella,* a little Pimelodus; *gracilis, slender*

South America   Western Location Map A15 to V22   Length, 6 inches

HERE are many very similar species of *Pimelodella,* and it is impossible to be certain of identification without alcohol specimens and having accurate locality data. The species illustrated is typical of most of those imported. It came in as *P. gracilis* (Valenciennes) but we are not at all sure that it really is that species. For the practical purposes of the aquarists, however, it seems that we had best continue to call the fish by its trade name until such time as we may know better.

It happens that in this illustration the extremely long barbels show very plainly, but this development is not at all unusual with this type of fish. What we would like to know about these thread-like extensions is their purpose, for it would seem there must be one, other than a decoration of doubtful beauty. As most catfishes are night prowlers, and even in daytime seek dimly lighted places and muddy bottoms, it is not at all unlikely that the barbels are sensory organs, to be used as a help to, or instead of eyes.

The fish from which this photograph was made had beautiful silvery sides with slight herring-bone depressions, divided about equally in half down the middle by a brilliant black line. A very active little fellow. The sexes appear to be exactly alike, and for that reason we show but one specimen.

Microglànis parahỳbœ (STEINDACHNER)

Pronounced My'kro-glay"niss par'a-high"bee

MEANING OF NAME: *Microglanis,* little catfish; *parahyboe,* from the Rio Parahyba, Brazil

Also known as *Pseudopimelodus parahyboe*

S. E. Brazil   Western Location Map S33 to U31   Length, 2 inches

A CHOICE little Catfish that has been with us in small numbers for a long time. Evidently they are not plentiful where collected, for the price has never been low.

Species very similar to this are found in other parts of South America, notably in Guiana.

The markings are pinkish gray on a background of dark brown. The illustration shows ventral and dorsal views as an aid to identification. It will be observed that there are 3 pairs of barbels, each being marked with alternating light and dark sections. Never bred in captivity. A peaceful little fish, but not a particularly active one. Easily fed. Temperature range, 70-85 degrees.

A nocturnal fish.

THE ELECTRIC CATFISH
Family Malapteruridae
Pronounced Mal ap′ te ru″ ri dee

This family contains only one species, the African Electric Catfish. It has a large adipose fin, but no rayed dorsal fin.

Malápterùrus eléctricus (GMELIN)

Pronounced Mal-ap-te-ru′rus e-lek′tree-kus   *Popular name,* Electric Catfish

MEANING OF NAME: *Malapterurus,* soft fin on tail, referring to the adipose fin; *electricus,* electric

Most of Tropical Africa   Length, 6 inches

Western Location Map x45; A52; D59; L71; P68

IN color the fish is medium grayish, flecked irregularly dark. Design shown on the tail region is dark gray on a lighter background.

During the day the species is quiet and not aggressive. At night smaller fishes kept with it are apt to jump out of the water or otherwise disappear. It is not definitely known how far the peculiar gifts of electric catfishes (and of electric eels) are used for offensive or defensive action.

They are tough and easily fed. Not known to have been bred in captivity.

THE BANJO CATFISHES
Family Bunocephalidae
Pronounced Bu'no sef al"i dee

The Bunocephallids are small unarmored Catfishes with a very wide head and a slender, elongated body. All are from South America.

Bunocéphalus species

Pronounced Bew'no-seff"a-lus by'col-or   *Popular name,* Banjo Catfish

MEANING OF NAME: *Bunocephalus,* with hills (bumps) on the head

Amazon   Western Location Map K9 to G24   Length, 5 inches

THIS is one of several very similar species of Banjo Cats that are imported from time to time. Few of them are ever correctly identified by aquarium dealers. They are similar in appearance and are not easily told apart. They all have broad but flat heads. When the tail fin is spread, which is seldom, it shows a rounded form. The colors are dark and mottled above and light beneath. They have very small, beady eyes.

Seldom bred. Seventy or eighty years ago Dr. Jeffries Wyman reported that catfishes of this family carry the eggs adhering to the abdomen of the fish. This has been observed with one species of Banjo Cat in an aquarium but others report that the eggs are laid in the sand.

Another type of Banjo Cat appeared on the market in 1955, in importations from British Guiana. This new fish, *Agmus lyriformis,* has the general form and finnage of *Bunocephalus* but the head is not only broad but also very thick and covered with very large bumps.

THE SMOOTH ARMORED CATFISHES
Family Callichthyidae
Pronounced Call ick thy' i dee

The Smooth Armored Cats are just that. The body is encased in a coat of bony mail formed of two series of overlapping plates along each side. In no case is the armor completely covered with fine but evident prickles and the mouth is never modified into a sucker disc. The adipose fin is supported by a spine. All the Smooth Armored Catfishes are South American. All come up once in a while for air, making a quick dash to the surface and back again.

Callichthys callichthys   (LINNAEUS)
Pronounced Kal-lick'thiss   kal-lick'thiss   *Popular name,* Callichthys
MEANING OF NAME: *Callichthys,* Pretty fish
N. South America   Western Location Map y19 to F29 and V22   Length, 4½ inches

THE even rows of marks along the sides of the fishes in the illustration are the edges of overlapping armor plates, common to the so-called "Armored Cats." The fishes do not have ordinary scales.

The fish is quite a good scavenger; in fact, was one of the first used by aquarists in that capacity. It is harmless, and therefore well suited to the community tank. Not to be confused with the commoner "Hoplo" Cat (see next page).

Eggs are placed in bubble-nest in plants at the surface. Parents guard eggs and young. Breeding temperature, 70-75. Bred occasionally.

Hòplostérnum thòracàtum (CUVIER AND VALENCIENNES)

Pronounced Hope'low-stern"um   tho'ra-ca"tum   *Popular name,* Hoplo Cat

MEANING OF NAME: *Hoplosternum,* armed sternum; *thoracatum,* refers to the thorax.

Panama to Brazil   Western Location map y 4 to K 26   Length 6 inches

OFTEN wrongly known as a spotted *Callichthys*. While *Callichthys callichthys* (Panzerwels) was reputed to be a bubble-nest builder, we personally know of no successful breedings, so when this fish built its nest at the water's surface, it was taken for granted that it was indeed a spotted *Callichthys*. It is not, but it *is* a close relative, with certain differences in bony structure. (In 1955, still another closely related fish appeared on the market, *Dianema longibarbis.* It has a very deeply forked tail.)

The general color is brownish gray with dark brown, variable markings and dots. The fins, especially in the male, are reddish brown and his body color in general is darker. The fish is an active "scavenger," and is quite peaceful. Breeds readily at about 2½ inches and in the aquarium seldom exceeds 4 inches.

The method of fertilization is similar to that described for the *Corydoras,* except that eggs are placed on the underside of a large floating leaf or an object such as an anchored floating saucer.

THE CORYDORAS

OUR knowledge regarding the characteristics of the individual species of *Corydoras* is so limited that it seems advisable to consider them as a whole. They are all a genus of the family Callichthyidae, popularly but erroneously called "South American Cats." Instead of having ordinary scales, they are covered with two main rows of overlapping, bony laminations or plates. Many of these armored fishes reach a size that would make them quite impossible in a household aquarium, but, fortunately for us, *Corydoras* are the dwarfs of the family. We say *fortunately* because these fishes have proved themselves of great value and interest to aquarists.

They are droll, gnome-like little beings, going about their business of life in what seems to us a serio-comic fashion. This business, as far as the aquarist is concerned, is that of scavenger. It would hardly be going too far to give them the title of health officers, for their self-appointed task is going about the bottom of the aquarium, seeking bits of food that other fishes have overlooked, and which would soon contaminate the water. They go farther than this, as they consume dead leaves, dead snails and even dead Daphnia. However, one should not "work a willing horse to death," as their eating capacity is limited. This family of fishes is subject to few diseases. In experiments to learn how much salt treatment different species can stand, *Corydoras* died first.

Although many of us like these fishes for their own marked individualities and their contrast to other aquarium species, it is as scavengers that they have permanently established themselves in popular favor, having largely replaced snails for that purpose. True, they will not work on the side glasses as will snails, for they are strictly bottom-feeders. The important point is that no fish attacks a *Corydoras* of moderate size, whereas many of our exotic fishes make short work of snails. Then, again, snails eat fish eggs. Unless eggs are on the bottom a *Corydoras* will not seek them out. Finally, snails once established are difficult to get rid of, which is not true of our little scavenger fish. However, under suitable circumstances, snails should be used as auxiliary cleaners. That is, in association with such fishes as will not kill them, and where the question of egg-eating does not arise, as among live-bearers.

Corydoras occasionally dash to the surface for a bubble of air. This does not indicate distress, nor that they are full-fledged air-breathers.

Some beginners get the idea that at least one *Corydoras* is a "must" in every tank. This is not strictly true. Many experts prefer to keep their tanks in such condition that no assistant "scavenger" is needed.

The first *Corydoras* to become well established among aquarists were *paleatus* and *nattereri*. They and *aeneus* are the most easily obtained and the ones we know most about, for we have good accounts of their breeding habits, which at this time is more than can be said of most of the other species, although it is reasonable to expect that their methods would be at least closely similar.

In the majority of species the female is somewhat the larger. We believe that in *C. paleatus* the ventral fins are slightly more rounded in the female. Our accompanying illustration shows this difference. Not having seen the other species breed, we do not know whether this applies to them all, but it possibly does. As breeding approaches, the belly of the female takes on a reddish hue. Also the strong first ray of her pectoral fins reddens and thickens. In addition to these indications we have the old rule to select the more round and full-bodied fish as the female. It has long been claimed that the males have more pointed dorsal fins. Our observations do not confirm this.

Lower fish is the male with slightly more pointed ventral fins. This difference happens to be exaggerated here by their partially folded position. Inset shows eggs being pursed between ventral fins of female, just prior to her attaching them to plants.

Still referring to *C. paleatus*, the first sign indicating that spawning is soon to follow is when the male persistently swims over the back of the female, bringing his barbels into occasional contact with the place where her neck ought to be, if she had one. Presently the pair comes to rest on the aquarium bottom, and assumes a strange position, not easily de-scribed. The male rolls over, nearly on his back. The female then clasps him at a right-angle position, crossing breasts. Her right-side barbels are caught beneath his left-side pectoral fin. In this position they remain still for about half a minute. Upon freeing themselves they swim independ-ently of each other. It can then be seen that the female has pursed her ventral fins together, and that between them she is carrying 4 eggs. She searches for a suitable place to attach them, going up and down different plant leaves with her mouth. A firm Sagittaria leaf seems to please her most. In an upside-down position she clasps the leaf with her ventral fins and firmly presses the large eggs against the leaf, where they adhere tena-ciously. First, 2 eggs are attached, and, in a few moments, 2 more. The process is repeated at intervals over a period of about 2 hours, at which time a large female will have deposited nearly 100 eggs. The curtain has fallen on the interesting show when the pair starts rooting in the sand.

The male does not follow the female when the eggs are deposited. Neither does he pay any attention to them. Certain it is there is no in-ternal fertilization, as with live-bearers. It is stated by some that the female takes the sperm in her mouth and applies it to the spot where the eggs are to be placed. From her actions in mounting the plants this would seem reasonable. Observing the embrace in brilliant light we could see no possibility of her gathering the sperm in this way.

Unless parents provide some definite care for the young, we favor for all species their removal from the eggs and babies, regardless of possible well-established good reputations.

The young *Corydoras* soon take refuge in the natural sediment of the aquarium. These settlings should be at least a quarter inch deep. The babies make themselves scarce for about 2 weeks.

In a properly prepared aquarium they will not need to be fed at once. If there is not plenty of sediment for them to root through, a little paste from boiled oatmeal should be provided. At the same time snails should be introduced to eat the surplus oatmeal. There need be no hurry about supplying live Daphnia. Small sifted sizes may be provided in a month.

These spawnings occurred in slightly alkaline water (pH 7.4) and at temperatures of 74, 68 and 65 degrees. At the higher temperature a slight aeration was supplied. Eggs hatch in from 4 to 6 days, according to tem-perature.

Considering that so many thousands of *Corydoras* are now kept in aquariums, it is remarkable that one so seldom hears of their breeding. This may be because they are not considered in feeding, except as second-table guests, pursuing their humble occupation of taking left-overs. To place them in good breeding condition, they should have plenty of live Daphnia and tubifex worms. Like pigs, they do not *prefer* left-overs, but take what they can get.

Added to their chief merit of nosing about the obscure parts of the aquarium and clearing up sources of contamination, they also do a good service in keeping the surface of the sand loose and free from caking. If the bottom is dirty they roil the water, which may prove to be an annoyance. Many aquarists make a point of having one or two *Corydoras* in company with other fishes in every aquarium, except, of course, where breeders should be by themselves. They do not eat any young the size of live-bearers, and probably no others.

Sometimes tubifex worms become established in the soil of an aquarium and present an unsightly appearance. *Corydoras* will dig them out.

No *Corydoras* knows the meaning of "fight." Even rival males at breeding time seem to be the best of friends. Most of them successfully endure a range of temperature from 62 to 82 degrees.

EGGS OF *Corydoras paleatus*, SLIGHTLY ENLARGED

They were on the under side of the leaves which were turned over for photographing by use of the glass rod seen in front of the picture.

Còrydòras œnèus   (GILL)

Pronounced Ko'ree-do"rass ee-nee'us   *Popular name,* Bronze Cat

MEANING OF NAME: *Corydoras,* helmeted Doras (Doras is another genus of Catfishes; *œneus,* bronzy

Trinidad   Western Location Map x between 19 and 20   Length, 2¾ inches

A VERY good scavenger fish, freely introduced in 1933. A popular method of distinguishing the species is by the diffused large dark area beginning just in back of the head, somewhat like an indistinct, horizontal oval. Also by the absence of any pattern markings on either body or fins. Now perhaps our commonest *Corydoras.*

Mr. Lawrence Shaw, in "The Aquarium" for December, 1935, reports that the male cleans a spot on the glass with his mouth, then spreads sperm on it, after which the female presses 4 to 6 large eggs on the same spot, where they adhere tightly. Total spawn, about 125 eggs. Parents were removed after spawning. Eggs hatch in about four days. Temperature, 75 degrees. They were successfullyreared on finely powdered fishfood.

A FAMILY OF *Corydoras aeneus*

Còrydòras ärcuàtus ELWIN
Pronounced Ko'ree-doe"russ ark'you-ay"tus   *Popular name,* Bowline Cat
  MEANING OF NAME: *arcuatus,* arched like a bow, with reference to the stripe
Upper Amazon   Western Location Map H17   Length, 2½ inches

A VERY distinctive *Corydoras,* the bright pearly body being traversed by a clear, arching black line. No need to confuse this with any other species. It was described and named by the English ichthyologist, Margery Elwin, and since its importation in 1939 has not, to our knowledge, been bred. It was brought in by the noted collector, Rabaut. For lack of an established scientific name when first imported, dealers called it "Tabatinga," after the name of a tributary of the far reaches of the Amazon, where it was collected. That name stuck, and is still the popular designation.

Very active and hardy, having a temperature range from the low sixties to the high eighties.

Like the other *Corydoras,* it does not seem to have an atom of fighting spirit. Perhaps its defense, as with most other catfish, consists in stiff fin spines, always spread when caught, or in danger, making a nasty wound in the throat of any fish trying to swallow it.

Còrydòras hastàtus EIGENMANN AND EIGENMANN

Pronounced Ko′ree-do″rass hass-tay″tus   *Popular name,* Micro Cat

MEANING OF NAME: *hastatus,* with a spear, in reference to the spearhead-like
spot on tail root

Also known as Microcorydoras

The Amazon   Western Location Map G23   Length, 1¾ inches

℘ HIS fish looks delicate, but it is really quite hardy. It is interestingly individual. Its movements are unlike those of other Catfishes, possibly excepting the Glass Catfish, *Kryptopterus bicirrhus.* It does not always grub about the bottom, but balances itself by a rapid motion of the pectoral and caudal fins, ready to dart quickly in any direction.

The body is translucent olive. Usually the dark stripe on the sides is a little clearer than shown here. An easily outstanding feature for identification is the white crescent at the base of the tail, standing out all the more clearly on account of arching around a black spot.

A few large, single eggs are deposited on the sides of the glass. Neither eggs nor young are eaten by the parents. The babies are about ¼ inch long when hatched, and are easily reared on sifted Daphnia. Domestic-raised specimens of this species seem to do better in the aquarium than imported stock.

The fish takes ordinary food and breeds at about 75 degrees.

Corydoras elegans STEINDACHNER
Pronounced Ko'ree-do"rass el'ee gans
MEANING OF NAME: elegant
Upper Brazilian and lower Peruvian Amazon
Western Location Map C15 and M11 Length, 2 inches

A CORYDORAS, running true to type and therefore not outstanding
in color. On closer examination and association it reveals interesting marks and movements. The body is not deep in comparison to
length, and is characterized by dark double longitudinal stripes, perhaps
more clearly shown in life than in our illustration. The eyes are set a bit
lower than in most of its cousins. The dorsal fin is ornamented by a few
gray dots. In some specimens these take on an arching pattern, as indicated in the one shown at the right of the plate. This is believed to be
the male.

Besides in the body markings, which are in shades of gray and black
on an olive background, the fish has the interesting habit of often swimming rather freely in the upper levels of the aquarium.

Not being such a constant rooter in the soil, it disturbs the sediment
less than do most of its relatives, thus registering a point in its favor.

It was at first sold under the wrong name of *C. lineatus.*

COLOR PLATE PAGE 562

Còrydòras rabauti   LAMONTE

Pronounced Ko′ree-doe″rus   ra-boat″-eye   Formerly called *C. myersi*

MEANING OF NAME: named in honor of the collector, Auguste Rabaut

Upper Amazon   Western Location Map H17   Length, 2¼ inches

*A*CCORDING to our recollection, both this species and *C. arcuatus* were imported in 1939; neither named at the time. *C. rabauti* was later named by Miss Lamonte from immature specimens. Still later, the ichthyologist Miranda-Ribeiro, working on mature specimens, named it *C. myersi*. This was found to be in error, so the name seems to have permanently reverted to *C. rabauti*.

While most of the *Corydoras* have interesting and distinctive overlaid patterns, this is the only one, so far, that can lay claim to enough color to justify the use here of a color printing plate.

The sexes are difficult to distinguish, but we suspect the one with the most green color on the gill plate is the male. The other seems to fill with spawn, but nothing happens. Occasional chance successful, but unobserved, spawnings are recorded. The species is an active bottom feeder. Temperatures, 64-82.

Còrydòras jùlii STEINDACHNER

Pronounced Ko're-do"rass jew'lee-eye   *Popular name,* Leopard Corydoras

MEANING OF NAME: *julii,* it is not known for what Julius this species was named. Formerly known as *Corydoras leopardus*

E. and N. E. Brazil   Western Location Map L30 to 31   Length, 2½ inches

A DISTINCTIVE importation of 1933. They came in large numbers and promptly gained many friends, who, for the most part, consider them to be the best of the *Corydoras.* This is because they are prettily marked, very active, hardy and not too large. They can be roughly recognized by the triple stripe on the sides, the black spot above the centre of the dorsal fin, and the spots extending over the nose.

Too bad the name of this species had to be changed after it had achieved general popularity.

Còrydòras melanístius REGAN

Pronounced Ko'ree-do"rass mel'an-iss"tee-us

MEANING OF NAME: melanistius, black sail, referring to the dorsal fin

Popular name, Guiana Cat

Guianas and Venezuela   Western Location Map A15 to A22   Length, 2½ inches

*A*NOTHER spotted South American Catfish in which the spots extend over the nose. However, the two characteristic dark markings noted in the photograph are quite different from the ornamentations on *Corydoras julii,* and, besides, there is no side stripe. This interesting species is often imported in quantities and has made many friends.

Còrydòras náttereri STEINDACHNER
Pronounced Ko'ree-do"rass nat'ter-er-eye
Named for Johann Natterer, its discoverer

E. Brazil   Western Location Map X28 to U31   Length, 2½ inches

A HIGHLY-REGARDED scavenger fish," quite as good as the following, but not in such good supply. There is no pattern in the fairly clear fins. The ventrals are light, opaque yellow. Highlights seen about the gill plates are green. Belly, yellowish. A pronounced dark stripe the length of the body suggests being deep in the somewhat translucent flesh. General color of the body is light, tending towards yellow; eye, gold. Breeds per description. Not as commonly found as it used to be.

Còrydòras pàleàtus　(JENYNS)

Pronounced Ko'ree-do"rass pay'le-a"tus

MEANING OF NAME: *Corydoras,* helmet-doras. Doras, having darts, referring to the barbels; *paleatus,* with dappled markings.

Argentina and S. E. Brazil　　Western Location Map V22 to Z27　　Length, 2¾ inches

PROBABLY this is the most generally used of the Armored Catfishes. It is hardy, low-priced and is nearly always obtainable.

The tail and dorsal fins are nearly clear, marked with a dark pattern. Pectorals (side fins) yellow; anal and ventrals, opaque ivory. The body is yellow, shot with a few green scales, especially about the head. The dark body markings in the photographs are black to bluish. Eye, light gold. A detailed description of the breeding actions of the species is on the second page under the heading "The Corydoras."

THE SUCKERMOUTH ARMORED CATFISHES
or Spiny Armored Catfishes
Family Loricariidae
Pronounced Lo' ri car i'' i dee

The Spiny Armored Cats are elongate, flattened Catfishes with a full coating (except sometimes on the abdomen) of bony plates which are rough with a thick coating of fine prickles. The mouth forms a sucking disk under the head. The adipose fin, if present, is supported by a bony spine covered with fine prickles. The Spiny Armored Cats inhabit South America and northward in Central America to Nicaragua.

Plecostomus species
Pronounced Ple-kos'tow-muss
Meaning of name: *Plecostomus*, folded mouth.

Nearly all of South America East of Andes   Length, up to 10 inches

HERE are many species of this genus and several have been imported. With their peculiar mouths they can cling tenaciously to any smooth surface. They are well equipped for eating algae, which they do industriously, even going up and down Sagittaria leaves without injuring them. It is most active at night.

What appears in the illustration to be a very large mouth is only a marking. The mouth is like that shown on *Otocinclus*. Color, gray with brown markings. Eats anything. They have a keen sense of property rights and bully or kill other scavenger fish, even their own smaller brethren. One to a tank is best. Never bred. Temperature 62 to 80.

Loricaria species

Pronounced Lor-i-care'i-a   *Popular name,* Whiptail Loricaria
MEANING OF NAME: *Loricaria,* armored one.
Tropical South America   Length, 3 inches

 ANY species of *Loricaria* have been imported but few identified. Purchasers of this species need not suspect damaged goods because there is no thread on the lower half of the tail. The "whip" is on the upper part only. Body markings are olive grays and near-blacks. Dorsal fin not white, as shown here, but translucent. Body quite shallow and rather broad. Not a very active fish, but good algae eater.

Few people have bred them. Mr. Carroll Friswold, of Altadena, supplied the description and also the good photograph by F. P. Fox. Forty very large amber-colored adhesive eggs were placed in the form of a narrow triangle on top of a clean rock. Temperature, 78. Male sits over eggs, crudely fanning them for the incubation period of 8 days. He cleans them with his mouth, removing any fungus. Ignores the babies.

After close observations of the process, the breeding habits are only partially known. Three days prior to spawning the female attached her mouth for half a minute to the vent of the male. Male has broader head. During spawning, each fish separately paid excited visits to the eggs.

Otocinclus species

Pronounced O'to-sin"klus

MEANING OF NAME: *Otocinclus,* sieve-ear, in allusion to the holes in the skull in the ear region.

Tropical South America east of the Andes   Length, 1¾ inches

MANY species have been imported but few identified. The one pictured is *O. affinis,* which is seldom available. A very interesting little "scavenger fish." It probably goes over leaves more thoroughly, above and below, than any other fish. When tired it seems to take a nap, perched in some odd posture, usually atop a leaf. The illustration is made with a view to showing the extended sucker organ, with which it goes about eating algae or other food. This is really an extension of the lips. A pèculiar thing the fish sometimes does is to swim upside down at the surface of the water, clinging to it like snails do, and apparently clearing it with its sucker mouth.

Otocinclus has seldom been bred. A well-known American wholesale breeder who has been successful with the fish writes: "On the glass side of an aquarium, much in the manner of *Corydoras aeneus,* they lay single eggs the size of a small pinhead. They hatch in about 48 hours, the transparent young sticking to the glass for two days before venturing to the bottom to look for food. It would be interesting, but not important, to know whether they adhere by suction lips, or from body tackiness, like other baby fishes."

This species causes the large wholesaler many a financial grief, for when newly received and crowded in bare containers, lacking plant life, they die off like flies. Under the conditions supplied by the retail dealer and the aquarist, they are more at home, and live satisfactorily.

A most inoffensive fish and, once acclimated, seems fairly hardy. Temperature range, 68 to 82 degrees.

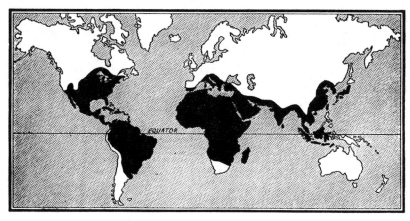

THE KILLIFISHES
FAMILY CYPRINODONTIDAE
Pronounced Sy-prin'o-don'ti-dee

The Killifishes, or Egg-laying Tooth-carps, belong to the order Micro-cyprini (or Cyprinodontes) along with their live-bearing relatives, the Gambusinos. The Killies are well distinguished from the Gambusinos by the absence of the external sex organ or gonopodium (the modified anal fin) of the males.

According to the classification of these fishes used by Dr. Myers, the authority on the group, the fishes covered in the following pages belong to several subfamilies, as follows:

Cyprinodontinae (the Pursy Minnows), including *Aphanius* and *Jordanella*. Fundulinae (the Fundulins), including *Fundulus, Leptolucania, Chriopeops,* and *Cubanichthys*. Oryziatinae (the Medakas), including only *Oryzias*. *Procatopodinae* (the Lampeyes), including *Microphanchax*. Rivulinae (the Rivulins), including *Aplocheilus, Epiplatys, Pachypanchax, Rivulus, Aphyosemion, Nothobranchius, Cynolebias,* and *Pterolebias*.

There are over 200 species of Cyprinodontidae known, most of them inhabiting Africa and America. Southern Asia has only a few species.

Culture of the Killifishes is broadly described under "Breeding the Egg-Scatterers," but there are several specific features where they differ from most other families. For one thing, few or none give one big spawning all at one time. Pairs usually spawn a few eggs a day over a more or

288

less extended period. The eggs are tough-shelled, usually with a few to many long thin filaments or "hairs" attached to them, and are more often placed singly among dense, bushy plant growths (such as *Riccia*), or (in certain genera) placed in the mud of the bottom. Finally the eggs take longer to hatch than those of most other small aquarium fishes. The shortest time is about one week, the average is about two weeks, while with some of the annual species, the eggs may take several months to hatch. With the tropical species, spawning often takes place in an aquarium for several extended periods throughout the year. Few of the North American species have been spawned extensively by aquarists.

After the sexes have been separated for one or two weeks and well fed with nourishing food, spawning will usually commence as soon as they are placed together in a well lighted, healthy aquarium containing the necessary bushy plants (see later under "Annual Species" for the mud spawners). Nylon spawning mops may be used instead of the plants. As the spawning goes on day after day, the easiest method of handling the eggs is to remove the bushy plants (or spawning mops) containing the eggs about once a week and place them in a rearing tank. The rearing tank should be large enough and well enough planted to enable smaller, more recently hatched young to escape their older brethren. Eggs laid over two or three weeks apart should not be placed in one rearing tank.

Spawning behavior is almost always the same throughout the family. The male comes up alongside the female and pushes her broadside against the plant growth. There, with fluttering fins and trembling bodies, a single egg is laid and fertilized. Then the process is repeated. Only one pair spawns together at one time. Extra males should not be present, but one male may spawn with several females.

In some genera of this family (*Chriopeops, Cubanichthys* and *Oryzias*) the spawning is not done against the plants, although the spawning act is much the same. Instead, each separate egg that is laid and fertilized during the day remains attached to the vent of the female by its long filaments, the day's clutch resembling a small bunch of tiny, transparent grapes. (See illustration of *Cubanichthys*.) During the next few hours the eggs are rubbed off one by one by the female and remain suspended from the plants or the sides of the tank by the filaments.

The eggs are about the size of a pin head, which is considered fairly large, and consequently produce fry of good size, needing Infusoria for only a short time before graduating to sifted Daphnia or newly-hatched brine shrimp. Growth from that point on is rather rapid.

The large babies sometimes eat the small ones. While the dwarfs of any large hatching of fishes may as well be disposed of in that way, it must be remembered that there is usually a week's difference in age of a lot of killifish young and it would not be fair to assume that the small ones are runts. To save the little fellows through their infancy they should be occasionally sorted for size. A female may produce 400 eggs during a breeding season. The eggs at a tempreature of 75 degrees hatch in 2 weeks or a little more.

For the mud spawners, see the special section on "Annual Species" further on.

Many of the Killies are great jumpers, and will leap through very small openings left in the tank cover. This is especially true of the species of *Rivulus*. In its native habitat, *Rivulus* is known to take journeys over-land through the wet forest, flipping its way along and often being found in little pools and puddles (sometimes even the water-filled hooftracks of cattle) at a considerable distance from the closest permanent stream or pond. In the aquarium, *Rivulus* often lies atop the surface plants and may even be found now and then adhering to the sides of the aquarium out of water or even sticking to the under side of the glass cover. Most of the species are very inactive. The most active, in our experience, is *R. cylindraceus*.

The species of *Aplocheilus, Epiplatys* and *Pachypanchax* have flat heads and large mouths. With some others more or less similar in appearance, they are sometimes spoken of as "the *Panchax* group," but this grouping has no basis in classification. The eggs of these genera, like those of *Rivulus*, take about two weeks to hatch at 75° F.

Some killies, such as the larger species of *Aplocheilus, Epiplatys, Aphyosemion* and *Pachypanchax*, some of the kinds of *Rivulus*, and all or nearly all the annuals, possess a somewhat combative temperament, and males often attack and sometimes kill other killies and occasionally even members of other groups. Spawning females should always have a place to retire from the attentions of overly ardent or combative males. Species of such disposition are better left out of a community aquarium.

Aphànius sòphiae (HECKEL)

Pronounced A-fain'e-us so'fee-ee

MEANING OF NAME: *Aphanius,* indistinct; *sophiae,* after Sofia, Persia

Persia   Western Location Map o81 to m71   Length 1½ inches

HE male of this species is one of the most beautifully spotted fishes in the aquarium. The regular small spots in the fins and the large, slightly irregular ones on the body are light blue to white, and stand out like pearls against a dark setting, the body being olive-brown and the fins blue. This color description, it will be at once seen, fits only the male. As is usual with fishes, the female gets the worst of it as far as fine raiment is concerned.

This is one of those species which can live in ordinary aquarium water, but does better with about 10% of sea water added, or a teaspoon of salt to each gallon of fresh water. This is not strong enough to harm the ordinary aquatic plants.

They breed among plant thickets, and as the male is an aggressive driver when breeding, plenty of refuge should be available to the female. She deposits clear eggs which hatch in about 10 days at a temperature of about 75 degrees. These fish have a great preference for live food, and ordinarily will not touch their eggs unless pressed by hunger. As there is no point to leaving the babies with the parents, they may as well be separated in the beginning.

Fishes of the genus *Aphanius* have a wide temperature tolerance, ranging from 60 to 90, but do best at 72 to 76 degrees.

An active, beautiful aquarium fish, unfortunately not always available. It should be more extensively cultivated. It likes sun.

Aphànius ibèrus　(CUVIER AND VALENCIENNES)

Pronounced A-fain'e-us eye-bee'rus

MEANING OF NAME: *iberus,* from the Spanish peninsula, Iberia

Spain and Morocco　　　　Western Location Map k52; 152　　　　Length, 1½ inches

℘ HIS fish may briefly be described as a striped edition of the foregoing. All comments regarding breeding and temperature are ditto.
In place of the 12 silver-blue bars of the male, the female has about the
same number of dark dots along her sides. As will be seen, the fish is of
a slightly more slender build than A. *sophiae.* Some writers describe
4 curved, gray bars in the tail fin, but our specimens do not show these.
Minor variations in fish markings, for many reasons, must not be taken
too seriously.

Both species of *Aphanius* get along well with other small fishes. Very
quick in their movements. They will take any food, but prosper best on
live Daphnia, etc.

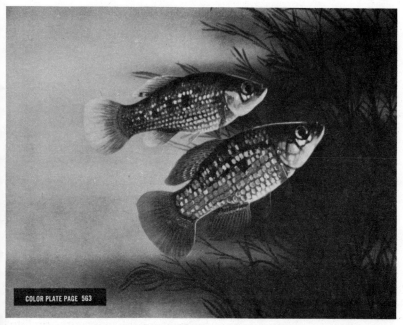

COLOR PLATE PAGE 563

Jordanélla flòridae GOODE AND BEAN

Pronounced Jor'dan-el"la flo'ri-dee   *Popular name,* Flag Fish
          Named for David Starr Jordan and the State of Florida
Florida   Western Location Map g25 to j26   Length, 2 inches

*A*QUARISTS have not always been as successful with this beautiful and interesting species as they could have been had the food requirements been better understood. There seems to be an impression that *Jordanella* is a sunfish, and that it is strictly carnivorous. It is largely the lack of algæ as food that is responsible for failures.

As the male is a strenuous courter, the breeding aquarium should be thickly planted, including, if possible, some Riccia. A well-established 5-to-10 gallon tank containing soft algæ is best. For several days about 20 eggs are deposited at the bottom. At 75 degrees they hatch in 5 to 6 days. The male fans the eggs, guards and protects the babies.

The species is rather combative, and is a heavy eater. In the absence of algae, some boiled spinach should be alternated with other foods. Florida dealers supply this attractive, interesting fish. It prefers alkaline water.

Spawn is deposited in depressions or among rootlets at the bottom, and is cared for by the male, who proves himself an excellent parent. The eggs hatch in a week at 74 degrees, and are easily raised.

Fúndulus chrysòtus   HOLBROOK

Pronounced Fun'dew-lus kry-so'tus

MEANING OF NAME: Fundulus, bottom fish; *chrysotus,* golden-ear, with reference
to golden gill plates

Popular name, Goldear Killy

S. E. United States   Western Location Map d26 to j26   Length, 3 inches

ALTHOUGH this handsome fish is very variable, it is easily recognized. On its olive sides are a few spangles of green gold, usually mixed, on the male, with round red dots. Sometimes added to these are irregular islands of black. Extremely beautiful specimens are sometimes seen in which the red dots strongly predominate, while a deep reddish hue extends into all of the fins, even with the female, which in the ordinary form has them clear. The light spot shown on the gill plate is green to gold. Eyes, usually yellow. There is another strain that is spotted heavily with black, somewhat like a male *Gambusia holbrookii.*

The species is a typical egg-dropper, preferring such plants as Myriophyllum for spawning purposes. The eggs at 75 degrees hatch in about 12 days, and the young are easily reared. Female (above) has larger anal.

The fish is highly regarded by European aquarists and even by some Americans. A snail-killer, and sometimes rips fins of other fishes.

Leptolucània ommàta (JORDAN)
Pronounced Lep'toe-lew-cane"e-a om-may'ta
MEANING OF NAME: *Leptolucania,* slender *Lucania,* another genus
bearing a coined name; *ommata,* with eye-like spots.

Okefinokee Swamp, Georgia and N. Florida   Length, 1½ inches
Western Location Map f25; h25

THESE fishes are moderately well-known to aquarists of Europe and
America, especially to those who like to have comprehensive collections. They are not what would be called generally popular.

The male is a light but warm golden color, while the female is duller and verges towards green. Both have the long dark body stripe, but in the male it is less clear towards the end and is traversed by light vertical bars. A difference in the sexes will also be noted in the shape of the fins, the upper figure being the male.

This, as will be seen at the heading, is one of our native fishes, and is not new to the aquarium. The author has not found it to be very durable, but there are others who succeed with it.

The species spawns at a temperature of about 74 degrees, and likes to deposit eggs in thickets of fine plants. Incubation period, approximately 10 days. The babies are very small and at first require minute Infusoria.

A perfectly peaceful species. Although small, it should have plenty of room. Eats anything, but needs occasional feedings of live food. Temperature range, 65 to 80 degrees.

COLOR PLATE PAGE 563

Chriòpeops goodei   (JORDAN)

Pronounced Kry-o'pee-ops good'eye   *Popular name,* Bluefin Killy

MEANING OF NAME: Chriopeops, similar to Chriope, a minnow;
goodei, for George Brown Goode

S. E. United States   Western Location Map f25 to i26   Length, 2 inches

THE "Bluefin" is one of the most delightful small freshwater fishes from
Florida, and is well suited to life in the aquarium, although it does
not like to be crowded. Tanks under 10-gallon size are not recommended.

The male has a spirited style, the two iridescent blue fins being nearly
always fully spread as shown in the illustration. This color should be
seen in a light reflected from the fish to the observer, direct sunlight being
the very best. Otherwise the blue is rather fleeting and variable.

Visitors to Florida who like to explore the small streams occasionally
see a small school of these little fellows at their very best, sporting themselves in the sunny waters. The species does not care for much heat.

Sexes are easily told, for the fins of the female are smaller and without
color. They spawn somewhat in the manner of *Cubanichthys cubensis*
(following), and may be bred in large groups. Eggs hatch in about a
week at 72 degrees.

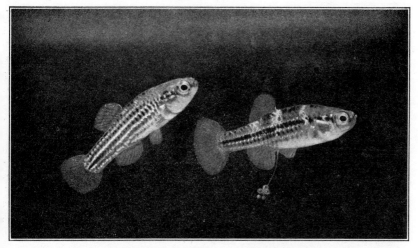

Cùbanichthys cubénsis (EIGENMANN)

Pronounced Kew'ban-ick"this kew-ben'sis   *Popular name,* Cuban Killie
MEANING OF NAME: Cuban fish inhabiting Cuba
Cuba   Western Location Map 1 and m25 and 26   Length, 1¾ inches

THIS fish has not only some degree of individual beauty, but among known aquarium fishes it has a detail in breeding habits which is unique. The large eggs, as will be seen in the photograph, are suspended in a bunch at the end of a web-like thread. This thread withstands quite a bit of jerking about without breaking, but it finally catches in some aquarium plants, is torn loose from the fish and the eggs hatch where they hang. Possibly in Nature they continue to dangle from the fish until hatched. The fertilization has not been observed, but in common with nearly all other fish eggs it is quite probable they are fertilized immediately after being extruded. Fish eggs are at first slightly flattened like a rubber ball that has been lightly pressed. As an egg quickly rounds itself into a sphere, it sucks in a little of the surrounding water which has just been charged with the sperm of the male fish, and so helps fertilize itself.

The lighter lines on the sides are electric blue. These lines, as will be observed, are considerably brighter in the male. The general color is olive.

The fish has not yet become freely distributed, but it no doubt will be, for it is interesting, it has been bred several times, the original source of supply is easily reached, it is peaceful and easily kept.

A range of 70-80 degrees suits it very well.

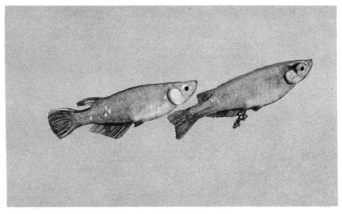

Orỳzias làtipes (SCHLEGEL)

Pronounced O-rye′zee-as lay′ti-pes   Formerly *Aplocheilus latipes*

MEANING OF NAME: Oryzias, referring to rice plant Oryza, i.e., a rice-paddy fish;
latipes, broad-foot—foot meaning fin.

Popular names, Medaka, or Rice Fish

Japan, China and Korea Eastern Location Map e57; g54; d51 to 139 Length, 1¾ in.

NATURE'S infinite variety is strikingly shown in the many breeding methods of fishes. This demure little fish, having no great beauty, offers us one of the spawning novelties. In the spring and early summer the males chase the females in conventional custom, but instead of the eggs scattering, they stick to her vent like a miniature bunch of tiny glass grapes, where they are fertilized by the male. The eggs do not long remain in this position. Within a day they are brushed off, seemingly by accident, on aquarium plants, where they remain from a week to 10 days before hatching. The parents do not eat either eggs or young, which makes their breeding a simple matter for beginners.

The species is prolific, stands a temperature range of from 40 to 80 degrees, and breeds at about 64 to 68. It likes plenty of sun.

The color of the original wild strain is olive, with silvery, white belly. In the cultivated stock a pale gold replaces the olive, but the light belly remains unchanged. There is said to be a deeper orange stock which the writer has never seen.

While the colors of the sexes are the same, the male is easily distinguished by his longer dorsal, with the last ray somewhat separated from the others, and by a much broader anal fin. Both sexes have light green eyes and perfectly clear fins.

These are among the most peaceful fishes known to aquarists. Any food.

Orўzias javánicus (BLEEKER)

Pronounced O-riz'ee-as ja-van'e-kus   *Popular name,* Java Killy

MEANING OF NAME: *javanicus,* from Java

Java and Malay Peninsula   Eastern Location Map F39; L44   Length, 1½ inches

VERY much the same as the foregoing, except that it is smaller in size and deeper in proportion to length. The fin difference in the sexes does not appear to be as great as in the Medaka. The species comes from Java, and is more uncommon as an aquarium fish.

Coming from a strictly tropical part of the world, it would seem likely to require more heat than the Medaka.

This species and the others belonging to the genus *Oryzias* comprise a very distinctive subfamily of the Killifishes which differs from all the others in the fact that the upper jaw (the premaxillary bones) cannot be moved forward when the mouth is opened. They also differ in their translucent coloration.

Micropanchax macrophthalmus (MEINKEN)

Pronounced Mike-row-pan'-chax mack'roff-thal''muss   *Popular name,* Lamp-eye

MEANING OF NAME: *Micropanchax,* little Panchax

macrophthalmus, with big eyes

Lagos, Nigeria   Western Location Map A55   Length, 1¼ inches

cA NOVELTY introduction of 1931, this interesting species has had several subsequent importations which were rapidly disposed of. It has been occasionally propagated by a few breeders in this country. This is one of those species which is reasonably hardy if kept under favorable conditions. One of the conditions they require is old water.

The name "Lamp-eyes" proved a good selling label for the fish. No matter what merit a species may have, a name cleverly capitalizing its outstanding characteristic has a popularizing effect. Our little exotic here has sufficient merit to sell itself, but an interesting or imaginative interpretation of its striking peculiarity gives an added charm.

This peculiarity lies in the eyes. The upper part of the eye-ball is a light metallic green, which, when played upon by a top light, and especially with a dark background, reminds one of the mysterious lamp-eyes of the deep-sea fishes. However much they may appear to give forth a light of their own, they really do not, for in darkness they show nothing. The pale green translucent body offers the eyes no competitive brilliance, the only other outstanding feature being the dotted metallic line down the side, which, instead of taking away effect from the "lamp," only adds to it by giving the fish the appearance of a miniature comet. The dorsal, anal and tail fins are flushed with delicate blue, the latter fin also being lightly dotted with red.

The sexes may be distinguished by the fact that the dorsal and ventral fins of the male are more pointed than those of the female.

The species likes a temperature of 72-80. Eggs are placed singly in thickets, are not eaten and hatch in about 10 days at a temperature of 80.

COLOR PLATE PAGE 564

Aplocheìlus lineàtus   (CUVIER AND VALENCIENNES)

Pronounced Ap'low-kyle"us   linn'e-ay"tus   *Popular name,* Malabar Killy

MEANING OF NAME: *Aplocheilus,* simple lip, *lineatus,* striped
Formerly known as *Haplochilus rubrostigma* and *Panchax lineatus*

India   Eastern Location Map z19   Length, 3½ to 4 inches

THE colors of this species vary so much according to the light in which it is placed that no one picture can show a composite of the truth. Our color plate is the best of many we have made of this difficult subject, but it is lacking that important metallic sparkle which has so far eluded the arts of the photographer and the photo-engraver. At times the lines of metallic scales seem like rows of tiny mirrors of burnished gold. Again both fishes may be of a uniform, pale green color, but the female always has more and stronger vertical bars and very few red dots. The black spot at the base of the dorsal also identifies her. The white markings on the upper and lower edges of the tail fin are absent in some individuals.

This is the best known of the *Aplocheilus* species, as well as the easiest to breed. It has a mouth of considerable capacity and in its larger sizes the fish can suddenly dispose of a half-grown Guppy.

Aplocheilus blocki　ARNOLD

Pronounced Ap'low-kyle"us block'eye　　　　　　*Popular name,* Madras Killy

MEANING OF NAME: *Aplocheilus,* simple lip; *blockii,* after Capt. Block, the original collector. Formerly known as *Panchax blockii*

More usually known in the trade and by American aquarists as *Panchax parvus*

S. India and Ceylon　　　　Eastern Location Map A19; x22　　　　Length, 1¾ inches

⟲HIS is the smallest *Aplocheilus* known and perhaps the prettiest. To be fully appreciated, its sparkling facets should be bathed in direct sunlight. Olive sides, darkening towards the top, furnish good backgrounds for the dazzling regular rows of red dots which alternate with sparkling scales of greenish-yellow tone. The spots in the fins of the fish to the right, which will be recognized as the male, are warm brown. The dark edging of his fins represents yellow. It will be observed that the female has an oblique dark bar in the dorsal fin just at its base. Her colors are merely a pale suggestion of those in the male. When the photograph was taken her anal fin was folded, giving an erroneous impression of its form. Gill plates transparent, showing the rosy color of the gills. The eyes of both sexes are pale gold. Specimens are seldom quite as large as our illustration.

The fish is a good breeder and an aquarium of 3-gallon capacity is sufficiently large for it to spawn in. One should always remember, however, that young fishes grow better in large aquariums than in small ones. They breed like the other Panchax. Temperature range, 70-84 degrees.

Epiplàtys séxfasciàtus GILL

Pronounced Ep'ee-play"tiss sex'fas-see-ay"tus

MEANING OF NAME: *Epiplatys,* very flat above, with reference to the head; *sexfasciatus,* with six bands.

Popular name, Six-banded Killy

Tropical W. Africa   Western Location Map A47; E59; F59; E62   Length, 4 inches

HE first and substantially correct impression one gets of this species is a greenish yellow, strongly barred fish. Although in size and general characteristics it resembles *Aplocheilus lineatus,* it has none of the sparkle of that distinguished member of the family. The spots on the sides between the bars are dark, but are occasionally relieved by a few flashes of metallic green. Fins of the female (upper fish), clear or tinged yellow; in the male, strong greenish yellow, except the ventrals, which are orange-gray. The tail fin is faintly tipped with red. A black lower lip presents a rather unusual appearance. Both sexes have pale gold eyes.

While the male does not have the decidedly pointed fins of some of the species, nevertheless his strong color and considerable breadth of anal fin are characteristics by which the sex can easily be told.

The fish is not especially difficult to breed, but few seem interested in propagating it. For that reason the stock is rather scarce. Temperature, about 75-80 degrees.

Like most of its relatives, it is a jumper. Cover at all times.

COLOR PLATE PAGE 564

Aplocheìlus pánchax (HAMILTON-BUCHANAN)

Pronounced Ap'low-kyle"us pan'chax

MEANING OF NAME: *Panchas,* after a native name, Pang-chax *Popular name,* Panchax
India and Malayan region   Length, 2¾ inches

Eastern Location Map q17 to F39; H38; M45; H46

RATHER easily-bred old favorite aquarium fish, known for years as *Panchax panchax.* There are several subspecies, or geographical races, differing somewhat in body shape and color. These are at present (1956) being studied in India and at Stanford University.

The basic color of the body is olive in different shades. Females rather colorless. In our illustration we are fortunate to be able to show the two main color varieties in the males—red and yellow.

This is one of those species with which it is practically impossible for the aquarist to go astray in the matter of identification.

Fairly peaceful and a good breeder. Temperature range, 70-84 degrees.

COLOR PLATE PAGE 565

Epiplàtys chàperi   (SAUVAGE)
Pronounced Ep'ee-play"tiss chap"er-eye (not cha-peer'ee)
MEANING OF NAME: *Epiplatys,* very flat above, with reference to the heaᴅ;
chaperi, after M. Chaper, its discoverer
Sometimes known to aquarists as *Panchax chaperi*
Popular name, Redjaw Killy
Gabon, W. Africa   Western Location Map y47; B52   Length, 2 inches

ONE of the true old favorites, and while of recent years it has been
crowded by more showy species, it holds a place in many collections. It is fairly hardy and of a popular size.

A small but very individual color characteristic of the male is the fiery
appearance of the lower lip and sometimes also the throat, best seen from
the front view. Another peculiarity of the species which makes it easy
to recognize, and at the same time tell the sex, is the pointed extension,
in the male, of the lower part of the tail fin. This is a peculiarity that sets
the species clearly apart from any of its relatives, near or far.

Temperature range, 65 to 90 degrees. It is a free breeder.

Epiplàtys màcrostigma (BOULENGER)

Pronounced Ep'ee-play"tiss mack'row-stig"ma

MEANING OF NAME: *macrostigma*, with large spots   *Popular name,* Bigspot Killy
Known also as *Haplochilus* or *Panchax macrostigma*

Cameroon, W. Africa   Western Location Map G59; H60   Length, 2¼ inches

ONE of the rarer and more delicate of the *Epiplatys* species. It is a
little larger than *Aplocheilus blockii.* Lower half of the side is blue-
green, which shades up to brown-olive on the back. The feature which
to the aquarist gives it its individuality is the large, deep carmine or wine-
colored dots on the sides. In the male the dots extend into a blue-green
field in the 3 single fins. The back edge of the gill plate in the female is
transparent, and shows the rosy tint of the gills. Her ventrals and anal
are tipped light blue-green.

A color variation having the lips bordered with red and having other
slight color differences was for a time listed as *E. grahami,* but *grahami*
is a different fish.

A charming fish which is not seen as often as could be wished for.

While not a fighting fish, it nevertheless belongs in an aquarium with
only its own kind. It does not seem to be happy nor at home in a tank of
mixed fishes. Should occasionally have live food, especially Daphnia or
white worms.

The species is rather difficult to spawn, although its breeding habits
conform to those of its near relatives. Needs old water and a temperature
of 72-82 degrees.

Epiplàtys fásciolàtus (GUENTHER)

Pronounced Ep'ee-play"tiss fas'see-o-lay"tus

MEANING OF NAME: *fasciolatus,* with bands on side

Sierra Leone   Western Location Map z47   Length, 3 inches

SEVERAL writers have stated that this species is difficult to distinguish from *E. sexfasciatus.* While it is true that the greenish-brown color in both species is somewhat similar, the two species are not at all similar in life. It will be seen that the dark markings in the dorsal, tail and anal fins in *E. fasciolatus* are lacking in *E. sexfasciatus.* Also the female in *E. fasciolatus* has a yellow edging to the anal fin, whereas in *E. sexfasciatus* it is clear.

Under too strong a light or in water that is too fresh or too cool, the fish is an insipid yellowish color, almost devoid of markings, but when in old, warm water and it comes out into the light from a position well shaded by plants, it is a very beautiful fish. The ground color is olive-yellow, the light spots are green, while the dark body line and the pattern and dots in the fins are maroon. Fins in the male, greenish yellow; in female, nearly clear. About 10 light bars sometimes appear on the sides. Breeding and habits as described for the group. Temperature, about 75 degrees. The species is somewhat difficult to procure commercially.

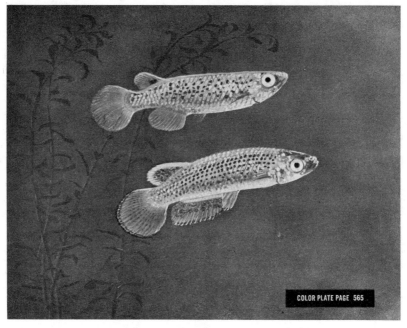

COLOR PLATE PAGE 565

Pachypanchax playfairi (GUENTHER)

Pronounced Pay'ky-pan"chax play-fair'-eye   *Popular name,* Rough-back Killy
MEANING OF NAME: *Pachypanchax,* thick Panchax; *playfairi,* after R. L. Playfair
Seychelles Islands, Zanzibar and E. Africa   Length, 3½ inches
Western Location Map H-174 and LM6 on Eastern Location Map

ANY of our aquarium fishes are so nearly alike that trained
observers have difficulty in distinguishing species, and a writer
has double trouble in naming some simple points of identification for his
readers. It is with pleasure that we pounce upon *P. playfairi,* for here is
a fish that literally could be identified by a blind man. The scales, especially in the male, stand out slightly on end, like in a fish having the
disease called dropsy. It is the only aquarium fish known to the writer
having this peculiarity. The picture shows it.

This is one of the fishes that can be easily caught in the aquarium by
very slow approach with the net, but once captured it should be covered
at all times until the transfer is completed, for it is then a real "escape
artist."

The fish has an interesting appearance, but is known as "a bad actor."
It picks on other fishes and eats its own eggs and young. For breeding it
requires extra thick planting and early separation of breeders and their
eggs. Temperature, 72-85 degrees. Rather carnivorous.

COLOR PLATE PAGE 566

Rívulus cylindràceus POEY

Pronounced Riv'you-lus   sill'in-dray"see-us   *Popular name,* Cuban Rivulus
MEANING OF NAME: *Rivulus,* a little river or brook; *cylindraceus,* cylindrical
Cuba   Western Location Map m25 to m27   Length, 2 inches

ONE of the most satisfactory of the genus *Rivulus.* It is hardy, active, peaceful and prolific. In color it varies considerably, our illustration here being one of its most frequent phases. Sometimes the body is sprinkled irregularly with dark green or red dots. Dorsal fin is often greenish yellow, touched with a white margin. The anal fin, where it joins the body is occasionally flaked with red. These color variations are not so much temporary changes in individuals, but differences according to the locality where they are found (in Cuba).

Although not one of the biggest of the *Rivulus* group, it is one of the "jumpingest," easily clearing a barrier of 10 inches. It behooves the aquarist to always remember to replace the aquarium cover where these fish are kept. A thickly planted tank has a tendency to curb the jumping urge in any fish.

The female is drab compared with the male. It is easy to tell her sex by the usual female "Rivulus spot" at the upper edge of her tail base.

Female has small ovipositor at breeding time, and drops large eggs near the surface. Thick plants like Myriophyllum catch many of them before the breeders can gobble them.

Rivulus härti (Boulenger)

Pronounced Riv'you-lus hart'-eye

Meaning of name: *harti,* after the collector, Hart   *Popular name,* Hart's Rivulus

Venezuela and Trinidad   Length, 3½ inches

Western Location Map x between 19 and 20; x 18

SOMETIMES confused with *Rivulus urophthalmus,* but is not the same fish. It is one of the larger members of the genus.

The body is warm gray to pinkish, overlaid with dots of red that form themselves into rows, as illustrated. The tail fin is yellow on the upper and lower edges, with black adjoining the yellow on the inside. The centre of the end of the fin is also black. Eye, light gold.

Aquarists travelling in Trinidad report them plentiful everywhere. Very tough, and flop from one pool to another in damp weather. In the upland streams they lack color. They eat smaller fishes.

They breed like other *Rivulus,* and for several days deposit quite large eggs in fine grass. These they do not eat. Although not shown in the photograph, fine transparent dots will be seen in the tail fin of the male. These are absent in the female. In this species the usual ocellated spot at the upper base of the tail of the female (top fish in illustration) barely shows. Her color is more muddy and the red dots duller than in the male. Temperature range, 70 to 85 degrees.

Rívulus ocellàtus HENSEL

Pronounced Riv'you-lus o-sell-ay'tus

MEANING OF NAME: *ocellatus,* with eye-like spot *Popular name,* Marbled Rivulus

S. E. Brazil Western Location Map V30 Length, 2¾ inches

NEARLY all of the females of the different species of *Rivulus* have the "eye spot" near the upper base of the tail. In *ocellatus* it is particularly clear and attractive. Some writers claim that both sexes exhibit this spot, but this author seldom finds any in the male, except perhaps a vague one. The upper fish is the female.

Bright colors in this species are conspicuous by their absence. For all that the fish is not unattractive. The markings shown in the photograph are composed of harmonious shades of brown and gray. The only actual bit of color is in the anal fin, which is tinged yellow.

The position this pair has taken for their portrait is not out of keeping with the many comical angles at which they cock themselves—a true *Rivulus* habit.

This is one of the species that is either very plentiful or very scarce. At this writing, the supply is low. The fish accepts almost any food.

A hardy, friendly species, easily kept and bred. In general appearance and actions it reminds one very much of our own popularly-named "Mud Minnow" *(Umbra pygmœa).*

They stand any reasonable temperature such as is usually provided for exotic fishes, an average of 70-76 suiting them quite well.

COLOR PLATE PAGE 566

Rivulus urophthálmus   GUENTHER
Pronounced Riv′you-lus your′off-thal″muss
MEANING OF NAME: *urophthalmus*, with eye-spot in tail
Popular names, Red Rivulus and Blue Rivulus

Amazon   Western Location Map H12 to G28   Length, 2½ inches

THERE are 2 distinct color varieties of this species, so different that it is difficult to realize that they are the same fish. The one pictured here is the "Golden." All that needs to be explained is that the lower figure, showing no red dots, and lacking the usual tail spot of *Rivulus* females *is* the female.

The other color variety is called the "Blue," although not very blue. In this case the female *has* the "Rivulus spot." In color the "blue" variety is considerably darker and from a distance the color is rather nondescript. Closer examination shows alternating rows of red and green scales. The fins are grayish and in both sexes the 3 unpaired fins are spotted with red, more strongly in the male.

This species, in either color, is rather hardy and can stand a temperature range of 65-85. Breeding, at about 75 degrees. They are inclined to be cannibals with their young. Breeding and care as per description.

Rívulus strigàtus   REGAN

Pronounced Riv'you-lus   stry-gay'tus

MEANING OF NAME: *strigatus*, streaked   *Popular name*, Herring-bone Rivulus

Amazon   Exact locality not known   Length, 1½ inches

*I*F the reader will vision the dark lines of the herring-bone pattern on the sides of the male as being a rich red, and the light parts a beautiful blue-green, he will have a good idea of the principal impression made by this stunning little fish, as well as a sure method of identification, for no other known aquarium species of *Rivulus* presents this particular pattern.

While the colors in the female are the same, only in reduced degree, the herring-bone design is absent or only vaguely suggested.

The centre of the tail fin suggests the same color scheme as the body, but the upper and lower edges are yellow to orange. Ventrals and anal in the male are yellow, tipped with red. Pectorals, yellow. Dorsal, light yellow with a few red dots. Fins in the female are nearly clear, but she shows the characteristic female *Rivulus* spot in the upper tail base. Eyes in both sexes, pale with dark outer edge. The species is not so given to the long holding of poses as are most of its cousins.

Rivulus strigatus is rather touchy. It likes a temperature of about 75 and breeds at 80 degrees. Its breeding habits conform to the standard description for the genus, and while it is one of the more difficult ones to succeed with, it is by no means impossible, and is well worth the effort.

COLOR PLATE PAGE 567

Aphyosèmion austràle   (RACHOW)

Pronounced Aff'ee-o-see"me-on   aws-tray'lee   *Popular name,* Lyretail

MEANING OF NAME: *Aphyosemion,* a fish with a banner; *australe,* southern

Known to American aquarists as "Cameronensis," in Germany as the "Kap Lopez"

Cape Lopez, Africa   Western Location Map E58   Length, 2½ inches

(O)UR color plate gives a true representation of this beautiful fish in health. When not kept in conditions to its liking, it "folds up," becomes narrower, does not spread its fins and is apt to resign from life altogether. In a favorable environment, it is not a delicate fish.

Considering that it comes from tropical Africa, it stands water of moderate temperature very well, 68 to 70 degrees suiting it admirably, although for breeding it should be kept warmer, say 72 to 74 degrees. What it is most particular about is *old* water, preferably a little acid, about pH 6.8. This is important in breeding. Lower figure is the male.

Eggs are deposited, a few at a time, among such plants as Riccia. They are rather easily seen, but the parents do not touch them. Hatching period, about 10 to 12 days. There is no advantage, however, in keeping the breeders with the eggs, once they are through a spawning period, which is likely to last several days. On plenty of Infusoria, preferably from a pond, the young grow rapidly and soon require sifted Daphnia, or newly hatched brine shrimp.

Aphyosèmion cámeronénse   (BOULENGER)

Pronounced Aff'ee-o-see"me-on kam'er-on-en"see

MEANING OF NAME: *cameronense,* from Cameroon   *Popular name,* Cameroon Killy
Equatorial W. Africa   Length, 2¼ inches
        Western Location Map F58 and 59; H60; C58 and 59

GIVING this fish its true name and place caused aquarists some mental
  irritation, for we had become confirmed in the habit of placing the
name of "Cameronensis" on *A. australe.* It was some time after having
this error drawn to our attention that the rightful claimant of the name
appeared on the scene. This fish was only imported here in 1933, many
years later than the one that was innocently parading under a false name.

Considering the outstanding beauty of the false *A. cameronense,* it was
rather a let-down to see the real one, although it is rather attractive. The
tail fin, as the illustration shows, is rounded instead of lyre-shape, and
all the colors, by comparison, are pale. It is simply a light fish of a
creamy shade, striped with red lines which are a series of dots. Between
these dotted lines are stripes of a pretty metallic green, which at some
angles change to blue. The spots and lines shown in the fins of the male
are the same shade of red, surrounded by metallic blue borderings. On
the outer edges of these fins, except the centre of the caudal, we find a
pale lemon tint. Pectorals, edged blue. Eye, green. The female (lower
fish) is barely dotted red. Breeds like other members of the genus.

Likes old, slightly acid water, and not much strong light.

Aphyosèmion calliùrum   (BOULENGER)

Pronounced Aff'ee-o-see"me-on kal'lee-you"rum

MEANING OF NAME: *Aphyosemion,* fish carrying a flag; *calliurum,* with beautiful tail

West Coast of Equatorial Africa   Western Location Map B48   Length, 2½ inches

*A*PHYOSEMION AUSTRALE was originally considered to be only a color variation of the above species. While there is still doubt as to whether they are separate species, aquarists need a distinction, and since Myers and Ahl have joined in classifying them separately, we have good grounds for doing the same.

The principal color differences seem to be that A. *calliurum* is in general a lighter and more yellow-brown color, lacking somewhat in the bluish richness on the sides, and having more of a tendency to show fine vertical bars on the rear portion of the body. Also the fin points are a little shorter. They are said to be more tender, as well as more difficult to breed. Otherwise all remarks regarding one species apply to the other. This includes breeding habits.

There is always a ready demand for both of these similar *Aphyosemions.* In addition to being most beautiful, they are also very peaceful.

To see them at their best (and it is indeed an impressive sight), the light should come from over one's shoulder. It is especially beautiful when struck by sun from that direction. The upper fish is the male.

The Aphyosemions ought to be fed on live food or fresh sea food, such as bits of crab meat. Daphnia or white worms are perfect for them. Prepared food will do "in a pinch." They like a subdued light.

COLOR PLATE PAGE 567

Aphyosèmion cognàtum   MEINKEN
Pronounced Aff'ee-o-see' me-on cog-nay" tum
MEANING OF NAME: *cognatum*, related to (apparently australe)
Popular name, Red-speckled Killy
Congo, W. Africa   Length, 1¾ inches   Western Location Map G63

*I*NTRODUCED in Germany in 1931, this is one of the most showy of the many beautiful *Aphyosemions*, the male being strongly speckled with crimson dots as shown in our plate. Those touches of white in the fins add pleasantly to the contrast. While a little smaller in size than most of them, this does not seem to detract from their beauty.

Like most of its cousins, *cognatum* often stands still, rapidly vibrating its pectoral fins, and then moves suddenly, a characteristic of many fishes depending for life and health on the capture of live food. In small species like this one, that usually means various forms of crustacea. As a rule they do not attack smaller fishes nor their fry; nor are they aggressive in a community tank.

Breeding is virtually the same as that described for *A. australe*, preferring soft, old water. Temperatures 70-77.

While preferring living fish foods, they gladly take frozen brine shrimp, canned shrimp or even (when quite hungry) some dried foods, especially those containing a high percentage of animal substance.

Aphyosèmion spléndopleùris (MEINKEN)

Pronounced Aff'ee-o-see"me-on splen'do-plew"riss

MEANING OF NAME: *Aphyosemion*, a small fish with a banner (referring to colorful
tail fins); *splendopleuris, splendid sides*

Also known as *Fundulopanchax splendopleuris*

Tropical W. Africa   Western Location Map C59; B58   Length, 2 inches

𝒯HIS species appears somewhat like a yellow edition of the better
known *Aphyosemion bivittatum*, although the body is more slender
and the fins of the male are shaped differently. Also it is quite lacking
those delightful blue tints and reddish markings. The female is remarkably similar to that of the species mentioned, but the reddish markings
on the body are absent. The only warmth of color in the species is the
reddish brown dots in the dorsal fin of the male. His tail fin is a pretty
yellow in the ends, finally tipped white. The yellow anal fin is narrowly
edged black. Body, yellow to golden brown. As shown in the photograph, the two dark horizontal lines on the female are much stronger than on the male. This species is very similar to *Aphyosemion loen-
bergii.*

Breeds like related species, but lays the eggs among floating plants. It
is seldom propagated for the reason that the stock is scarce. Eggs hatch
in about 2 weeks at a temperature of 73 degrees.

Although not requiring a high temperature, this is one of the fishes
which is susceptible to chill if the water goes below 70 degrees.

COLOR PLATE PAGE 568

Aphyosèmion bìvittàtum (LOENNBERG)
Pronounced Aff'ee-o-see"me-on by'vi-tay"tum

MEANING OF NAME: *bivittatum*, two-striped   *Popular name,* Two-striped Killy
Also formerly known as *Fundulus bivittatus* and *Fundulopanchax bivittatus*
Tropical W. Africa   Western Location Map B58; C58; D59   Length, 2½ inches

PROBABLY printing inks on this plate do as well as might be expected. They are approximately correct, but miss a delicate translucent beauty which the fish possesses. The fish itself varies considerably in color, only showing its best in old water in a well-planted aquarium, in not too much light. Live food is important to it.

Its manner of moving about the aquarium is peculiar. It darts and then stands still, balanced by a continuous movement of the pectoral fins.

Like other members of the family, it deposits eggs among plant thickets. These hatch in about 12 days, at a temperature of 72 degrees. The young vary much in size and should be graded to prevent cannibalism.

By nature the species is suited to living with other fishes, but it is very particular about the quality of water, especially as to not being placed in water that is even slightly new. On the whole, we would say that this is one of the "touchy" species, requiring skilled handling.

THE ANNUAL KILLIFISHES
(Mud Spawners)

𝒯HE remaining Killifishes differ from the preceding ones in the fact that they do not deposit the eggs on plants, but place them in the mud or very fine sand at the bottom of the aquarium. Even more remarkable is that most of the species, including more especially the South American *Cynolebias* and *Pterolebias* and the African *Nothobranchius*, are annual fishes, completing the life span in less than one year. Whether they are completely annual or not, all of the fishes in this division are short lived. We know of no specimen that has lived to be two years old. On the other hand, these annuals include the most brilliantly colored of all Killifishes, and the males of some of them are among the most gorgeously colored of all fishes.

The information that some of these killies are annuals became known to aquarists in Germany as early as the 1920's but the fact that there is a large group of annual species, all belonging to a group of closely related genera, was not generally known until Dr. Geo. S. Myers presented the evidence in two papers published in 1942 (in Stanford Ichthyological Bulletin) and 1952 (in the Aquarium Journal). It was he who first called them "annuals."

In their native habitats, these fishes live in mud-bottomed ponds and sloughs, sometimes connected with a permanent body of water, but more often not. Towards the end of the rainy season, they spawn in the mud, and the adults then mostly wither and die, usually because the pond simply dries up. The eggs, however, survive, buried in the damp mud under the surface crust. There they remain, for a month and a half to several months. The heat of the sun apparently *slows up* the development of the eggs, for it has been noticed that eggs kept in water hatch sooner in cooler water than in warmer (see below).

When the rains again begin to fill the pool, hatching occurs almost at once, and a new generation of fishes, born of parents long dead, grows very rapidly. However, the same sort of life cycle is gone through even if the body of water in which the fish live does not dry up completely.

Although these several species come from tropical Africa and South America it is well to remember that they naturally inhabit well-shaded, still pools where the temperature does not rise excessively. Many capable aquarists have failed with these fishes, because of the fixed idea that all exotic fishes must be kept at a high temperature, an error caused by a too inflexible interpretation of the word "tropical" as applied to aquarium fishes.

While these fishes are among the more tedious to breed and difficult to handle, their great beauty makes the effort worthwhile and challenges our ability as aquarists.

Another peculiarity is the reversal of rules in regard to the effect of temperatures on the incubation period of the eggs. We usually expect an increase in heat to shorten the time. With these species the eggs hatch in about 7 weeks at a temperature of 70. At 78 it takes about 16 weeks!

The breeding aquarium should be at least 10-gallon size, but 15 is better. Water ought to be—*must* be—old, and about 7 inches deep. If available, use one part of marine to 20 parts of fresh water. Otherwise one ounce of genuine sea salt to 8 gallons of water. Bottom: sand, with a top layer of natural sediment. Temperature, 74. Use floating vegetation for a light screen and plenty of growing, bushy plants on the light side of the aquarium for the same purpose. These may also serve as a refuge for the female if the male becomes too boisterous.

While the courtship is not elaborate, the spawning is peculiar. After the pair comes to an understanding they select a spot at the bottom, take a side-by-side position, interlock fins, tremble, deliver and fertilize a single egg and deposit it on or in the dirt or sand. Stoye records an observation in which the female forces the egg into the sand by the use of a chute made by cupping her ventral fins together. A pair will deposit about 25 eggs per day for a period of 5 days, after which the male should be removed. After a week he may be returned to the same aquarium to resume operations, for if the eggs are properly buried and the female has been well fed, there is no danger of the eggs being eaten. So far as the safety of the eggs is concerned, the spawning may be repeated over a period of 5 weeks, at which time both breeders should be removed, for the young, soon to appear, would be devoured. By this plan the young will vary proportionately in size with their different ages, and as they are very carnivorous, assortment into size is necessary. If one is content to handle a week's spawning as a unit, this precaution may not be necessary.

So used have these fishes become to subdued light that any eggs not properly covered will not hatch if left in strong light.

For general maintenance these species do well in a temperature range from 68 to 78 degrees, with 71 to 74 as ideal. Every effort should be made to feed them on a carnivorous diet, preferably living, even to the extent of young live-bearers, if Daphnia and mosquito larvae cannot be had. Chopped earthworms, excellent. The best substitutes are bits of fish, shrimp, crab, oyster, etc.

One difficulty is that the males of the annuals, especially those of some species of *Cynolebias*, often fight with each other as fiercely as the males of *Betta!* And remember, *they jump.*

COLOR PLATE PAGE 568

Aphyosèmion cœrùleum (BOULENGER)
Pronounced Aff'ee-o-see"me-on see-rue'lee-um   *Popular name,* Blue Gularis
MEANING OF NAME: *caeruleum,* blue
The "Blue Gularis" of aquarists, also known as *Fundulopanchax cœruleum*
Equatorial W. Africa   Western Location Map C59; B56; A56   Length, 4 inches

℘HIS is not only one of the handsomest members of its family, but is probably in the best supply commercially. For all that, it can scarcely be said to be a popular fish. This may be for one or all of several reasons. It is cannibalistic towards fishes small enough to be swallowed but is not quarrelsome, nor a fin-ripper, although the male may mutilate the female at breeding time. A strong jumper that must always be closely covered. Has decided preference for live foods, but will take dried ones. Stands still with a slow weaving motion and makes sudden dashes. Needs old water, plenty of plants not much light, and a temperature of about 72 degrees. Breeds best at 68 to 72 degrees. Individuals vary, especially in the length of fins and also in coloration. The intensity of the brownish red in the lower portion of the tail fin is especially variable.

Our photograph, taken by the natural color process (this plate made in 1920, being the first aquarium fish ever recorded by that method), gives a sufficiently good idea of the fish, so that further elaboration is unnecessary. The illustration is of a male fish. The female has a rounded tail fin, and much less color.

The fish is hardier than might be imagined, but few of them dying on their long voyages of importation, although on arrival their colors are apt to be poor.

Eggs are deposited singly on or near the bottom, take a long time to hatch and the young are easily raised. They breed true to type as previously described for the family. Temperature range, 68-82 degrees.

As a postscript touching on the jumpiness of this fish it is recalled that many years ago a fellow enthusiast and the author imported a score of them. Prior to dividing them they were placed over night in a large covered trough. The lid was a half inch short of complete coverage. By morning every fish had leaped out and *dried* out!

Aphyosèmion gàrdneri (BOULENGER)

Pronounced Aff'ee-o-see"me-on gard'ner-eye   *Popular name,* Gardner's Killy

MEANING OF NAME: *Aphyosemion,* a small fish with a banner (referring to colorful tail fins); *gardneri,* for its collector, Captain Gardner

Togoland, Africa   Length—male, 2¼ inches; female, 1½ inches

Western Location Map A55; B56

ONE of the most brilliant and bizarre of a beautiful family of fishes. Unfortunately it is rare, delicate and difficult to breed.

It is suffused with light blue, strikingly overlaid with brown and deep crimson markings, represented by the dark parts of the illustration. The most intense crimson markings are those about the head, the large spots on the anal and the wavy line going through the lower part of the tail fin. The upper and lower edges of this fin are light yellow, while the centre carries an extension of the color effect in the body. Both the anal and dorsal fins shade from blue to yellow and both are naturally fringed. Eye, light green to blue. Should be kept at 70 degrees or higher.

The female is considerably the smaller of the pair, reaching a size of only about 1½ inches. Her fins, as will be observed, are very different in shape, as well as color, from those of the male. She is of a plain, light olive shade, over which, and into the dorsal and anal fins, are pale red dots. Eggs hatch in 2 weeks.

COLOR PLATE PAGE 569

Aphyosèmion sjoestedti (LOENNBERG)

Pronounced Aff'ee-o-see"me-on shuss'ted-eye (not so-jess'tedy)
MEANING OF NAME: After Yngve Sjoested   *Popular name,* Golden Pheasant Killy
Tropical W. Africa   Length, 3 inches
Western Location Map B57, between A46 and z47; CD59

NOT often imported and rather difficult to breed, this striking *Aphyo-semion* may be considered in the "select" class among aquarium fishes.

It likes old water and a rather subdued light, and does best on live foods. Should not be placed with fishes much smaller than itself. Capable of jumping over an aquarium edge which is several inches above water level. Keep closely covered at all times.

As with most of the *Aphyosemions,* the sexes are easy to tell on account of the pronounced differences between the tail fin of the male and female. In this instance, the male (lower fish) has a pattern in the fin, while the female has none. As might be expected, his coloring is much the brighter.

This fish is rather slender up to two years of age, when it becomes heavier, such as we see here. The colors continue to intensify, especially the indigo. The odd, lower extension of the anal fin also appears with late maturity. Breeding and care as under *Fundulopanchax* group. Single large eggs hatch in about sixty days. Temperature range 70-80.

COLOR PLATE PAGE 569

Nothobranchius rachovi AHL

Pronounced No'tho-brank"ee-us ra-kov'-eye   *Popular name,* Fire Killy
MEANING OF NAME: *Nothobranchius,* with pseudobranchiae (inside gill cover);
rachovii, after Arthur Rachaw

Portuguese East Africa   Western Location Map P71   Length, 1⅜ inches

OUR color plate shows the fish about ⅓ larger than life. The male's intense brilliance is hard to match. Most males have much more blue than indicated here. Unfortunately the species is seldom imported.

In Africa these fish live mostly in small pools that dry up annually. The parents die, but the buried eggs hatch and mature rapidly in the next rainy season. This gives the clue to breeding. Aquarium bottom should be covered with one inch of boiled and rinsed peat or fine sand, where eggs are laid singly. Eggs should not be disturbed for two months, when the water should be drained and the spawning medium kept barely moist for a week. When placed in water again, they usually hatch in minutes. During a spawning period, a female may lay hundreds of eggs. Fry eat newly hatched brine shrimp immediately.

Live food is recommended and a temperature of 70-80 degrees, with not too much light. Soft, slightly acid water is required. This species must have conditions to its liking. Given them, it is not delicate.

COLOR PLATE PAGE 570

Pterolèbias peruénsis MYERS
Pronounced Ter'o-lee"bee-as pe-ru-en'sis
MEANING OF NAME: *Pterolebias,* winged Lebias, *peruensis,* inhabiting Peru
Popular name, Peruvian Longfin

Eastern Peru   Western Location Map H-12   Length 3 inches

ONE of the striking introductions of recent years, this species is rather odd in several ways.

Evidently one of the "annual" fishes, it is rather difficult to breed in captivity, and requires much patience.

From a side-by-side position with the male, the female drops single, rather large egg into the soft soil. As a substitution for Nature's requirement of partially drying out the eggs, Mr. Rosario S. La Corte, first successful breeder of the species, placed them, after the spawning, in lightly moist peat for a period of 2 weeks. On removal to plain water they hatched, and were quickly reared on brine shrimp and other foods. At all ages they have enormous appetites, and will eat almost anything, although they are not particularly carnivorous.

The tail fin of the male soon develops into a handsome banner which he swishes in a grand manner, but the dark parts on the tips do not develop until later. Temperature, 68-76 degrees.

Cỳnolèbias bellóttii   STEINDACHNER

Pronounced Sy'no-lee"be-ass bel-lot'ee-eye   *Popular name,* Argentine Pearl Fish

MEANING OF NAME: *Cynolebias,* dog-toothed Lebias;
bellottii, after Dr. Bellotti, of Italy

Argentina   Western Location Map √21   Length, 3 inches

THERE is an elusive charm about *Cynolebias bellottii,* at least in the male fish, not easily described. It is even hard to pin him down to his principal color. So much depends upon his condition and the light he is in. At his best there is a strong touch of indigo about him, shading to olive. Sometimes he is olive to yellow. Our color plate shows him at his best, with his sides and fins ornamented by blue-white pearly dots. The female varies little in color, but she is so different from the male not only in markings, but in fin formation, that one wonders whether they are really identical species, but they *are.*

The illustration of the male shows a purplish crescent on the end of the tail fin. This wrong effect is in some way produced in the photograph by dark colors in the background, showing through the transparent fin.

The conditions under which they breed in mudholes in the plains of Argentina are so peculiar that one can hardly hope to breed them in an aquarium. Temperature, about 70.

COLOR PLATE PAGE 571

Nothobranchius palmquisti (LOENNBERG)

Pronounced No'tho-brank"ee-us palm'quist'eye

MEANING OF NAME: *Nothobranchius*—inside gill cover

Tanganyika   Western Location Map H70   Length, 2¾ inches

*O*NE of the annuals, *Nothobranchius palmquisti* holds a position as one of the most colorful. The head of the male in good light is a vivid blue green, scales on the body are edged in red and the red seems to pick up as it reaches the tail that is bright red. Dorsal is brownish red and sometimes appears a yellowish red. Pectoral and ventral fins are shot with blue. The females are grey-brown, underside yellowish white.

Considered a bottom spawner, the small aquarium is prepared with water that has been filtered through peat moss, and peat moss is used to cover the aquarium floor in a thick layer. Two or three females will keep the male from driving any one of them too hard. After a period of two or three weeks the peat is removed and stored in a slightly moist condition in a dark place for 6 to 8 weeks. After this period has passed, the peat is placed in a small tank filled with aged water. The eggs hatch in from 4 to 6 hours. The youngsters will take newly hatched brine shrimp.

The fish will only accept live food and brine shrimp and Daphnia usually make up their fare. Temperatures between 73 and 75 degrees F. seem to be best. Photo by Richard Lugenbeel. Edited by H. S.

THE GOODEIDS

FAMILY GOODEIDAE
Pronounced Good e'i dee

Viviparous fishes, but the males lack the long gonopodium common to the Poeciliidae, having, instead, the first rays of the anal fin stiffened and slightly separated into a point. Confined to Central Mexico. Turner found that females nourish unborn young in a way resembling mammals. For general information regarding breeding live-bearers, see under the following family, The Gambusinos.

Neótoca bìlineàta (BEAN)
Pronounced Nee-ot'o-ca by'linn-e-ay"ta
MEANING OF NAME: *Neotoca,* neos, meaning new (type of) and tocus, meaning offspring; *bilineata,* with 2 lines. Formerly known as *Skiffia bilineata*

Rio Lerma, Mexico   Length—male, 1½ inches; female, 2 inches

Western Location Map o12

GOODEIDS are different from Gambusinos in that the female requires a new fertilization for each brood of young. Under favorable conditions there are 5 broods per year, numbering from 5 to 40, according to the size of the female. The parents do not eat their young and are not fighters. Maturity takes place in from 3 to 6 months.

The species is silvery with gray in the fins as shown. An interesting blue-green arched line divides the belly of the female from the upper body. Best temperature, 70 to 77 degrees.

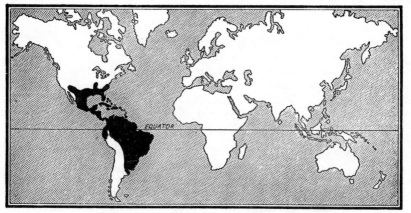

THE GAMBUSINOS
OR LIVE-BEARING TOOTH-CARPS

FAMILY POECILIIDAE
Pronounced Pee'sill-ee"i-dee

The Gambusinos, or Live-bearing tooth-carps, are the "live-bearers" of the aquarist. They are easily distinguished from the Killies by the elongated gonopodium or intromittent anal fin of the male. It is largely by differences in structure of this organ that the various genera are classified. As will be seen from the accompanying map, all the Poeciliids are from the New World, the greatest number of genera in the species occurring in Central America and the West Indies.

There are several groups of viviparous or "live-bearing" fishes, such as the family Goodeidae (just preceding), some members of the Half-beak family (dealt with later in the book), and a number of others not yet known to aquarists. However, the Gambusino family includes most of the live-bearers kept in home aquaria, and we interrupt the sequence at this point to give a general account of live-bearer breeding.

Breeding the Live-bearers

NOT many years ago the author was often in receipt of letters, usually to "settle a bet," asking whether fishes really have their young born alive. The popularity of exotic fishes has become so general that the public now accepts the phenomenon of viviparous or live-bearing fishes without surprise. No more letters on that point are received.

However, there is some basis of truth in the idea that only mammals give birth to their young, for, while many of our aquarium fishes do indeed present developed young to the world, apparently without going through the egg period, this is not precisely true. Fully formed eggs are in the egg duct of the female, where they become fertilized, are hatched and grown to the same point of maturity as the young of egg-laying fishes which have absorbed their yolk-sacs and are ready to swim freely. In other words, the eggs of viviparous fishes have the protective advantage of hatching within the body of the female, and of entering the world well equipped to meet life on a competitive basis.

While it is true that an egg is the medium through which every live-bearing animal (whether warm- or cold-blooded) transmits the spark of life, there is a great difference between the internal process in mammals and fishes. In mammals, the ovum or egg after fertilization becomes attached to and is part of the mother. Its life stream proceeds from her. Except for the mother's supplying oxygen to the eggs and young, no such relationship exists between ordinary viviparous fishes and their babies.

Period of Development

She has no definite period of gestation as do warm-blooded animals. The young develop according to temperature, and after maturity are delivered at somewhat variable times, dependent upon conditions. Possibly the urge of the mother is a factor, for we know that if one fish is selected from a number of apparently "ripe" females and placed in fresh water, she is liable, through stimulation or excitement, to deliver within an hour. The babies are likely to be just as perfect as those coming from the other females several days later, indicating that they have been well formed for some time.

In the mother they lie folded once, with head and tail meeting, and are delivered in this form, one at a time, or occasionally two. Very soon they straighten out and swim for the best refuge they can find. The young when first introduced to the world are about a quarter inch long, which is considerably larger than from most species whose eggs hatch externally.

As has been stated, temperature has a bearing on the period of incubation, but to give the reader an approximate idea of what to expect from average conditions, it may be said that at 75 degrees the time from fertilization to delivery is about 4 to 5 weeks. The time may be greatly protracted by a few degrees less temperature. At 67 degrees it may be as long as 12 weeks. As with the egg-layers, however, it is believed that fairly rapid incubation produces the stronger young.

Maturity Age Different species vary considerably in this respect, and all species vary according to the conditions under which they are reared. A young Guppy, male or female, raised at an average temperature of 75 to 80, given plenty of room and live food, will be ready for breeding in 6 to 8 weeks. Platies are almost as rapid, while the minimum time for the maturity of Mollienisias is approximately twice as long. Early breeding of females does not affect final size.

Fertilization Interesting as are the facts already related regarding the live-bearers, they would be incomplete without an account of the fertilization itself. Those not already acquainted with the process will find it instructive. Many aquarist friends have found the theme of reproduction of live-bearing fishes to be an easy and natural medium for preparing young people for the "facts of life."

To outward appearances the sexes are the same at birth. In a few weeks the anal fin of the male fish becomes just a trifle more pointed. As time for maturity approaches, it rapidly lengthens into a straight, rod-like projection, carried backward and parallel to the body, and usually close to it, although capable of being quickly moved at any angle, forward or sideways. All appearances of a fin have disappeared. This is now called the *gonopodium*. In form and length it varies with different fishes. In Platies it is small and not always easily seen. In Guppies and *Gambusia* it is unmistakable, while in such genera as *Phallichthys* and *Poecilistes* it is quite obvious. The tip of the gonopodium varies in shape in different species. This fact was once believed to set up a mechanical barrier against crossing certain species, but this is now doubted, as we are not certain that the gonopodium actually enters the egg duct (which is at the vent of the female).

The male in courting grandly spreads all fins and excitedly approaches the female, usually parallel to her and a little from the rear. He may circle her, all the while on the *qui vive*, ready to make a quick thrust from a position of vantage. The act is over in a second. The female never seems to be flattered by these attentions. Perhaps she dimly realizes with true world-old feminine instinct, that she is only his desire of the moment. At any rate the author has never seen nor heard report of her willingly accepting his attentions, nor of responding to them. Neverthe-

less, "love finds a way," and live-bearing fishes continue to multiply even
faster than the rapidly increasing ranks of aquarists.

The live-bearers do not mate in the sense that the Cichlids do, nor
the nest-builders. They are not even polygamous, but strictly promiscuous. Reproduction with them is conducted on a basis of what might be
termed *impersonal opportunism.*

**Subsequent
Fertilization**
Here is a subject of which we know little, but we have
an idea. As previously stated, a single fertilization is
sufficient for 4 or 5 broods. Immediately after a female
has delivered her young, the males are intensely attracted to her and
double their attentions. Although she is probably able to deliver another
brood without further male contact, the question is whether such subsequent contact would result in part or all of the young inheriting the
characteristics of the last male mate. This is brought up for the reason
that if a fish breeder wishes to establish the characteristics of a certain
male in its descendants, such, for instance, as particularly attractive
markings in a Guppy, he would not be safe in assuming that the first
4 or 5 broods are necessarily fertilized by him if the female has, prior
to the fifth delivery, been exposed to another male. That presents an
interesting subject for research.

It is, of course, also a possibility that a second male contact any time
after the first delivery of young, but before the fifth, would have no
influence on the first 5 broods, but might fertilize later ones.

**Repeated
Broods**
Owing to physiological reasons not fully understood, a
female may have 4 or even 5 lots of young from a single
fertilization. These will be about the same distance apart
in time as the time between fertilization and the first delivery.

**When Is a
Female "Ripe"?**
Except with those few live-bearers which are
black, or nearly so, there is a contrasting dark
area on the female's body, close to the vent. It
varies in shape and clearness in different species, but tends towards a
crescent form, or sometimes a triangle. This is called the "gravid spot,"
caused by the dark portions of the internal organs showing through the
stretched abdominal walls. More important, the sides of the fish bulge
when seen from a top or side view. A little experience will give an idea
of how far matters have progressed. With fishes we have not all the guiding facts that help our own medicos to make their computations in
timing human births, but sometimes our guess is just as good!

Frequency
Frequent breeding does not seem to shorten the life nor
affect the final growth of either egg-layers or live-bearers.
Interference with Nature is more questionable.

Number of Young

Broods may be as few as 3 in number, or well over 200. A fair average for a grown fish to deliver is 40 to 50. Anything over 100 is considered unusual. Some species have fewer and larger young than others. As previously stated, while the size of the female greatly influences the number of young she delivers, it has no effect on the size of the babies. TWINS, attached belly-to-belly, are occasionally delivered. The usually die within weeks.

Saving the Young

With all prolific animals Nature seems to set up some barrier so they do not overrun the world. With live-bearing fishes in the aquarium, it is cannibalism on the part of parents. Aquarists can easily circumvent this tendency and save the babies.

First of all, the fewer fishes present at the time of delivery, the better. This includes the male also, his function having been completed weeks or months previously.

There are two general methods of saving the young. One is by providing them with hiding places, such as plant thickets, and the other is by the use of some mechanical contrivance which prevents the mother from getting at her babies.

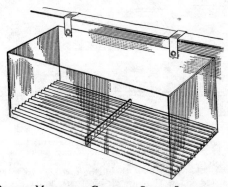

PLASTIC MATERNITY CAGE FOR SMALL LIVEBEARERS

Rods in bottom are spaced apart. Cage is suspended from aquarium side, and partially submerged. Fishes larger than Guppies should never be placed in small, suspended cages.

Many such mechanical devices have been developed for the preservation of newly-delivered baby fishes. They have their points of merit. The central idea, with all of them, is to confine the ripe female in a space where she can live and which provides a small opening (or openings) through which the young fall or swim, and through which they cannot well return.

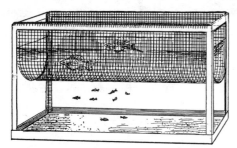

A simple scheme for saving the babies consists in using a single sheet of plastic screen suspended as shown from the long sides of an aquarium. The ends must fit snugly against the short sides. Special screen with openings twice as large as flyscreen is needed. In a 10-gallon tank this can be made suitable for livebearers that are too big for confinement in small traps.

V-shaped arrangements of sheets of glass in aquaria, with the bottom of the V slightly open, can be used in a large way for a number of ripe females at one time. Also a single sheet of sloping glass with the lower edge nearly against one side of the aquarium glass is another variation.

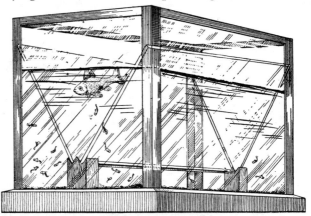

V-TRAP FOR SAVING YOUNG LIVE-BEARERS

This may be quite large, according to the size of the aquarium. A number of ripe females can be placed in it at the same time. Some wholesale breeders use this method. If prepared food is used, snails should be present to eat any surplus which falls through the slot. The water level should be low enough to allow the snails to reach the air at the side edges. They are air-breathers, and will suffocate if not able to reach the surface.

These various mechanical devices have their uses, especially if the aquarist is not in a position to place the expectant mother in a thickly planted tank. It will be found, however, that in well-equipped establishments, where the breeding of live-bearers is conducted on a large scale, traps are seldom used. Preference is given to the other method, utilizing thickets of plants as hiding places. The ideal aquarium for the purpose is an oblong one of from 3- to 8-gallon capacity, one-half of which is planted thickly across the narrow way with either *Sagittaria natans* or *subulata*. Loosely among the plants and at the surface should be some floating aquatics such as Riccia or *Utricularia minor*. Any other planting which provides a thicket is satisfactory, such, for instance, as masses of Anacharis, Myriophyllum or Nitella.

The planted side of the aquarium should be *towards the light*, as this is the natural direction for the young to take. The parent will not give chase among the plants, or will do so only feebly. The young sense their danger and are pretty cute at dodging.

There are several advantages to this plan of delivery. The female can be placed alone in the aquarium well in advance of expected appearance of young, thereby avoiding a certain amount of danger in handling her at a later time which might cause injury, and more probably, premature birth. In such an aquarium she can be well fed and kept in fine condition. With the aid of the open space she can easily be caught and removed after the completion of her duty to her species—and to her owner. By this schéme practically no young are lost and they grow well when left in the planted aquarium.

Shallow water seems best adapted to the needs of the young of the live-bearing species, although this is not an absolute requirement. From birth to 2 weeks old they seem safer in depths of 7 inches or less.

Premature Births   As has already been stated, the handling of a live-bearing female shortly prior to her time for delivery is liable to result in premature births, even with gentle care. Some kinds of fishes are more sensitive than others. Guppies are seldom affected, while Mollienisias are touchy. The invariable sign of a premature delivery is when the yolk-sac is not fully absorbed, and is to be seen attached to the belly of the baby. Such young are heavy, and unable to rise from the bottom without effort. Few of them survive. If the sac is small it is advisable to salt the water, one full teaspoon to the gallon.

Feeding Young Live-bearers   Young live-bearers remove from the aquarist one of his burdens. Being born a good size, it is not necessary to fuss about live microscopic food for them. They can take small sifted Daphnia or newly-hatched brine shrimp at once, or will do fairly well on finely powdered fish food of almost any kind. Manufacturers have grades especially for them, but this is only a matter of size. Any granular food can be pulverized for the purpose. Size of food can be increased as the babies grow. They like "Mikro" worms.

At a reasonably high temperature, say about 75 degrees, they should be fed from 2 to 4 times daily. Whether the food be prepared or living, there should be only enough of it to last a quarter hour. Excess prepared food fouls the water. Too many Daphnia reduce the oxygen content. Snails dispose of prepared food the fishes have not taken. For this reason *it is advisable to have plenty of them with young fishes of all kinds that are being raised on prepared foods.* As the fishes grow, some species will kill the snails. If there is evidence of this, the snails may as well be removed and *Corydoras* substituted.

Sometimes beginner aquarists write that their baby fishes have not grown appreciably in several months. This state of affairs is likely to end in permanently stunting them, even though better conditions are later provided. Some causes of retarded growth are: too small aquariums, too many fishes, too low temperature, too little food, too little live food, infrequent feeding. See paragraph on "Forcing Growth."

When May Young Be Placed with Adults? The answer to this question depends much on the size of the parents. Large parents of a given species do not have larger young than small parents, but they can swallow bigger fishes. The offspring of average parents are safe to place with the parents when the young have tripled their length, which should be in a month, with correct feeding. When placing *any* small fish in *any* aquarium, consider what the largest fish in that aquarium might be able to do to the little stranger. Can the big fish swallow the little fish?

Live-bearers seem to be quite impersonal as to their own particular young or the young of their own species. They are neither more nor less liable to eat them than the young of other parents or of other species. Their own appetites and the size of the proposed victim are the only considerations.

Generally speaking, the live-bearers will not eat young fishes if they have a good supply of choice live food for themselves. And, while generally speaking, it should be said that any fish introduced into an aquarium is apt to fare better if its hosts and future companions are in that mellow humor which is produced by having had a good meal, particularly if the new arrival happens to be small!

Keeping Species Separate As a matter of avoiding later confusion, it is best to keep the young of all similar species separate. This is particularly true of the live-bearers. Many of them not only look alike before maturity, but they are liable to breed much earlier than would be expected.

Hybridization between different species is not very likely to occur in an aquarium of mixed fishes, but undesired crosses are quite liable to happen between different color strains of the same species, such, for instance, as between red and blue Platies. This causes a degeneracy of pure types. When crosses are wanted, they should be deliberate.

Mollienisias In some respects the breeding of Mollienisias requires separate directions. Where required these will always be found under the individual headings comprising the genus.

Gambùsia áffinis hólbrooki   (GIRARD)
Pronounced Gam-bew'see-a aff'in-iss hol'brook-eye
MEANING OF NAME: *Gambusia,* worthless; *affinis,* related;
holbrooki, after J. E. Holbrook
Atlantic Coast States, Delaware to Florida   Length—males, 1½ in.; female, 2¼ in.
Western Location Map a28 to j26 and f21
Western form, *Gambusia affinis* (Baird and Girard), from b20 to f21 and o15

TO many aquarists, at least in the United States, *Gambusia affinis* represents the beginning of an epoch. It was our first live-bearer. The species was advertised by dealers as the eighth wonder of the world. All flocked with their $2 per pair to prove or disprove for themselves all claims for this strange fish. All placed them in with fancy lace-tail Goldfish. Soon the beautiful fins of the Goldfish were in shreds and the Gambusias were banished. But they were kept long enough to prove that they have their young born alive, and to demonstrate that they bred faster than purchasers could be found. This is not surprising, for in appearance they have no merit sufficient to offset the disadvantage of their destructive natures. Like other efficient fighters, they give no notice of attack.

G. affinis is a justly famed fish, for it has saved many human lives by eating mosquito larvae. It has been introduced into many parts of the world for this purpose, but its chief service to man has been in destroying the larvae of the mosquito which carries the germs of malarial and yellow fevers. In tropical countries in situations where the draining of mosquito ditches is impossible or too expensive, the little fish has been successfully brought into service. Its practical value is enhanced because it can live in good or bad water, and will stand a temperature range from 40 to 100 degrees. Success in building and maintaining the Panama Canal depended partly on the solution of the fever problem. *G. affinis* was and still is largely responsible for making Panama habitable to the white man.

There is much confusion in the minds of aquarists about the differences between the 2 common forms of *Gambusia* in our southern states. The worst error, and the hardest to eradicate, is the idea that the black-spotted Gambusias form a distinct species, *holbrooki. The black spotting has nothing whatsoever to do with separating the two forms!* The facts of the case are these: In the southern United States (excluding Texas for the moment), there are two forms of *Gambusia,* an eastern and a western, practically identical in color, form, size and habits. The eastern form *(holbrooki),* which is found in lowland streams of the eastern seaboard from Delaware to Florida and Alabama, has 8 rays in the dorsal fin and the third ray of the gonopodium shows a deep split when examined under the microscope. The western form *(affinis)* occurs in lowland streams from Alabama to southern Illinois and south in the Texas coastal region to Tampico, Mexico. It has only 7 rays in the dorsal fin and the microscopic split in the third ray of the gonopodium is absent. In Alabama the eastern and western forms meet and merge their distinctive features so that certain individuals from this area cannot be placed definitely as one or the other form. Hence they are not nowadays regarded as distinct species, the western one being known as *G. affinis* and the eastern one as a race of it, *G. affinis holbrooki.*

Both sexes of both *affinis* and *holbrooki* are ordinarily pale gray fishes, often with faint bluish metallic reflections. The dorsal and tail are usually marked with rows of tiny dark dots. The dots in the tail easily distinguish the plain females from female Guppies. Otherwise they look much alike.

The velvet black spotting or blotching which is prized in aquarium specimens may be present in either *affinis* or *holbrooki.* Dr. George Myers, who has collected *affinis* wild in North Carolina, says: "Schools of several hundred Gambusias were to be seen swimming in shallow water near shore. In every second or third school a single, or at most 2, black males were observed; they were very conspicuous among their pale brothers. The original collectors who sent Gambusias north used to catch out these colored 'freaks' with a dip net, pair them with any large females caught in the schools, and ship them as a different species, the so-called '*G. holbrooki.*' These black freaks seem in many cases to breed true, and at least some of our southern dealers seem to have developed strains which breed consistently. Wild black-blotched females are extremely rare, but in the course of man's selective breeding for black fish, a proportion of fairly dark females appear. So far as available data go, the black blotching of either sex occurs about as frequently in the western *affinis* as in the eastern *holbrooki*, but the black color, as can be seen from the foregoing, no more indicates specific difference than does the black color of the black Molly."

Neither of our illustrations includes a normal pale-colored male of either variety, since these are almost never shipped by the southern dealers. The first figure shows a normal female and a partially black-spotted male of the same form.

For breeding in the aquarium, it prefers a temperature of about 75 degrees. It conforms to the usual type of breeding described for "Live-bearers," but is one of the species which is particularly likely to eat its young if given the opportunity. Since they multiply with such tremendous rapidity when in the wild state, it must be that the young very quickly take themselves off to good hiding places. With plenty of natural food they soon develop to a size which is too large to be swallowed by the parents.

In the matter of food they are easily suited. While preferring animal substance, they will take any of the prepared articles.

The species is very seldom attacked by any kind of disease.

In some of the streams of southern and western Texas there are 3 or 4 other, very different species of *Gambusia*, at least one of which, the golden Gambusia *(G. nobilis)*, has found its way into aquariums.

Gambusia (either *affinis* or *holbrooki*)
Black-spotted male and female

Gambùsia punctàta POEY

Pronounced Gam-bew'see-a punk-tay'ta   *Popular name,* Blue Gambusia
MEANING OF NAME: *punctata,* dotted
Cuba Western Location Map m25 to m29 Length—male, 2 inches; female, 3 inches

THE writer hesitates to express his full admiration of this species, for it is a fish which must be seen in the right light in order to be appreciated, and at best its beauty is not of the showy sort. For that reason an enthusiastic description might easily lead the reader to disappointment through expecting too much. The beauty of the fish is quite simple. It consists almost entirely of a delicate suffusion of a rich light blue over a gray-to-olive body color. The blue is also in the lower part of the tail fin, the first ray of the anal, the gonopodium of the male, and is intensified about the head, reaching a point of actual brilliance in the violet-colored eye. This blue eye is unique among all the aquarium fishes known to the writer, the only one approaching it being that of *Cichlasoma cutteri,* which is blue, tinged with green. The dorsal is pale yellow, edged black. Rows of dark brown dots further adorn the male.

The illustration of the male might give the reader an incorrect idea as to the form of his tail fin. It happened to be photographed in movement. In reality it is shaped as shown on the female.

To see this fish properly the light must come from the direction of the observer and strike on the side of the fish. A dark background is best.

While this is a hardy live-bearer, the temperature on it should not drop below 68.

Breeding temperature, 75. Quite apt to eat young. Not prolific.

Considered a peaceful fish, but a correspondent says that in a community tank it chews the tail fins of other fishes.

Heterándria formòsa AGASSIZ

Pronounced Het'er-an"dree-a for-mo'sa   *Popular name,* Mosquito Fish
MEANING OF NAME: *Heterandria,* male different from female; *formosa,* comely
North Carolina—Florida; also locally in Louisiana   Male, ¾ inch; female, 1⅛ inches
Western Location Map c27 to i26

THIS tiny fish is unquestionably the smallest of the aquarium live-bearers. The male is of breeding size when only a half inch long, while the female is not much larger.

There seem to be 3 fishes bearing the popular name "Mosquito Fish," 2 of them (Guppy and Gambusia) because they are extensively used for the extermination of mosquitoes by eating their aquatic larvae. The name is also applied to the present subject, *Heterandria formosa,* possibly because the male is not much bigger than a large mosquito.

The coloring is not bright, but pleasant. Ground color, olive, with the rather clear, horizontal dark line. Vertical bars in the photograph are black. Below the long dark line the belly is bright white. An interesting touch of color is a red spot just above the black spot in the dorsal. The female has a slight dark mark in the anal fin, but as they are live-bearers, the sex is usually distinguished by the physiological formation of the males.

In breeding they are different from the usual type, inasmuch that a brood of young is not all delivered within a few hours, but over a period of a week to 10 days. Each day for that time the tiny mother will drop 2 or 3 young. Among plenty of floating plants they do not need to be removed from parents, but require smaller food than the young of larger live-bearers. Temperature, 55 to 85. Breeds at about 70 degrees.

The species in general is very active, a good little aquarium fish, and not expensive. In its native haunts it inhabits thick, matted growths of fine-leaved plants. It is our opinion that this diminutive species should be kept only among its own kind.

Pseùdoxíphophòrus bimaculàtus (HECKEL)

Pronounced Soo'do-ziff-o-fo"rus by-mac'you-lay"tus (Soo'do-zif-fof"o-rus is allowable)
MEANING OF NAME: *Pseudoxiphophorus,* false *Xiphophorus; bimaculatus,* with 2 spots
Central America   Length—male, 1¾ inches; female, 3½ inches
       Western Location Map p15 to s21

*A*LTHOUGH this species was commonly kept in the early days of exotic aquariums when anything that was a live-bearer was considered good, it is being gradually crowded out by more attractive and better-tempered fishes.

Our subject here is just a live-bearer with a rather savage nature. The female, twice as large as the male, usually vents her temper on him, with fatal results. Possibly she has more sense than most fishes and realizes the trouble he causes her. The young when delivered are about half an inch long, and grow rapidly. Temperature range, 70-85 degrees.

In color the fish is an olive-brown on the back, shading down to a yellow-white belly. There are flashes of metallic green about the head and along the back. Scales are edged black, and rather attractive. The 2 black dots for which the fish gets its specific name are not particularly conspicuous. They will be seen in the photograph just in back of the gill plate and at the base of the tail. Also the illustration gives a picture of a reduced female live-bearer that has just delivered her young.

Should have live food, but will take prepared ones.

This is a fish for any of those ardent fanciers who take pride in possessing a large number of species. Temperature range, 68-82 degrees.

Phallóceros caudimaculàtus (HENSEL)

Pronounced Fal-los'ser-os caw'dee-mac'you-lay"tus
MEANING OF NAME: *Phalloceros,* with horns on the gonopodium; *caudimaculatus,*
with spot on caudal peduncle   *Popular name,* Barrigudinyo
Also incorrectly known as *Girardinus reticulatus* and *Girardinus januarius*
S. E. Brazil   Length—male, 1¼ inches; female, 2¼ inches
Western Location Map U31 to V22

THERE are two recognized strains of this species, the plain and the spotted, the latter known as *reticulatus.* Our illustration is of the spotted variety, but serves for either.

Of the live-bearers this was one of the first introduced, and in Europe excited the same comment that *Gambusia affinis* did in the United States.

In the matter of color, the plain variety has little to boast of. The spotted strain is rather attractive. The background color of both is a greenish gray, shading lighter towards the belly, which is nearly white. There is a little green under the throat. Eye, pale green to gold. Good breeders and fairly hardy. It will be noticed that in this species the gonopodium turns sharply downward at the very end. An average temperature of 72 suits it very well. They have been known to withstand 55 degrees. Any food. Will not molest other fishes.

A yellow variety of this fish has erroneously been introduced as "Golden *Gambusia,*" or "Golden Leopard Fish." It is quite attractive.

Phallichthys amàtes MILLER

Pronounced Fal-lick'thiss a-mah'tees   *Popular name,* Merry Widow

MEANING OF NAME: *Phallichthys,* fish with a phallus or gonopodium; *amates,* after the locality where found (Los Amates)

Honduras   Western Location Map s23   Length, male 1 inch; female 2 inches

*H*ERE is an instance in which the fishes did not display all their markings at the time they were photographed, thus making necessary an amplified description. A black line runs through the eye, similar to that shown in the illustration of *P. isthmensis.* The male often shows as many as ten narrow, vertical dark lines on the sides. A faint dark line crosses the body from above the ventral fins to the base of the tail. Body, olive brown, shading to golden on the belly. Gill covers and chin are iridescent blue-green. The sides show a flush of this elusive color.

The really outstanding feature of the fish, at least to the aquarist, is the snappy dorsal fin of the male. Nearly always erect, it is marked with two arches, which, if brighter-hued, might be called a double rainbow. Both arches are dark, the outer one the more intense. This does not quite reach to the outer edge, as the photograph would seem to indicate, for the fin is tipped with a hair-line edge of enamel white. They are free breeders.

Lively habits, plus the mourning edge on the dorsal fin, prompted Mr. F.H. Stoye to suggest "Merry Widow" as a good popular name for the fish. As *Gymnocorymbus ternetzi,* known as the "Black Tetra," has also been called the "Merry Widow," we suggest the avoidance of confusion by applying the name only to *P. amates.* Breeds at about 76 degrees.

A slightly smaller fish, *P. pitteri* (Meek), earlier imported from Costa Rica and Panama, is very similar, and may prove to be identical.

Phallichthys isthménsis (REGAN)

Pronounced Fal-lick'thiss isth-men'sis   Also known as *Phallichthys pittieri*

MEANING OF NAME: *Phallichthys*, fish with a phallus, or gonopodium;
isthmensis, isthmus (of Panama; really Costa Rica)

Costa Rica Western Location Map w25 Length—Male, 1½ inches; female, 2½ inches

HILE this agreeable live-bearer has no marked or outstanding characteristics which at once reveal its identity, a closer look will show a combination of points which make it readily recognized. It is interesting to see how far careful amateur observation can go in the absence of exact measurements and the records of tooth, scale and fin counts of ichthyologists. Looking at the plate, we see that the extremely long gonopodium reaches almost to the tail fin. It is turned slightly downwards at the end. The first ray of the dorsal fin is almost at the highest point of the body. The dorsal of the female is nearly as large as the male's. There is a black line running through the eye and extending just below it, giving the effect of a clown's make-up. An observer of the fish in life would see that the dorsal fin is edged orange with another line of black just inside the orange; that the anal fin of the female is yellow at the rear edge; that the ventrals of both sexes are edged pale blue; that the tail fin is clear; that the scales are edged black. Enough points for a reasonably good identification of *Phallichthys isthmensis*.

A moderately fertile live-bearer, preferring a temperature range between 70 and 80 degrees. Easily fed and is a satisfactory fish in the company of other species.

Pœcilistes pleurospilus   (GUENTHER)

Pronounced Pee'sil-iss"tees plu'row-spy"lus

MEANING OF NAME: *Poecilistes,* like Poecilia; *pleurospilus,* spotted sides

Also known as *Poeciliopsis pleurospilus*

Central America   Length—male, 1½ inches; female, 2 inches

Western Location Map p15 to s20

SIX or seven dark spots evenly spaced along the sides where they interrupt a thin line of highlight, give this attractive live-bearer its character. The body is in color what might be called "fish olive," while the fins have a faint tinge of brown. In the tail fin will be observed two delicately dark vertical bars which eluded our camera.

Not a well-known live-bearing species, but one that is well established and likely to remain with us, for in addition to being something out of the ordinary in appearance, it is also a fairly good breeder. A peaceful, desirable fish. Temperature, 70-84 degrees.

There are several similar species of *Poecilistes* in Central America, some of which may have been imported as aquarium fishes.

Girardìnus metállicus POEY

Pronounced Jir'ar-dy"nus me-tal'li-cus

MEANING OF NAME: *Girardinus,* after the French-Amercian ichthyologist, Charles Girard; *metallicus,* metallic

Cuba   Western Location Map m25   Length—male, 2 inches; female, 3 inches

WHILE this fish is possessed of a fairly bright metallic sheen, it is not so outstanding that one would expect the characteristic to be incorporated in the name of the species. About 15 back-slanting silvery bars cross the sides, the intervening spaces being darker. Small, greenish dots are sprinkled under the eyes and on the gill plates. The dorsal fin in both sexes displays a dark dot where the base joins the body. The sex organ of the male is double-pointed and the longer point is slightly hooked. If the tail fin of the female in the illustration appears to be double-pointed, this is due to its curved position.

An active, hardy species. Eats anything, and succeeds when confined in a small aquarium. They are not very likely to eat their own young, especially if well fed.

In a certain strain of the species, found in the Hongolosongo River (Cuba), a proportion of black or nearly black males are found. In general, a satisfactory fish, requiring a temperature of between 68 and 84 degrees.

Quintàna atrizòna HUBBS

Pronounced Quin-tay'na at'ri-zo"na   *Popular name,* Quintana

MEANING OF NAME: *Quintana,* pertaining to the fifth (referring to the peculiar fifth
ray of the gonopodium); *atrizona,* divided into zones (by the black bars)

Cuba and Isle of Pines   Length—male, 1 inch; female, 1¾ inches

Western Location Map m25 to m31; between m and n, 25 and 26

A PLEASING little live-bearer of comparatively recent introduction. In general color it is olive. The dark bars shown in the illustration are dark gray to black. The dorsal is rather attractive, the centre being lemon color, while the front and back edges are dark. The prettiest feature, however, is a pleasing pale metallic blue in the ventrals and particularly in the anal fin of the female. She is considerably larger than the male. Somewhat the same sort of blue sometimes flashes from the gill covers. The upper part of the eye is golden.

These fish are pleasingly active in the aquarium when kept at a temperature of about 73-80 degrees. On the average they have about 20 young at a delivery. They are easily raised and make excellent growth if kept at a temperature of 75 degrees or higher, and given alternating meals of live and prepared foods. It is possible to mature them to breeding size in 16 weeks. To accomplish this the same thing is necessary that we find with most of our young fishes. That is, they ought to have frequent, small meals—several a day.

The species lives at peace with other fishes.

Poecília vivípara BLOCH AND SCHNEIDER
Pronounced Pee-sill'e-a vi-vip'a-ra
MEANING OF NAME: *Poecilia*, a fish with reticulated markings, *vivipara*, live-bearing
E. South America, Porto Rico, Leeward Islands Length—male, 1½ in.; female 2¾ in.
Western Location Map z21 to B26 to J38 to Y28

*A*S with so many of the live-bearing species, the male is comically smaller than the female, but what he lacks in size he makes up with bristling activity and a color superiority.

This is not, however, one of the brilliant species, even with the male. His dorsal fin is attractively colored, being a variable orange shade, darkest at the base. It has two dark, arching bands, one of them at the outer edge of the fin. The spot shown on the side of the body is dark with a golden border at the rear. A dark patch (not a gravid spot) appears on the belly just above the ventral fins. This is more prominent in the female. The general body color is silver and olive, with a bluish over-tone. Different strains of the species vary considerably, especially in the richness of the dorsal tints of the male, and with some there is a distinct brassiness about the throat.

A very satisfactory live-bearer, and a peaceful one, easily fed and managed. Temperature range, 68-82 degrees.

Lìmia caudofasciàta   REGAN

Pronounced Lim'ee-a caw'do-fas'see-ay"ta   *Popular name,* Blue Poecilia

MEANING OF NAME: *Limia,* mud, referring to mud-eating habit of *Limia vittata; caudofasciata,* banded tail, referring to bars near tail fin

Incorrectly, *Limia arnoldi*

Jamaica   Length—male, 1¾ inches; female, 2½ inches

Western Location Map o and p29 and 30

A FISH flecked with blue fire. The vertical small highlights shown in the illustration are spangles of sapphire. These no doubt give the fish its popular name, for there is no other blue coloration. The general background is olive, but with sufficient dark markings along the sides to make the metallic scales even more vivid by contrast. Fins in the female are clear, except for a faint tinge of orange at the base of the dorsal. In the male this is stronger, and has a black spot in the centre of the orange, next to the body. Tail fin in male, orange shading to clear. The male also has a somewhat golden belly. Both sexes have golden eyes.

Breeders find the fish rather keen on eating its young. Care should be taken to protect the babies, for this is a species well worth cultivating. A properly lighted aquarium containing a number of *L. caudofasciata* is beautiful. They should be seen by reflected light, as described for other species.

Live-bearers. Breeding temperature, 75 degrees.

Lìmia melànogaster (GUENTHER)

Pronounced Lim'ee-a mel-lay"no-gas'ter　　　　Formerly known as *Limia tricolor*

MEANING OF NAME: *melanogaster*, with black abdomen, referring to the large "pregnant spot" of the female

Jamaica　　　　Length—female, 2½ inches; male, 2 inches

Western Location Map, just above p30

SOME question exists as to whether this is the same species as the foregoing, *L. caudofasciata*. Certainly to the eye of the aquarist there are distinct differences. The most obvious one is the very large and very clear gravid spot near the vent of *L. melanogaster*. The spot in *L. caudofasciata* barely shows. Otherwise the markings are similar. *L. melanogaster* we observe to be of a more lively disposition.

The photographs of the two species might lead the reader to expect them to be of different sizes. They are not. This is due to the difference in the specimens themselves.

The species when crossed with *Limia nigrofasciata* produces an interesting hybrid, shown under the heading "Hybridizing."

The writer has not found them to be very durable.

Lìmia nìgrofasciàta	REGAN
Pronounced Lim'ee-a ny'grow-fas'see-ay"ta
MEANING OF NAME: *nigrofasciata,* black banded	*Popular name,* Hunchback Limia
Haiti		Western Location Map n to o33 to 34		Length, 2 inches

A NUMBER of fishes appreciably change shape with age, but with this species it is very marked in the male. As he reaches towards his full size, the forward part of his back humps in a very pronounced degree. This certainly does not improve the appearance of the fish, but here the law of compensation again comes into evidence, for while the back acquires a sort of old-man's-hump, the dorsal fin develops in size until it is a thing to be proud of, and as he spreads it roundly in courting the female, he is quite a dandy.

The outer half of the dorsal is black, while the base is slightly yellow. Tail fin and belly, yellow in male; lighter in female.

About 10 dark bars on the body account for the specific name. The body is gray and somewhat translucent, so that the spine can be seen.

This fish, a live-bearer, is hardy and easily bred at a temperature of about 72 to 75.

As has been stated, on previous page, the species has been crossed with *Limia melanogaster,* giving very interesting and attractive hybrids.

Lìmia vittàta (GUICHENOT)

Pronounced Lim'ee-a vy-tay'ta   *Popular name,* Cuban Limia

MEANING OF NAME: *vittata,* with a band

Cuba Western Location Map m25 to n30 Length—male, 2½ inches; female, 3¾ inches

A RATHER robust species, as the photograph indicates. Often not brightly colored in any respect, but the scales are delicately overcast with a pleasing light blue. Body color, olive-brown. In the female this is overlaid with about 4 dark dotted lines, going lengthwise, while the male has rather irregular, dark, broken vertical bars. These are variable, and may be absent. Dorsal and tail fins in both sexes are slightly yellow, and in some examples brilliantly so. In the male both these fins are dotted, but in the female the tail fin is clear.

The light dots on the female are photographic high lights, and do not represent metallic scales. Eye, silver.

Not a showy fish, but a friendly one. The rather generous dorsal of the male is a feature.

Breeds freely at about 74 degrees. Easily cared for.

One of these females (at the Shedd Aquarium in Chicago) holds the known record for all species for the greatest number of young delivered in a single litter—242!

Móllienísia velífera REGAN

Pronounced Moll'le-en-iss"ee-a vel-if'era   *Popular name,* Yucatan Sailfin

MEANING OF NAME: *Mollienisia,* named for M. Mollien; *velifera,* sail bearer

Yucatan   Western Location Map o20 to n22   Length, 5 inches

ALTHOUGH *velifera* is not often to be had, aquarists generally consider it to be the aristocrat of the Mollienisias. This is on account of its enormous dorsal fin, which it spreads frequently but not constantly. The coloring is about the same as *latipinna,* but with a little more gold overcast, and a brighter brassy belly. A few blacks have been seen. Ichthyologists recognize three characteristics of its dorsal fin. It is set very far forward and the numerous small light spots on it are rounded, and encircled by dark borders. The fin has about 18 rays, whereas *latipinna* has about 14. Otherwise the comments following on *latipinna* also apply to this species, except that the young are larger when born (½ inch) and that the parents are more liable to eat them. Broods may run as high as 100.

A peculiar fact, also noted elsewhere, is that very few aquarium-bred *latipinnas* develop sail-fins, whereas with *velifera* the dorsal is always big, but not always as gorgeous as the one here photographed by Dr. Carl L. Hubbs, the leading authority on Mollienisias.

Móllienísia látipínna LE SUEUR

Pronounced Moll'le-en-iss"ee-a lat'i-pin"na   *Popular names,* Sail-fin or Mollie

MEANING OF NAME: *latipinna,* broad-fin

Coast of North Carolina to Florida; Gulf Coast and N. E. Mexico   Length, 3¾ inches

Western Location Map c27 to j26, h20 and o15

THIS is the usual "Mollie" of commerce. Coming from a considerable geographic range, it varies correspondingly in appearance,
especially in that point of importance—the dorsal fin. This varies so
greatly that it may class the individual either as a super-fish or as simply
"another Mollie." In a highly developed specimen, his resplendent dorsal
fin is truly a crown of glory. To witness this "sail" fully exhibited in its
royal splendor is to see something unforgettable — at least to an appre-
ciative fish fancier or ichthyologist. Naturally his best display is put on
either in a sham battle with another male (they seldom come to blows),
or before what might be called his lady of the moment. With all sails
set he comes alongside her with insinuating motions, and then takes a
position across her path as if, with a flurry of quivering fins, to prevent
her escape. The colors displayed in these rapid and tense actions do

not seem to be produced by excitement. It is merely an unfolding of the hidden tints which are always present but displayed only on occasions. The dorsal shows a gentle blue iridescence, but it is in the tail fin that the real color display takes place. The upper and lower thirds become a flashing, light metallic blue, while the centre is a beautiful golden yellow. Yellow also covers the forward part of the belly.

. The body of the fish is olive, with 5 narrow brown stripes, separated by rows of a lighter, sawtooth pattern.

Mollienisias require more care in breeding than most of the live-bearing species, but that extra attention bears fruit. They must have plenty of room, a temperature close to 78 degrees and plenty of the right kind of food. Mildly alkaline or slightly salted water is desirable. By nature largely vegetarian and, being active, it eats often, especially in the matter of nibbling at algae, which it does almost constantly. For this reason alone the fish should be in a large, well-lighted aquarium, which is conducive to the growth of algae. If there is insufficient of this growth for the purpose, some should be scraped from other aquariums. If this is impossible, then they ought to frequently have a little chopped boiled spinach, or finely chopped crisp lettuce. Ground shrimp or boiled foods containing shrimp and spinach in addition to a cereal, form good staple diets. Live Daphnia, or mosquito larvae should be given frequently but not constantly. Feeding 4 to 6 times in 24 hours is desirable, provided each meal is entirely consumed within 10 minutes. This frequent feeding is important, both to breeding stock and the growing young. Prepared food should be in quite small sizes.

At the first sign that a female is ripening, she should be removed to a well-planted delivery tank of about 10 or more gallons capacity. Gravid females of all Mollienisias are adversely affected by handling, and the results are reflected in the young being born dead or defective in some respect, usually too heavy to leave the bottom. In fact, Mollienisias in general and M. latipinna in particular, had best be handled and moved from one aquarium to another as little as possible. If things are going well with them, a good motto is "Let good enough alone." If only a single pair is being bred, it is preferable to keep the expectant female where she is and remove the male as a matter of precaution, although in the majority of cases, M. latipinna does not eat its young.

No female Mollienisia should ever be placed in a small breeding trap. They need room and plenty of greens. All "Mollies" fail if crowded.

The one puzzle no one has so far been able to overcome is the fact that in aquariums it is seldom possible to produce Sail-fin young from Sail-fin stock. For one thing, it requires two years' growth.

Móllienísia látipunctàta (MEEK)
Pronounced Moll'le-en-iss"ee-a lat'i-punk-tay"ta
MEANING OF NAME: *latipunctata,* broad-spotted
Mexico   Western Location Map n14   Length, 2½ inches

ONE of the smaller, newly introduced species of *Mollienisia.* Males may be recognized by the black vertical bars on the mid-sides, and by the rows of orange spots along the lower sides of the body. The rather large dorsal and tail fins are strongly sprinkled with small, irregularly placed black dots. Females always show a line of black spots along the sides. The young are few, but are large at birth.

Mollienisia formosa

We give this name a heading only because for years it has been extensively listed in books and commercial catalogs. In reality it is a natural cross between *M. latipinna* and *M. sphenops,* and is a composite of both parents, being intermediate in the number of rays in the fins, and in the position of the dorsal fin. This fish has received worldwide magazine and newspaper publicity because in certain large areas where it is very abundant it seems to defy the laws of inheritance, maintaining itself as a race of females that have none of their own kind of males with which to mate. They mate with either *M. sphenops* or *M. latipinna,* producing only female hybrids similar to themselves.

(There has been a proposal on the part of some ichthyologists to spell the generic name with two e's rather than three i's (*Mollienesia*). The Editor is not sure the change is justified, and we retain the old spelling for the present.)

Xiphophòrus species
Erroneously called X. *montezumae*
Mexico   Length, exclusive of tail spike—female, 2¼ in.; male, 1¾ in.
Western Location Map n14

*X*IPHOPHORUS MONTEZUMAE seems to be elusive. First named in 1900 by Jordan and Snyder, it has never yet been imported (up to 1956). In the 1920's, a large, yellow-red fish (probably a hybrid) was popularly known as "*montezumae*". Some time later, Drs. Hubbs and Gordon identified the fish pictured above as the true *montezumae*. With its gray-green color and short sword, it is not too attractive. Our Editor, Dr. Myers, long doubted this identification, for the original preserved type specimens of *montezumae* at Stanford University represent a large species with a long sword. After examining these original specimens (in 1956) Drs. Gordon and Rosen justify Dr. Myers' doubt. The fish we portray is not *montezumae* but an unnamed species which we trust Drs. Gordon and Rosen will soon name.

The species, considered by itself, is not without a quiet sort of attractiveness. An interesting novelty for the ambitious aquarist. Temperature, about 70 to 80 degrees.

There are also other forms (species and subspecies) of Swordtails, most of which have been imported for genetic research by Dr. Myron Gordon, but are not yet common in the aquarium trade. Most of them are not as striking as the ones we include.

COLOR PLATE PAGE 574

"Orange Tail" variety of *Mollienisia sphenops*
(CUVIER AND VALENCIENNES)

*M*OLLIENISIA SPHENOPS is the most widely distributed species of the genus, so it is not surprising that it is also the most variable as to size and color, and, to some extent in disposition.

Although scattered members of the species are black, some have a strong orange crescent at the end of the tail fin, and some have beautiful dorsal fins as shown on "Liberties." None of these colors, nor their variations or combinations, has much bearing on the identification of the species. Even the ordinary color, an olive gray with darker markings, means little. The aquarist's usual problem is to tell *sphenops* from *latipinna*. Fortunately this is not difficult. In *latipinna* the first ray of the dorsal fin starts in *front* of the highest point of the back. With *sphenops* it starts *in back* of the hump. The males are the more easily classified.

Mollienisias are particularly subject to injury in shipment, resulting in Mouth Fungus, "Ich" and "Shimmies." Early salt baths are effective.

COLOR PLATE PAGE 574

"Liberty" variety of *Móllienísia sphènops*
Pronounced Moll'le-en-iss"ee-a sfee'nops
MEANING OF NAME: *Mollienisia* for M. Mollen; *sphenops*, wedge-face
Gulf Coast of Texas to Venezuela   Length, 2 to 4 inches
Western Location Map k13 to w31, w12 to y4

COMING unheralded from Yucatan and imported by Wm. A. Sternke to OpaLocka, Florida, in 1935, this color variety of *M. sphenops* created quite a stir, and was soon widely distributed, as it proved to be a good breeder. The fish turned out to have so much exuberance (to put it politely) that is became something of a pest in chasing other fishes. This caused its popularity to wane, and possibly the strain lost some of its intense coloring through inter-breeding with other varieties of *M. sphenops,* which could readily be expected. At any rate, at the present writing it is unusual to secure specimens showing the original bright coloring.

Kept by themselves in a large aquarium they make a lively living picture. As they are jumpers their tanks should be covered with either screen or glass. Temperature range, 68-80 degrees.

Two added observations on all Mollienisias: In a tank of mixed species they are usually first to die because they suffer from crowding and a lack of their special feeding requirements.

COLOR PLATE PAGE 575

Black Mollienisias or Midnight Mollies
(Not *M. sphenops*)

*A*LL black Mollienisias were originally line-bred from rare natural black "sports" or freaks. These occur mostly among *latipinna*, sometimes *sphenops*, rarely *velifera*. The magnificent pair shown here, judging by the position and form of the dorsal fin of the male, is probably a cross between *velifera* and *latipinna*. The color tips of the fins are usually narrower and more yellow than displayed by the above grand specimen.

Blacks make advantageous contrasts with brighter-hued aquarium fishes.

When young from black sailfin mollies are born, some are light and some dark. Most become light in a few weeks, and when about an inch long they begin spotting black. Some become black in 6 months, some in 2 years, and some, never. It is a common belief that once they become black, they grow very little more. One of our biggest breeders of blacks does not consider this to be true.

Through persistent selective breeding a strain has been developed which is born black and remains so. These are called "Permablacks," and were placed on the market commercially in 1936.

COLOR PLATE PAGE 571

Lebístes retículàtus (PETERS)

Pronounced Le-biss"tees re-tik'you-lay"tus *Popular names,* Guppy and Rainbow Fish

MEANING OF NAME: *Lebistes,* probably from *Lebias* (=*Cyprinodon*), and *istion,* a sail; *reticulatus,* net marked, or mottled

Also known as *Girardinus reticulatus, Girardinus guppyi* and *Poecilia reticulata*

Trinidad, Guiana and Venezuela   Length—male, 1⅛ inches; female, 2¼ inches

Western Location Map x19 to A24

Artificially introduced into many other locations

"ᴍISSIONARY FISH" would be a fitting name for this little beauty, for it far exceeds any other species in the number of convert aquarists it has made. And many of these converts who branched out and became aquarists in a big way still keep Guppies, and still feel that, with their infinite variety of colors, they are the most interesting of all aquarium fishes. Each male is as individual as a thumbprint.

Besides its beauty the Guppy has other great merits. Scarcely any other fish combines so many cardinal points in such degree. It is a live-bearer, the most popular type of fish. It is an extremely fertile as well as a dependable breeder. It is unusually active. It will thrive in close confinement. It can stand foul water. It has an extreme temperature range of 40 degrees, from 60 to 100. It will take any kind of food. It does not fight. It is not timid. It matures rapidly, an important point for those aquarists breeding for special points. It is subject to few diseases. It can be had everywhere at prices available to everybody.

The activity of the male is extraordinary. Whether flashing about in pure joy of living, or paying court to a female, he is ever the embodiment of intensity. He might well be termed "the playboy˙of the aquarium."

The specimens chosen for use in our color plate were selected with the idea of illustrating certain color features. Five of these color standards are shown. The fish just below the head of the female displays two of them. He has the "Peacock" or "Lace" design in the tail. The fish in the lower left corner also embodies two definite points. First it is a "Chain Guppy." This refers to the irregular dark line from the head through the body. The eye in the dorsal also makes it a "Birdeye Guppy."

The large central figure, of course, is a "loaded" female. The gentleman craftily approaching from the rear is in typical position for action, with his gonopodium brought forward for an instant thrust.

In highly developed stocks some females appear not only showing traces of color in the tail fin, but also shiny highlights in it, as indicated in the single illustration. It is believed, but not certain, that such females throw youngsters of superior colors. Any color in female adds value to a show pair.

VERY RIPE FEMALE WITH HIGHLIGHTS IN TAIL FIN.

The Long-finned Guppies

The once closely-held remarkable strain of long-finned Guppies developed by the late Dr. Abbs, of New York, became scattered after his sudden death in about 1940, but many beautiful strains are now fairly well fixed, especially by Paul Hahnel in New York, Dr. John J. Rutkowski and Lawrence Konig, of New Jersey, and Wm. A. Sternke of Florida.

With the Lyretail, Swordtail and Veiltail types it is not uncommon for the tail fin to be longer than the body. Dorsal in proportion. No fancy breed can long be maintained without tireless vigilance in quickly discarding imperfect males, and in the early isolation of virgin line-bred females.

Maturity takes place very early, and a female once fertilized by an inferior male is "ruined" as a select breeder until she had dropped all his young—a matter of some 6 months—without attention from another male. Her previous mis-alliance then has no bad effects on offspring by a later and better mate. Perhaps the surest way of separating the sexes

VEILTAIL   LYRETAIL

is to place them singly in jars at one month. In selecting individuals from a large number we have found it easiest to place them all in about an inch of water in a shallow basin, lifting out each with the bowl of a tablespoon.

Breeding all sorts of animals for points, whether done on scientific Mendelian principles, or by "rule of thumb," involves the continual mating of the best close relatives. Unrelated breeders, of just as high grade, will not give as good results. As before stated regarding fishes, this can be carried on for generations without apparent physical deterioration, but breeders having both quality and good size should be chosen.

Excessive fin development does not occur in the young. Half-grown males of promise are best to use as breeders. The act of fertilizing requires more agility than that commonly possessed by fin-laden males. Besides, Guppies are old at two years.

We do not agree with those who theorize that color inheritance is carried only through the male line. According to sound principles the female, showing little or no colors, still transmits the influence of her ancestry.

At several points we have suggested that certain fishes appear to best advantage with the light striking directly on the side we see. That is, from the back of the observer toward the tank. This is especially true of male Guppies. With most aquariums the light comes from the wrong direction for that, but it is a rewarding effort to even temporarily place them in a viewing jar with the sun playing on them.

The Guppy seems to be the only exotic fish with enough variety of fixable points to establish it as a basis for fish fanciers. Guppy societies exist, having set standards for judging points to be used in shows.

Most of their diseases yield to the "progressive salt treatment" (see index). This may be carried far, as they can easily stand enough salt to kill most external enemies (and other fishes). The fatal "Hollowbelly" can usually be avoided by feeding several times daily on varying foods live, fresh and prepared. A good average temperature for Guppies, 70 to 88. They are apt to worry snails to death by nipping at them.

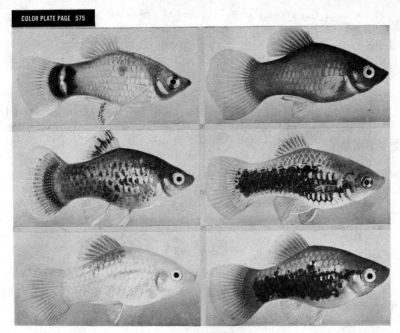

COLOR PLATE PAGE 575

Blue — Variegated — Golden   Red — Black — Berlin
Some Color Varieties of Platy Fish

Xíphophòrus maculatus (GUENTHER)
(Formerly *Platypoecilus maculatus*)
Pronounced Zi'fo-fo"rus mac'you-lay"tus (Zi-fof' o-rus is also correct)
MEANING OF NAME: *Xiphophorus*, sword-carrier *maculatus*, spotted
Popular names, Moonfish, Platy

Rio Papaloapan, S. Mexico   Length—male, 1½ inches; female, 2 inches
Western Location Map q16

*B*EYOND doubt, the general awakening of public interest in exotic aquarium fishes is due in large measure to the outstanding characteristics of a few species. The Platy Fish is one of the true early leaders, and one, through its many good points, that has retained favor while others have come and gone. The platy, in addition to being one of the most attractive and generally satisfactory fishes in its own right, has contributed to the aquarium a most interesting assortment of hybrids. It may be safely stated that no other fish has made possible such elaborate studies in the inheritance of characteristics. This valuable quality, however, is beginning to overwhelm us with complications and many finely-drawn distinctions. It is with that thought in mind that the writer here intends touching only on the straight Platy and its well-recognized variations.

The reason the species is known as "Moonfish" is because in many of the specimens first imported, there was a dark, moon-shaped mark at the base of the tail. This, however, proved to be one of the most variable points in the fish, and few are now found having a true moon.

BLUE PLATY

"Blue" embraces quite a range of shades in the Platy. Most of the wild stock, it has often been observed, has a tendency towards a blue or green gloss. This has been brought out in cultivated stock, and in the latest development nothing but blue appears. When lifted in the net, this fish is a distinct indigo color. Such specimens usually have no red in the dorsal fin. In the writer's opinion, this is the most beautiful type of blue Platy, especially when it possesses a true crescent in the tail, such as is shown in the illustration. Some specimens are deeper in blue than pictured here.

RED PLATY

For long after a deep red strain was brought into existence, it was peppered or stippled with the same kind of black dots that characterize the wild Platies. These marks have now b⌐en bred out and we have a modern strain of pure blood-reds, such as in the specimen used for our illustration. It is indeed a beautiful fish and has been bred in immense quantities in an effort to keep up with the demand. The color becomes deeper with age, usually ending in a mahogany red. For some reason the blood-reds are not quite as hardy as the others, nor as long-lived. It has been found that they do best in slightly acid water, and that they find aeration welcome.

BLACK PLATY

A broad black stripe extends along the body of this well-known variety. The remaining parts, above and below, are neutral shades, tending towards green or yellow. A handsome strain has come into existence which is nearly all black, except for the fins, which retain the blue-white front rays on the ventral and anal fins and the lower part of the tail, and which in this variety stand out in strong contrast with the black of the body. These ornamental white rays, prominent in the original stock, have persisted through most of the cultivated strains.

GOLDEN PLATY

Some years ago a European aquarist discovered a "sport" among his Platies, and from this break has been developed a popular line known as "golden." The shade is a rich yellow, scarcely deep enough to be

COLOR PLATE PAGE 572

"WAGTAIL" PLATY

called gold, yet better than our illustration, which is a little weak. The fish is somewhat translucent. They all have red dorsal fins and some, like our illustration, have red saddles on the back. A great difference of opinion exists as to whether this should be present in the variety, but as there is no recognized body of fish fanciers to settle this purely fanciers' problem, it will have to remain a matter of choice.

WAGTAIL PLATY

Among the many interesting Platy crosses developed by the famous geneticist, Dr. Myron Gordon, is the one he christened "Wagtail." Contrasting with a lighter body (either golden or red as illustrated) the blackish fins are conspicuous, especially while they are in motion, no doubt giving rise to the popular name. The strain has continued to breed fairly true, and is popular wherever exotic aquarium fishes are kept.

PLATY CROSS-BREEDS

The definitely established color strains which have been described have been crossed to make sub-varieties. An obvious instance of this is the figure in the color plate at the lower right, plainly a combination of the two types above it, and a pretty one, too, if the red remains pure, which it often fails to do.

The Variegated Platy at the left centre presents a sparkling array of rich colors. This is a mixture of several strains, the result being a beautiful fish.

The Spotted Platy, illustrated herewith, an interesting black-and-white

SPOTTED PLATY

fish, has an individuality worthy of notice. It is rather uncommon.

Fishes with markings like these, and also with smaller specks, or stipplings, are among the most common wild types.

BREEDING PLATIES

It should be remembered that all color strains or varieties of the species *Xiphophorus maculatus* are still the same species, and that they themselves in breeding pay no attention whatever to the colors of their mates. In practical application this means that if the aquarist is interested in maintaining pure strains he should keep all breeders of each variety in aquariums containing only their own kind.

Platies are bred very much the same as Guppies, except that they are a little less likely to eat their young. Also they do not take very kindly to the breeding trap, but should be placed in thickly planted aquaria and fed liberally when young are expected. They have a temperature range from 65 to 90, but do best at about 74 degrees. They are among those fishes that like to pick at algae, and it should be supplied them if possible. Platies drop their young early in the morning, and are through by 9 a.m. (Standard time). They are all good community tank fishes.

COLOR PLATE PAGE 572

Xiphophòrus variatus (MEEK)
(Formerly *Platypoecilus variatus*)
Pronounced Zi'fo-fo"rus vay'ree-ay"tus
MEANING OF NAME: *variatus,* varied or variable   *Popular name,* Variatus
Rio Panuco to Rio Cazones, E. Mexico   Length, 2 inches
Western Location Map m13 to n14

THE specific name of this fish, *variatus,* is surely appropriate. In coloration it is one of the most variable of aquarium fishes. For this reason it offers aquarists interesting problems in fixing colors.

There are two principal color strains—one with yellowish sides, brilliant canary-yellow dorsal and deep yellow-to-reddish tail. The other has considerable blue on the body, yellow in the dorsal and a deep red tail fin. They are respectively referred to as "yellows" and "blues." All imaginable intermediate variations occur. Among the later developments are solid reds, probably hybrids with red *X. maculatus.* Some have a large deep blue dot at the base of the tail fin. The males carry the colors, which begin to show at about 4 months, and are fully developed in a year. All the females are like the centre fish in the illustration.

This species is quite hardy and for short periods can stand a temperature as low as 50 degrees. It is a prolific live-bearer. If well fed with live Daphnia the parents are not likely to eat their young.

COLOR PLATE PAGE 573

Xiphophòrus hélleri   HECKEL

Pronounced Zi'fo-fo"rus hel'lereye (Zi-fof"o-rus also correct)
MEANING OF NAME: *Xiphophorus,* sword-carrier;
helleri, after the collector, Carl Heller
Popular names, Swordtail and Helleri

Eastern Mexico   Length, exclusive of tail spike, 2¾ inches
Western Location Map q16 to s21

(C) NE of the most important of aquarium fishes. Its striking appearance, interesting habits and lively ways have made many an aquarium convert of those who saw it by chance. Then its variable colors,
combined with the fact that it is a good breeder, have made it useful in
studying certain laws of inheritance. We have been able to create new
strains and new hybrids of great beauty.

The original imported stock, selling at the then fancy price of 10
dollars per pair, was strongly overcast with iridescent green and had
metallic green in the tail spike. The saw-tooth line along the centre of
the body was red and distinctly formed. The tail spikes were straight
and long. Only a small proportion of the stock now available has these
original characteristics in full measure. That variable quality which has
made the Swordtail a good subject for experimentation has also made it

difficult as to stability, so that clearly-drawn lines in varieties for purposes of competition in aquarium shows are hard, if not impossible, to maintain.

The principal color classifications are green body with green spike (called Green), green body with orange spike (called Orange), and a translucent yellow-brown fish with black-edged scales and a yellowish spike (called Golden). A sub-division of this latter class with an orange-red spike is now being developed.

In addition to the described main color divisions, there are markings to consider. One is a black crescent at the tail base and the other is a pair of separated dots similarly located. Dr. Myron Gordon, who has made a special study of the species, finds wild specimens comparable to all of the described variations except the Golden. In nearly all specimens, of whatever strains or crossings, the black edging of the spike remains, particularly the lower one. The Golden is an exception.

Our color plate shows the Orange variety, in which the reddish stripe along the side is broader and less clear-cut than in the original imported Green stock. Then there is a red hybrid with black-edged fins, called the "Tuxedo," as well as an albino with pink eyes. An odd but not very attractive variation is a red with red eyes. Care for any of these variants is the same as for the pure species, but they are liable to be less fertile.

The several Swordtails, in addition to being showy, are good aquarium fishes, but a few special characteristics should be remembered. They are wonderful jumpers, especially the males. Males are apt to bully one another, so it is best policy to have but one male in an aquarium. Like Mollienisias, they enjoy eating algae. It should be furnished them, if possible, even if it has to be scraped off another tank. In its absence a little finely chopped lettuce or boiled spinach is desirable. It is a species that feels the effect of a single chilling for a long time and may never recover from the "Shimmies" resulting from that cause. They should have an average temperature of 72-80 degrees and frequent small meals.

Otherwise, breeding and care as per standard description. The sexes at first look alike, but as the male develops to maturity, not only does his anal fin change into an organ of sex, but the lower rays of the tail fin elongate into the well-known spike. If this change occurs while the fish is still small, it will never grow much more. Good-sized males are secured only by growing them rapidly while young. This calls for plenty of room (aquarium of 10 gallons or more), no overcrowding, a warm temperature and plenty of live food. The species likes a flood of light, and shows best in it.

A large female is liable to deliver from 100 to 200 young.

A typical Simpson Hi-Fin Swordtail specially developed by Henry Kaufmann to have a full bright red coloration and pink eyes.

Simpson Hi Fin Swordtail

*E*ARLY in 1960 what is now commonly referred to as the Simpson Hi Fin Sword was introduced to the aquarium hobby. The mutation was developed by Mr. and Mrs. Thomas Simpson of Gardena, California. The Simpson Hi Fin Sword, as its name suggests, is noteworthy for its high, trailing dorsal fin. The male has retained its swordtail and its flowing dorsal terminates just after the caudal fin. Many color variations of this fish have appeared since it was first introduced, but probably the rich red velvet swords with their red eyes are the most striking. The females also have the trailing dorsal and the characteristic shows up in fry when it is still very young.

See *Xiphophorus helleri* for general care and breeding procedure, page 372.   Edited by H. S.

COLOR PLATE PAGE 573

Red Swordtail Hybrids

A BEAUTIFUL fish, similar to those in our illustration, appeared as the result of an unknown Red Platy Swordtail cross, in the aquarium of Mr. Samuel Silver in New York in 1922 or thereabout. He succeeded in fixing the strain and astounded the aquarium world by showing 20 perfect specimens at an exhibition where the author was a judge. Only some of the individuals were fertile, but the breed persisted and came into general use.

Another strain appeared in about 1930, of a beautiful translucent red color, with a good spike and a tendency to a white belly. This whiteness has largely been bred out. The strain is extremely prolific, which gave ground for the argument that the fish is not a hybrid, but a straight Red Swordtail, under which name it is known in trade. This argument by itself is not very sound, as fertile hybrids can be had by several re-crossings with one of the parent stocks. The lower fish in our color plate represents this later strain, but we find it impossible to reproduce its beautiful translucent quality. Red Swords and Platies are a bit tender.

There is still variation in the tail spike as to length and as to the presence of its black margin. The strain has proved extremely popular.

COLOR PLATE PAGE 576

Variegated Hybrids

*H*YBRIDS of this very variable and interesting type are usually the result of crosses between some color variety of *Xiphophorus maculatus* and *Xiphophorus hellerii*. Some are produced by various crossings of the hybrids themselves, and by back-crossings with one side or the other of the parent stock.

Truth to tell, much of it is done by chance, without any deliberate application of the Mendelian laws to attain a given objective.

Of the 3 shown, the upper fish, called the Black Spangled, is the most definitely established. It is produced by crossing the Niger variety of the Platyfish with a Green Swordtail. Those specimens in which the blue-green scales are carried evenly over the body, and into the head, are the most highly prized.

The ancestry of the centre fish, called the Calico, or Variegated Hybrid, is unknown to the writer, and probably to the owner as well. From appearances it easily could be the result of a cross between the Black Spangled fish and a hybrid Red Swordtail.

COLOR PLATE PAGE 576

Red Wagtail Swordtails

THIS is one of the latest and most striking of the Platy-Swordtail crosses. The parentage is not definitely known, but it seems certain that one of the parents must be the Red Wagtail. The other could well be the pure Swordtail, orange variety, or else the hybrid Red Swordtail; both shown on pages near this one.

The Wagtail would have been necessary to giving the black in the fins. This is the opinion of Dr. Myron Gordon, the eminent geneticist who produced the original Wagtail strain.

Not all specimens of this new cross have solid black in the fins, many showing only black in the fin *ribs*.

The red body color of this new variation is very good.

Females are usually fertile, but there is a great preponderance of males.

Like straight Swordtails, they are strong jumpers, and their aquarium should not be left uncovered.

THE HALF-BEAKS
FAMILY HEMIRHAMPHIDAE
Pronounced Hem i ram'fi dee

The Half-beaks live up to their name, for the easiest distinguishing feature of these peculiar fishes is the long lower jaw, prolonged into a beak. The Needle-fishes have *both* jaws prolonged. The Half-beaks are mostly salt-water fishes, but a few in the East Indies are from fresh water. These fresh-water forms are nearly all viviparous, in contradistinction to the salt-water species.

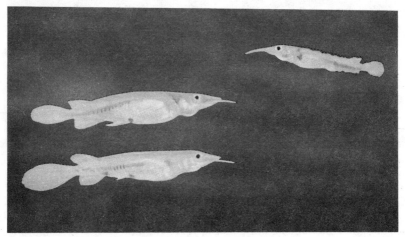

Dérmogénys pùsillus VAN HASSELT

Pronounced Der'mo-gen"iss pew'sill-us   *Popular name,* Live-bearing Half-beak

MEANING OF NAME: *Dermogenys,* with skin-like cheeks; *pusillus,* small, or weak

Siam to Java, Sumatra and Borneo   Length—male, 2 inches; female, 3 inches

Eastern Location Map x36 to 39; I40; L42 to M47; H45

*T*HIS grayish fish derives its quaint charm from its strange shape and its live-bearing habits, rather than color. The right-hand fish above is a male (note peculiar anal fin), the other two pregnant females.

A top swimmer, with mouth best equipped for surface feeding. Floating or live food suits it best, although it learns, if hungry, to take soft foods from the bottom. Young from 10 to 40 in number according to amount of live food given breeders, are born at night, and are eaten next day unless separated from parents. Baby brine shrimp is perfect food for babies and breeders. Temperature 68-80.

THE STICKLEBACKS
FAMILY GASTEROSTEIDAE
Pronounced Gas'ter os tee'i dee

The Sticklebacks are well-known nest-builders of the temperate and sub-arctic parts of the Northern Hemisphere. Their chief distinguishing feature is the series (2 to 15 or more) of free spines along the back in front of the dorsal fin.

COLOR PLATE PAGE 577

Gásterósteus acùleàtus LINNAEUS

Pronounced Gas'ter-os"tee-us ak-you'lee-ay"tus   *Popular name,* Three-spined Stickleback

MEANING OF NAME: *Gasterosteus,* with bony belly; *aculeatus,* sharp

Brackish and fresh coastal waters of the N. Atlantic and N. Pacific, South to New Jersey and Lower California   Length, 2½ inches

THIS fish, so brilliant in breeding season, is exotic but not tropical, covering a wide range of coastal waters of the Atlantic and the Pacific. Dealers in Europe and America sometimes have them for sale in the spring. To breed a pair is a very interesting experience. Habits and nature are similar to those of the Four-spined Stickleback, next described, but the breeding technique is different. The male fans out a depression in the sand and into this he sticks bits of loose plants, such as Riccia, and half covers them with sand, so that they are well anchored. In order to be sure of having a tunnel he burrows under and through the nest in the position showing the female in the color plate. In the meantime the female

Male puffing water through nest to force circulation among the eggs. He sometimes stands vertically, tail up.

stands aloof, at a distance, pretending to see nothing. He presently succeeds in coaxing her to the nest, but she coyly swims away. After a few such inspections she herself burrows through, followed by the male, who no doubt then fertilizes the eggs she has deposited. The pair goes through the nest several times. Spawning finished, the female takes a stand at a distant point, while the male stands guard over the nest, frequently blowing water through it, with a vigorous puffing. It is generally safer to then remove the female.

After 4 days of wear-and-tear, the nest is somewhat wrecked — a crater with loose bits of plants in it, but now peppered with babies. The father guards them savagely and does not eat them at any stage. They are easily reared on Infusoria, Brine Shrimp and sifted Daphnia.

The species is strictly carnivorous and must have live food throughout life.

Whether these young would breed next year without going through the cycle

Nest is now a loose mass in a large crater, so deep that it has loosened a Giant Sagittaria plant. The babies have hatched, but keep close to home for two days, under the watchful eyes of their faithful father.

of life in the ocean for the winter is not known by the writer. In the fall he liberated them in a stream that eventually led to the sea, taking a last fond look at them as they disappeared.

Apéltes quadràcus (MITCHILL)

Pronounced A-pel′tees quad-ray′kus   *Popular name,* Four-spined Stickleback

MEANING OF NAME: *Apeltes,* without plates or armor (which are formed on the sides of most Sticklebacks); *quadracus,* four-spined

Atlantic coast streams of United States, South to Virginia

Length—male, 1½ inches; female, 2 inches

REALLY marine fishes that come up fresh-water rivers and creeks of the Atlantic seaboard to spawn. They appear in large numbers in these streams in the early spring, about March. If netted at this time they are fairly sure to spawn in an aquarium. The water should be at about 65 to 70 degrees. Eastern dealers have them in season, at low prices.

The male builds a nest between the leaves of such plants as Vallisneria or Sagittaria, using bits of aquarium rubble for the purpose. Broken bits of Myriophyllum are ideal for his use. At the breeding season the male exudes from special glands in his body a sort of sticky cobweb, with which he glues the nest together and anchors it to nearby leaves. The nest is usually open at the top and has a hole in the side, insuring circulation of water as he blows into it during the several days of the hatching period. He does not eat the young. Sometimes several females will deposit their eggs in one nest.

The young must have Infusoria, followed by sifted Daphnia. Adults also need live food, preferably Daphnia.

Sticklebacks are pugnacious and should not be kept with other fishes. They cannot stand much heat. In breeding season the ventral fins of the male are brilliant red. With this species the parents do not usually live long after breeding is over.

THE SILVERSIDES
FAMILY ATHERINIDAE
Pronounced Ath er in'i dee

The Silversides are common salt-water fishes found on nearly all tropical and temperate coasts. A few permanently inhabit fresh water, including the two species here described. The separate spiny dorsal fin and the Cyprinodont-like mouth will identify fishes of this family.

Mélanotaènia nìgrans (RICHARDSON)

Pronounced Mel'an-o-tee"nee-à ny'grans   *Popular name,* Australian Rainbow Fish
MEANING OF NAME: *Melanotaenia,* with black band; *nigrans,* black
Australia   Eastern Location Map S56; R61; Q61   Length, 3 to 4 inches
L65 to V51 and °72

THIS is probably the most beautiful and generally satisfactory of the rather few aquarium fishes that have been brought from Australia. Under favorable conditions it is so prolific that it is liable to cause over-production. Those conditions are that a number of them be placed out-doors in summer in a concrete tank crowded with fine-leaved plants; that they be fed continuously with live food and left alone. Nature will do the rest. The young need not be separated from the old. Or a pair may be spawned in a large aquarium in the same manner as ordinary egg-droppers.

The striking feature of the species is a brilliant array of red and yellow stripes on the sides. The apparently dark spot on the gill plate is fiery red. The male (above) is smaller, slimmer and more brilliant. Very peaceful, hardy and easily fed. Temperature range, 60 to 90 degrees.

COLOR PLATE PAGE 577

Mélanotaènia maccúllochi AHL
Pronounced Mel'an-o-tee"nee-a mc-culloch-eye

MEANING OF NAME: *Melanotaenia,* with black band; *maccullochi,* named for the late Alan Riverstone MacCulloch, ichthyologist at the Australian Museum, Sydney

Australia   Exact locality not known   Length, 2¾ inches

*W*HILE this fish generally resembles M. *nigrans,* there are differences worth noting, especially by those aquarists who favor smaller fishes. This illustration is about ¼ larger than life size.

The colors as shown here speak for themselves, but it should be stated that they do not attain these hues until full-grown and under favorable aquarium conditions. Even half-grown specimens show little color.

In comparison with its cousin, M. *nigrans,* it is not quite as brilliant, but is livelier and keeps the fins spread much better.

The male (lower fish) is the more brightly colored, especially at breeding time. Spawning is accompanied by intense trembling, with the pair in close parallel position. Light yellow eggs, fairly large, are expelled against fine-leaved plants. They hatch in from 4 to 7 days. Except in large pools, the eggs and parents should be separated. Rear young as directed in "Spawning the Egg-layers." Temperature range for the species, 68-80 degrees.

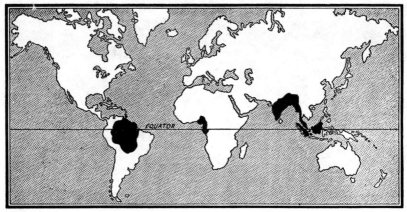

DISTRIBUTION MAP OF THE FAMILY NANDIDAE

THE NANDIDS
FAMILY NANDIDAE
Pronounced Nan'di-dee

Most spiny-rayed fishes are found in salt water and very few families of this type are restricted entirely to fresh water. The Cichlids, Sunfishes, true Perches, and Gouramis are among such fresh-water families. The Nandids also share this distinction, and of all such groups they are the most widely scattered in range.

Monocirrhus (one species) is found over most of the Amazon Basin and in the Essequibo River, British Guiana. *Polycentrus* (one species) is restricted to Guiana and the island of Trinidad. *Polycentropsis abbreviata* and *Afronandus sheljuzhkoi* (formerly described as *Nandopsis sheljuzkoi* by Meinken but he later changed the generic name to *Afronandus* as *Nandaposis* was being used) represent the family in Africa, where it is confined to a relatively small area about the mouth of the Niger and in Cameroon. In India there are *Badis* (two species), *Nandus* (two species), and *Pristolepis fasciata* in Burma, Thailand, Indo-China and islands of the Malay Archipelago.

The Nandids differ technically from other related families chiefly in features of the skeleton. All of them (except *Badis,* which may have to be placed in a separate family) have large mouths which can be opened out to a tremendous extent (see photo of *Monocirrhus*) and all (except *Badis* again) have the peculiar feature of having the tail fin and the rear ends of the dorsal and anal fins so transparent as to be hardly visible in the live fish. The transparent dorsal and anal fin ends are almost constantly in motion. All except *Badis* are voracious fish-eaters, with large mouths and strong teeth. They require live food, usually either fish or adult brine shrimp. Edited by H. S.

Badis badis (HAMILTON-BUCHANAN)
(Pronounced as spelled, either with the broad a as in ah or long a as in bay)
Name is based on a native name   *Popular name,* Badis
India   Eastern Location Map m19 to p31   Length, 2⅜ inches

ANY of our exotic fishes have extensive wardrobes of colored costumes which they wear according to whim on occasion, and an author attempting descriptions feels that he is helplessly repeating himself in saying very much the same thing about a number of species. However, *Badis badis* is one of the extreme cases. Our color plate saves words. The reader may imagine any intermediate shades he pleases and not be far wrong. The usual color is brown with black or red bars in a chain-like pattern. The clearness of the pattern as shown is not exaggerated.

Sexes cannot be told positively, but the males are more hollow-bellied and are apt to be darker and larger. Their fins are larger, too.

It was thought that this species preferred to spawn in a flower pot and as this became a standard prop, the actual spawning was not seen. An article by A. van den Nieuwenhuizen in an issue of The Aquarium Magazine dispelled the mystery, and we present Mr. Nieuwenhuizen's remarkable photographs here. A ten-gallon tank can be used, temperature should be from 78 to 80 degrees F. Edited by H. S.

FIG. 1. When a breeding tank is set up for *Badis badis* and only a flower pot is provided, exposed to considerable light, the male will seek a darker place to spawn.

FIG. 2. If the male and female have been separated but the female has been living in the breeding tank, she will have taken over the flower pot area and will not put out a welcoming mat for the male.

FIG. 3. Now that the male sumed the position of mast situation, he begins to pre spawning area by making a the gravel. The female wat procedure with interest.

FIG. 4. Immediately upon leaving his territory, the male lightens in color and shows zigzag stripes. As long as his colors change back and forth, spawning will not occur.

FIG. 5. When the male no longer changes color, the female approaches the spawning area. If the male remains dark and swims further into the breeding area, the female follows.

FIG. 6. Both fishes embrace to the manner of *Betta s* This action takes over the s area. The position accom fertilization of the eggs as male expels them.

FIG. 7. In this picture the male has relaxed his body somewhat and the female is slipping out of the embrace. The eggs are not too much in evidence.

FIG. 8. Now eggs are quite apparent under the female. In the movement of the spawning sequence, some eggs have been scattered and others have attached themselves to the wall of the flower pot.

FIG. 9. The spawning has an end and the male lies on the bottom at the right. male has become lighter and soon she will leave the

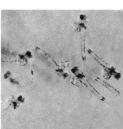

FIG. 10. *Badis badis* chooses the darkest area of the aquarium in which to spawn. The male guarded the eggs and later prepared a sandhole for the fry when they hatched.

FIG. 11. This shows a closeup of eggs photographed on plants. Here the spawning took place midst *Cabomba caroliniana*. After hatching the fry hang from little threads.

FIG. 12. *Badis badis* fry l this 48 hours after paren spawned. At the right side picture a fish changed positi movement was so fast that of a second of the flash enough to stop it.

Pólycentrópsis abbrèviàta BOULENGER

Pronounced Pol'lee-sen-trop"sis ab-bree'vee-ay"ta   *Popular name,* African Leaf-fish

MEANING OF NAME: *Polycentropsis,* resembling Polycentrus; abbreviata, abbreviated,
referring to the illusion that the fish has no tail fin

From a small area about Gulf of Guinea—See preceding family map

Western Location Map A55; B56   Length, 3 inches

INTRODUCING one of the very select fishes of the aquarium; a
recluse not often met with, one long honored by European aquarists;
a fish with an aura of mystery about it, and likely never to become common; it is even less known to ichthyologists.

The species in the main resembles the better-known *Polycentrus schom-
burgkii,* to which it is related, but the transparency of the soft-rayed fins
is even more striking. It takes a second look to be certain they have not
been sharply amputated.

There are no bright colors, only varying and changing shades of brown,
irregularly spotted black. The eye is the hub of 3 radiating dark lines,
seen in several Nandid species. Mouth very, very large and well adapted
to its particular pleasure of eating smaller fishes. It may take worms,
mosquito larvae and the larger water insects, but to be placed in breeding condition it should have fish.

The spawning resembles that of the Bubble-nest Builders but is not the
same. The male makes bubbles among the tops of leaves such as Cabomba, and the female deposits about 100 eggs singly on the plant
among the bubbles. Female should then be removed.

Polycentrus schomburgki (MUELLER AND TROSCHEL)

Pronounced Pol'lee-sen"trus   shom-burk'-eye   *Popular name,* Guiana Leaf-fish
MEANING OF NAME: *Polycentrus,* many-spined; *schomburgki,* after the
naturalist, Richard Schomburgk

Trinidad and Guiana   Length, 2½ inches
Western Location Map x between 19 and 20; A between 21 and 22

IN abrupt contrast with an ordinarily dark body, the transparent ends
of the dorsal and anal and the entire tail fin produce a startling effect.
Like most Nandids this species undergoes the most extreme changes in
color, from light brown to blue-black.

A number of aquarists succeed each year in multiplying the fish, but
it cannot be said to be easily bred. The pair should be in an aquarium
that is partially shaded and having, in addition, a plentiful screen of
growing aquatic plants. They like to spawn *inside* a flower-pot that has
been laid on its side, the opening *away* from the aquarist's view, and
towards a darkened corner. Female should be removed when spawning
is completed. Male fans eggs, which hatch in 4 days at a temperature
of 77 degrees. He, also, should then be removed.

Temperature range is 70 to 85 degrees.

The sexes are difficult to tell, but the male is usually the darker fish.

Mónocírrhus pólyacánthus HECKEL

Pronounced Mon'o-sir"rus   pol'lee-a-kan"thuss   *Popular name,* Amazon Leaf-fish

MEANING OF NAME: *Monocirrhus,* with one whisker; *polyacanthus,* many-spined

Amazon and Guiana Western Location Map A21 to H12 and G28 Length, 2½ inches

Evidently found over the whole Amazon Basin

*A*LTHOUGH this extremely odd fish was first described by Heckel as long ago as 1840, the type specimens in the Vienna Museum for many years remained the only ones of which we had any knowledge. In an interesting reprint from the "Biological Bulletin" for November, 1921, Dr. W. R. Allen describes a sluggish brook, overhung with tropical vegetation, from which he captured 3 specimens. The bottom was matted with fallen leaves. The fishes, of a leaf-brown, irregularly mottled color, were difficult to see. They moved about peculiarly like drifting leaves, and would not have been seen, except that the collector thought it strange that leaves should move at all in such sluggish water.

The species is most peculiar, and is a real novelty of decided exotic character. To begin with, the leafy color is much more apparent in life than a black-and-white photograph can show. It is really quite striking, and is not confined to any particular shade of brown, but changes greatly. Whether this is a chameleon-like power of protective coloration, we can only surmise. The eyes are difficult to distinguish, owing to the dark lines radiating from them. Usually the fins are spread, their saw-edges contributing much to the leaf-like effect. The beard on the lower jaw adds a stem to the leaf. Even the natives call the species the Leaf Fish.

They move about sedately and pose themselves at unusual angles, frequently head-down, as we see in the illustration. They do not seem to be particularly bored with life, but they gape or yawn prodigiously. Many fishes do this moderately, but the Leaf Fish puts on a startling act. The mouth seems to unfold from within itself until it becomes a veritable trumpet. Our camera caught the lower fish in the act.

They deposit, fertilize and fan their eggs somewhat like Cichlids, but their paternal care is not nearly so intense. The first spawn of this pair, placed in a dark vertical corner where the aquarium glasses join, was the most successful. Those later placed in pots did not do so well. The youngsters varied greatly in size, and after 3 weeks commenced disappearing. Removed from the parents and graded for size, the trouble ended. They have barbels for the first months, and when quite small are covered with tiny white dots which look like the parasitic disease, Ichthyophthirius. This is common to a number of kinds of very young fishes, and is probably protective coloration.

The Leaf Fish is most interesting, but unless one is prepared to feed it exclusively (and liberally) on small live fishes, all thoughts of keeping it should be abandoned, for it will touch nothing else. As the fish has a voracious appetite, it usually either wears out its welcome or starves to death, for few fanciers are equipped to maintain royalty demanding such expensive food. A thousand grown male Guppies per year just about keeps one of these adult cannibal aristocrats from feeling neglected. It does not attack fishes too large to be swallowed, but one should not underrate its capacity!

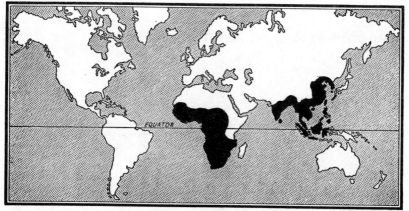

THE ANABANTIDS

FAMILY ANABANTIDAE
Pronounced An-a-ban'ti-dee

The Anabantids include the Climbing Perches and Gouramis. The family belongs to the order Labyrinthici, which is characterized by the presence of a labyrinthine chamber above the gills for the retention of air for breathing. The Anabantids differ from the Snakeheads in the spiny fins and in the more complicated breathing chamber structure. All of them are from Southern Asia and Africa.

The family is not a large one. The species and genera are most numerous and varied in the Asiatic part of their range, only 3 or 4 genera inhabiting Africa. Nearly all the species are useful in their native haunts as destroyers of mosquito larvae. Since only 2 or 3 are large enough to be considered as food fishes, it will be seen that most Anabantids are good aquarium material. Many of the species are combative, however, and all have sharp teeth. They usually kill snails.

These fishes are frequently known as "Labyrinth Fishes" because of the labyrinthine breathing organ, but the Snakeheads (see the next family) might also be called "Labyrinth Fishes", for they possess a somewhat similar organ.

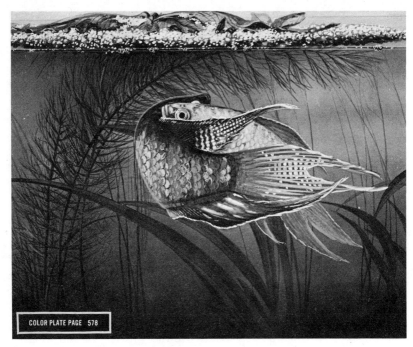

COLOR PLATE PAGE 578

NUPTIAL EMBRACE OF PARADISE FISH

The Labyrinth Bubble-nest Builders

LABYRINTH fishes are those having an auxiliary breathing apparatus in addition to the ordinary gills. Although not capable of independent muscular action, this organ is comparable to the lung of an air-breathing animal, and serves the same purpose. It is called a labyrinth on account of its involved structure which brings a great many fine capillaries into contact with the air forced through it. These capillaries absorb oxygen from the air and deliver it directly into the blood stream of the fish. The air, however, does not pass through the labyrinth in the same manner as we humans breathe, but is taken at intervals by the fish at the surface of the water. Simultaneously a new bubble is taken in the mouth and the old one is forced out through the edge of the gill covers, having first passed through the oxygen-absorbing labyrinth. This is in the head.

These fishes use the regular gills for oxygenating the blood to a much greater extent than is generally believed. Accurate experiments have been carried out in which a species of labyrinth fish (Paradise Fish) was sealed in a bottle of water in which there was no air surface. The fishes showed discomfort, but, contrary to what might be expected, they did not suffocate in 12 hours. Furthermore, measurements showed that they extracted almost as much oxygen from the water as did other species without labyrinths. On the other hand it is a great advantage to a fish to be equipped with both kinds of breathers, for in situations where the oxygen in the water is so deficient as to suffocate ordinary species, the labyrinth fishes maintain life without apparent distress. From this it will be seen why they may be kept in comparatively small containers.

On the mistaken theory that air-breathers take *no* oxygen from the water, aquarists sometimes add them to tanks which are already over-populated.

The intervals at which air in the labyrinth is changed varies with species and conditions. When excited the fish may come to the surface several times a minute, but at other times, especially in cool water, it may remain below for several minutes at a time.

Nearly all of the labyrinth fishes are what are known as "bubble-nest builders." As the description of this peculiar method of breeding applies to the several species under the heading, it will not be needlessly repeated in each instance, but where individual characteristics vary from the following description, they will be pointed out as occasion requires.

The outstanding feature of the breeding of this family of fishes is the floating nest of bubbles which they construct and in which the eggs are placed, hatched and the young tended. These bubbles are formed by the male as he comes to the surface, draws a little air in his mouth and envelops it in a film-like saliva. When released, the globule naturally floats to the surface. Endless repetition of this act piles up what looks like a little mound of very fine soap bubbles. They often select a building spot just under some floating aquatic leaves or a large single leaf.

When a male starts building a nest, even in a small way, it indicates that he is about ready for breeding. Unless a female is already present, it is the proper time to bring a pair together. It is better to move the male into the aquarium occupied by the female. Most of these fishes are quite harmless to species other than their own, but at breeding time there is danger of one being killed, usually the female. For this reason it is desirable to have plenty of room and a liberal supply of refuge plants, which, by the way, they never injure. The courting is conducted by a grand spreading of fins, first of the male, with ultimate response by the female if his suit is successful. His best holiday attire is used in courtship.

The male is often an impatient courter. After the nest is built, he drives the female towards it. If she is not ready for spawning her response will be slow, and it is then that he is liable to attack her, tearing her fins or perhaps killing her outright with a single head-on blow, de-livered against her side. It is at this time that the aquarist needs to be something of a strategist, as well as a diplomat, for the pair should not be separated at the very first sign of trouble. Like the wise judge at a Domestic Relations Court, he should give the contestants a reasonable chance to adjust their difficulties themselves. If matters grow worse, the strong arm of the aquarist should intervene, and give the parties an en-forced separation. A later trial mating may prove more successful.

But let us assume, as we should, that the courtship has been a normal one, and that the pair is ready for the Business of Life. She follows him to a position just below the prepared nest. He bends his body into a crescent which encircles her. As they slowly sink through the water, rolling over, she drops several eggs which are immediately fertilized dur-ing the embrace of the male. He releases himself, picks up the eggs in his mouth, and pushes them into the nest. This act is repeated for per-haps an hour, at the end of which time there may be from 100 to 500 eggs in the nest. In fish language it is unmistakable; the male then as-serts his rights as a father. He drives the female to the farthest limits of the aquarium and assumes full charge of the nest. At this point she should be removed, for she is likely to be killed, especially if the aquarium is a small one, say under 15 gallons.

To do this with as little agitation as possible, insert a glass divider between the pair. Female is then lifted without trouble.

With the presence of the eggs in the nest the male redoubles his efforts in producing bubbles, for the old ones gradually burst. In order to retard this evaporation, and for another reason to be explained shortly, the aquarium should be kept well covered with glass. The bubble-nest, originally about 3 inches wide and half an inch high, becomes perhaps an inch high and spreads out to 4 inches. The small eggs between the bubble suds can be seen, but sharp eyes are needed.

These labyrinth fishes like a breeding temperature of 78 to 82 degrees. The eggs hatch in about 2 days. At first they are like microscopic tadpoles among the foam, and are quite helpless. As they fall out of the nest through the water, the vigilant father gathers them up in his mouth and puts them back into their watery cradle. This continues about 3 days, the nest gradually becoming shallower and the young taking a position at the sur-face of the water just below it. By the time the young have absorbed the yolk sac and gained their balance it is nearly gone. Some observers have claimed that the male blows it to pieces, but this is doubtful, for it soon disintegrates without constant repairs. No schoolmaster ever had a busier time looking after his charges and no children could have a more vigilant caretaker. He looks after the wanderers with an eagle eye, ever alert and willing to give his life in their defense. In perhaps a week he considers his task done and that the young should be able to protect themselves. So thoroughly does he seem to enter into this idea that he is liable to start eating them himself! Perhaps this is Nature's method of eliminating those that can be caught. In the wild state his protection is no doubt necessary, but in an aquarium in which there are no fish enemies there is no reason to keep the father with the young after they are free-swimming.

There are several points of practical value in raising bubble-nest builders which may be covered briefly. It is a very, very common experience for beginners to become enthusiastic over prospects of raising a nest of these young, only to have them die off at an age of from 2 to 4 weeks. The principal reason for this is insufficient food of the right kind, and the causes in back of this are aquaria that are *too small* and *too clean*. These small fishes require a considerable amount of microscopic food, which can only be developed and maintained in old water. The proper aquarium for this purpose should be at the very least 15 gallons in size, well planted, containing old water from 6 to 8 inches deep, and with a fair amount of natural sediment on the bottom. The presence of a few decaying aquarium plants is desirable. No snails should be used. When the eggs are laid it is advisable to sprinkle a little dried and crumbled lettuce leaves on the water, and also a very little of any finely powdered fish food. The decomposition of these organic substances keeps up the culture of microscopic life which will later be needed. It is a fact that very small fishes of this character have been raised on a fine flour made of fish food, but it is quite likely that the resulting Infusoria which feed on the decomposition of this substance have something to do with the success attained. At any rate, while it is a good idea to have a separate source of Infusoria culture, as elsewhere explained (under "Fishfoods"), it is also desirable to cultivate a natural supply of it along with the baby fishes, especially when they are of a species which are extremely small. Aside from this suggested aquarium preparation, the young of labyrinth fishes may be raised as per the regular formula for egg-droppers. A little green water is good for them in the early stages. Daphnia should not be given until they are large enough to take finely sifted sizes. At the age of 7 to 10 days they can also eat newly-hatched Brine Shrimp, previously described. If suitable live food of the next size is not available, powdered salmon egg meal sprinkled on the surface of the water is good to use. It floats, and as the young come to the top they learn to eat it.

Another reasonably successful substitute for live food is the yellow of a 20-minute boiled egg. It should be squeezed through a cloth and a bit as big as a pea shaken up in a bottle of about 4-ounce size. A few drops of the agitated mixture may be lifted in a medicine-dropper and fed to the fry several times a day. These infusions should always be freshly mixed and should be fed with great care, as they can easily foul the water.

The other cause for losses is the failure to keep the aquarium well covered with glass during the critical period when the labyrinth is forming, for this organ does not begin to develop until the fish is about 3 weeks old. At this time they are particularly sensitive to draughts and temperature changes. If the surface of the water is at all dirty or filmy, it should be frequently cleaned by drawing a piece of newspaper across it.

The writer has, with marked success, bred 5 kinds of labyrinth fishes outdoors in a 6-foot lily pool, one species each season. Nests were always placed by the fish under a lily pad, with the exception of the *Colisa fasciata* (Giant Gourami), and *Belontia signata,* both these species allowing their floating eggs to scatter loosely at the surface, to be freely blown about by the winds. Temperature ranged from 60 to 90 degrees, averaging 73. Females were never killed. Several overlapping nestings per season were raised, none interfering with or apparently eating the others. Sometimes 2 pairs of breeders were used. No artificial culture of Infusoria was used. Daphnia occasionally. These were soon cleaned up by the parents or the young which were large enough to eat them. Never tried Bettas in the pool, distrusting our variable summer climate. The reader should not assume that conclusions from pond breeding are applicable to aquarium culture.

Members of this fish family are subject to much individual variation in temperament, especially in the action of males in breeding. Some kill one female after another; others devour their babies, while some refuse to mate at all. The most unpredictable is the Betta. Ingenuity by the aquarist is sometimes needed. A change of mates is often the answer.

The labyrinth fishes are by nature carnivorous, living principally on small crustacea and also on insects which fall on the water. They can be trained to take ordinary prepared dried foods, but this should often be supplemented by fresh animal diet, such as Daphnia, chopped worms, bits of fish, shrimp, crab meat, or scraped raw beef liver.

They are all suited to life in a community tank with fishes of approximately their own size, provided others of *their own species* are *not* present. Most of them, except Bettas, get along very well in tanks containing a *large number* of their own kind, apparently being content to ward off attacks from the rear. Females may be kept together.

Mácropòdus operculàris (LINNAEUS)

Pronounced Mak'ro-po"dus oh-per'ku-lay"riss   *Popular name,* Paradise Fish

MEANING OF NAME: *Macropodus,* large foot (fin), in reference to dorsal and
anal fins; *opercularis,* with spot on the gill cover

Formerly known as *Macropodus viridi-auratus*

Eastern Location Map s39 and s43 to l46 and d51   Length, 3 inches

IF ancient lineage is the true basis for aristocracy, then the Paradise
Fish is undoubtedly the Exalted Potentate of all tropical aquarium
fishes. It was introduced into Paris in 1868 by Carbonnier. This introduction undoubtedly marks the beginning of the study of fresh-warm-
water aquarium fishes as we have it today, and if any future enthusiasts
wish to observe centenaries of the occasion, that is the year on which to
base them. Goldfish and a few cold-water species, both fresh and marine,
had been kept in European and American aquariums some years previously. It is now difficult to realize that in about 1850-60, especially
in England, the household aquarium was a new and fashionable fad, and
that many books appeared on the subject. Judging from the now comical
misinformation contained in most of them, it is little wonder that the
mushroom growth soon passed and left no trace, except for a few musty
books. One of the earliest of them (Warrington 1850) contained the
first correct statement of the principles of the "balanced aquarium,"
indeed an epoch in itself, and one worthy of commemoration.

For many years following its introduction into America in 1876 by the
famous Adolphus Busch, of St. Louis, the Paradise Fish was regarded
as an aquarium novelty of doubtful value, for owners of Lace-tail Gold-

EMBRACE

White Paradise Fish beginning to spawn.

BARREL ROLL

At this moment the eggs are extruded and fertilized, the female being in an upside-down position.

RELEASE

The male now trembles a few seconds and then gathers the slowly sinking eggs in his mouth, soon floating them into the bubble-nest, which is over the plants.

fish rightly feared the presence of this menacing stranger among their highly developed but defenseless beauties. The Goldfish fins usually suffered when it was tried.

Because the Paradise Fish is so easily bred and can live in water down to 50 degrees, it is held cheaply. If rare it would be considered a great beauty. When the male's fins are at their best, the long, sweeping filaments at the tail-ends are blue white at the ends. The females have shorter fin tips.

The color-plate of a pair in breeding embrace gives a good idea of the intensified mating colors of the male, and of the reverse paleness of the female. When not excited they are more nearly of a color, the female not so pale and the male not so bright.

In contrast with Goldfish this species early acquired a reputation as a fighter, but in comparison with some other exotic fishes he is really not savage, but is untrustworthy in a small community tank.

A true albino strain of Paradise Fish with pink eyes was introduced from Europe in 1933. The bars on the sides are pinkish, becoming more red as the fish ages. Otherwise it is white, or cream color. It breeds true and is prolific. What fight there is in the original stock seems to have mostly disappeared in the albino, the male not usually attacking the female after she has finished spawning.

Macropodus opercularis, or Paradise Fish, breeds true to standard form as described for Bubble-nest Builders. It is particularly suited to pond culture, as it is not injured by moderate chilly spells.

This fish is very tame, and while preferring animal food, will take anything. Like the Betta, in perhaps a slightly lesser degree, it seems to have no sense of fear. It is long-lived, and can endure very dirty water.

The species has been the subject of an unusual amount of discussion, by the systematists, having undergone, since its first description by Linnaeus in 1758, nearly a dozen changes of name, and been the subject of many hundred papers by ichthyologists and aquarists.

Paradise Fish are common in the rice fields of China, where they successfully endure a wide range of temperature. Here in America we have known them to be retrieved, nearly dead, from ice-coated ponds, then gently heated and brought to full health.

Mácropòdus cupànus dàyi   (KOEIILER)

Pronounced Mak'ro-po"dus kew-pay'nus day'eye   Also known as *Polyacanthus dayi*
MEANING OF NAME: *cupanus,* after a river in India; *dayi,* for F. Day
Eastern Location Map C22 and z19 to q29   Length, 2¾ inches

꯳HE *dayi* part of the name of this fish probably only represents a race of *Macropodus cupanus,* slightly larger in size and a bit more intense in color. The true *cupanus* is a much paler, grayish fish, usually lacking the lateral stripes, and showing as its chief color the red ventral fins of the male. The edges of the fins are a peculiar white that might be called phosphorescent.

The body has 2 dark horizontal bands, the lower one being the stronger. Throat and belly, reddish. Tip of anal, red. General body color is in shades of brown. A hardy species which accommodates itself to temperatures between 60 and 90 degrees. Breeds at 75 to 80. It prefers old water.

This is rather more of a jumper than most bubble-nest builders, and its aquarium should be kept covered.

The majority of aquarists consider it to be a good community aquarium fish, but experiences in this matter often differ.

It is a good breeder and is not shy. The fish in the photograph with the longer fins and shallower body is the male. At the moment of the photograph, however, his tail fin was not spread. Breeding habits as per description under "The Labyrinth Bubble-nest Builders."

Belòntia signàta (GUENTHER)

Pronounced Bell-on'tee-a sig-nay'ta   *Popular name,* Comb-tail

MEANING OF NAME: *Belontia,* from native name of a related species in
Borneo; *signata,* significant

Ceylon   Eastern Location Map C22   Length, 3½ to 4 inches

ON reflection it will be found that most of the aquarists' labyrinth
fishes are easily identified; they have marked characteristics. In this
one we have not only a pronounced color pattern, but the long, soft-
rays of the ventral fins are split, while the rays of the tail fin extend well
past the web. The predominating color is reddish brown, with considerable red in the fins, particularly the tail. Darker scales on the male (upper
fish) are red. Male is likely to kill female unless they have a large tank.
Scattered eggs float with no nest. Both parents tend young.

Bétta pugnax   (CANTOR)

Pronounced Bet'ta pug'nax

MEANING OF NAME: *pugnax,* pugnacious

Malay Peninsula   Eastern Location Map, F39

Popular name, Malayan Betta

Formerly known as *B. brederi*

Length, 3½ inches

HIS species is much heavier than *B. splendens,* and is not nearly so flexible nor so brilliant in color, the indefinite pattern being of mixed browns and grays. The shining scales on the side of the male (lower fish) are blue spangles.

Large single eggs are expelled in the usual Betta manner, but the male cups them in his anal fin, to be picked up by the female and propelled into the mouth of the male, where they hatch in 3 days, remaining there until the babies are able to swim freely. The male does not attack the female.

This fish was named *B. brederi* when first imported. However, Dr. M. W. F. Tweedie has recently shown that *brederi* is only one of the forms of *pugnax.*

Both species like a living temperature of about 75 degrees and breed at 80.

Trìchogáster péctoràlis (REGAN)
Pronounced Try'ko-gas"ter pek-toe-ray"lis
Popular name, Snakeskin Gourami or Sepat Siam
MEANING OF NAME: *Trichogaster,* hair-belly, reference to ventral fins;
pectoralis, reference to long pectoral fins
Siam, French Indo-China Eastern Location Map 42w, 36x, 39F Length, 8-10 inches
Malay Peninsula   wild

ONE of the latest introductions among the bubble-nest builders, and a very good one from the aquarist's standpoint. It is not a showy fish, but is hardy, has a good disposition, and is perhaps the most easily-bred member of the family. Spawns are very large.

Contrary to the custom of most males comprised in this type of breeder, he does not attack the female at any stage in the routine, nor does either parent eat the young. In fact, one large professional breeder writes that they will not eat young fish of any kind, nor kill snails. It is quite an advantage to have a species with which one does not have to be on the alert to prevent cannibalism.

The somewhat irregular line along the length of the fish is dark-brown-to-black. Light wavy bars shown on sides are pale gold against an olive background. The anal fin, especially in the male, is slightly amber. As with the other Trichogasters, mature males have longer dorsal fins.

COLOR PLATE PAGE 579

Bétta spléndens REGAN

Pronounced Bet'ta (not bay-ta) splen'dens   *Popular name,* Siamese Fighting Fish
MEANING OF NAME: *Betta,* after a local native name, Ikan bettah; *splendens,* brilliant
Siam   Eastern Location Map x37; y39; v36   Length, 2½ inches

*W*ITH all due respect to the Guppy for having aroused the interest of an enormous number of persons in aquarium study, there seems little doubt that the modern Veiltail Betta launched the hobby in a big way in America. Its extraordinary, spectacular beauty made instantaneous conquests among those who would never have looked twice at any other fish, but who are now dyed-in-the-wool fanciers and doing all in their power to interest others in the hobby.

But let us leave superlatives for a moment and have a look at the humble ancestor of this flashy fish. It is shown further on as Original *Betta splendens.* Its body is yellowish brown with a few indistinct horizontal bands. At breeding time the male becomes darker and rows of metallic green scales on his sides become plainer. Dorsal, metallic green tipped with red; anal, red tipped blue. Ventrals always fiery red, tipped white. All fins of moderate size, tail fin being rounded.

Suddenly there appeared in our aquarium world a new comet—a cream-colored Betta with fiery, flowing fins. Two varieties, a dark and a light one, were in the shipment. These were brought into San Francisco in 1927 from Siam. Thinking he had a new species, Mr. Locke, the consignee who received and bred the fishes, called the light one *Betta cambodia*. This has since been proved, as have all the now numerous color variants, to be a race of *Betta splendens*. Other importations in varying colors soon followed, some of them coming through Europe. Breeders aimed for the darker colors and soon established the famous "Cornflower Blue," and finally a solid, rich purplish blue. There are now so many shades of this fish in blues, lavenders, greens and reds that a decorator could almost find specimens to match the color scheme of any room, but nearly all of them hold to the pair of drooping, fiery red ventral fins.

The specimens used in the color illustration are by no means the highest form of fin development reached by these fishes, probably not by 50 per cent.

Much misinformation exists as to the fighting qualities of this fish, some of it so amusing that we present it, even at risk of too much length.

The late Dr. Hugh M. Smith, ichthyologist and writer, former U.S. Commissioner of Fisheries and one-time Adviser in Fisheries to the Siamese Government, was qualified to speak on this fish from any standpoint, especially as he had taken a particular interest in the species and personally brought to the United States some of the original Veiltail Betta stock. In response to a letter asking him to settle the point as to whether the fishes are especially bred for fighting or are caught from the wild for the purpose, the following extracts from his interesting and amusing reply should decide the matter finally, not only for newspaper columnists, but for aquarium writers, too.

"The literature of Betta as a fighting fish is replete with inaccuracies and absurdities. An unusually large number of these occur in a short paragraph in the article entitled 'The Heavenly-Royal City of Siam' by Florence Burgess Meehan (Asia, March, 1921).

" 'The fighting fish are about the size of goldfish. You catch one and put it into a bottle. Your neighbor does likewise. You put your bottle close to your neighbor's. Your fish becomes enraged. So does your neighbor's fish. They both flash all colors of the rainbow. They swell up. You bet on your fish. Your friends back you. After a time one fish or the other, hurling itself against the glass in a vain effort to reach its adversary, becomes so angry that it literally bursts. If it is your neighbor's fish that bursts, you win. If it is yours, you lose.'

"The writer of this paragraph certainly never saw what she was writing about, and the untrustworthiness of the account may be judged from the following facts:

"The Siamese fighting fish cannot properly be described as 'about the size of a goldfish' whatever may be the meaning of the expression. The fish are not matched while in separate 'bottles,' and when not fighting are usually kept in special rectangular jars about 4 inches square and 10 inches high, and a little larger at the top than at the bottom. When fighting, the fish do not 'flash all colors of the rainbow,' do not 'swell up,' do not 'hurl themselves against the glass,' and do not 'literally burst.'

"With these exceptions, the account quoted is nearly correct, but not quite. For instance, the impression is conveyed that if you wish to stage a fight, you and your neighbor go out and catch wild fish, whereas practically all the combats are between domesticated fish. Fighting fish have been cultivated and domesticated among the Siamese for many years, and all of the noteworthy combats on which sums of money are wagered are with selected, often pedigreed, stock. They have short tail fins.

"There are in Bangkok 10 or 12 persons who breed fighting fish for sale, and about 1,000 persons who raise fighting fish for their own use. A dealer whom I recently visited reports an annual production of 50,000 young, but only a small percentage of these are carried to the fighting age and sold. For the best males the current retail price per fish is 1 to 2 ticals, females half price (1 tical equals 44 cents gold).

"The native wild fishes from which the ordinary cultivated fish has been derived rarely exceed 2 inches for the males, the females being smaller. The cultivated fish reach a length of 2½ inches for the males.

"The way in which the male fish are matched and their method of fighting are well known. It will suffice to state that the combatants are placed together in a bowl or jar and quickly come to close quarters, expanding their fins and branchial membranes and displaying the gorgeous red, blue and green shades that have made the fighting fish famous. They appoach one another quietly and may remain in close relation, side by side, for 10 to 15 seconds, or longer, without action. Then, in quick succession, or simultaneously, they launch an attack almost too swift for the observer's eye to follow, and this is repeated at short intervals during the continuance of the combat. The effect of the fierce onslaughts begins to be seen in the mutilation of the fins, which may soon present a ragged appearance and considerable loss of fin substance may occur. The branchial region (gills) may come in for attack, and blood may exceptionally be drawn. On two separate occasions my own fish locked jaws and remained in that position for a number of minutes. That fish is adjudged the victor which is ready to continue to fight while its opponent is no longer eager for the fray."

Dr. Smith's reference to the courage of the cultivated breed of *Bettas* may account for their truly remarkable absence of fear under a certain circumstance which frightens and intimidates nearly all other fishes, especially the fighting sorts. This is the sudden confinement of the fish in a very small space such, for instance, as a glass photographing cell, or a half-pint jar. Placed in such a situation he calmly surveys his miniature prison, makes a few eel-like turns in it, apparently to see whether it can be done, and is then ready for each or both of his twin interests in life— breeding and fighting. His movements are truly serpentine.

Owing to this intense fighting passion of the males, it is necessary, at the age of about 3 months, to rear them in individual jars or aquaria. This is the way all fine specimens are produced, for although fish fins recover from injuries, scars remain and the fish is never again perfect. For this reason the price of fine specimens will always remain fairly high.

Bettas conform to the described habits for bubble-nest builders. They like acid water, about 6.8, and do best in a well-planted aquarium with liberal light. Water should be clear, but with plenty of natural sediment.

These Veiltail *Betta splendens* are at their best appearance and vigor between the ages of 10 months and 2 years, and should be bred during that period. Prior to one year it is difficult to select the best specimens, and after 2 years they age rapidly.

There is no way of identifying the sexes until they are about an inch

BRIEF BETTA BLISS

long, when the fins of the males begin to point and lengthen. Soon after this change is noted the males should be kept separately. The females may be placed together. Fin length is the result of inheritance—not food.

This fish is almost as adaptable to foods as it is to its surroundings, but nevertheless it does best on animal substances such as Daphnia, mosquito larvae, chopped worms, bits of fish, crab, shrimp, etc.

A single male may be placed in a community aquarium, and possibly a female also, if the tank is a large one. In general the sexes should be kept separated; the males singly or else spread around so that 2 of the species are not in the same tank. Males placed in small adjoining aquariums with a cardboard divider between will always spread themselves when the board is removed. It is a show for visitors that never fails.

The breeding actions of Bettas are unpredictable. Some males are killers, some egg-eaters. None should be trusted with the babies after they become free-swimming. Breeding temperature, about 78, but stand 68 to 90.

ORIGINAL TYPE OF *Betta splendens*

Osphronèmus gorämy (LACÉPÈDE)

Pronounced Os'fro-nee"mus go-rah'mee   Also known as *Osphromenus olfax*

MEANING OF NAME: *Osphronemus* erroneously refers to the feelers as organs of smell; *goramy,* after the native name

E. Indies   Length—aquarium specimens, 3 to 5 inches; in nature, 24 inches

Eastern Location Map M46; F37; E46

THIS is the only true Gourami and is certainly the real Giant Gourami. In its native waters it is a food fish growing to a length of 2 feet. It will, however, breed in the aquarium at a 10-inch size.

The half dozen other species carrying the name "Gourami" do so only through courtesy of popular error, the first mis-application having been tacked on the innocent *C. lalia,* the "Dwarf Gourami."

Although the tail fin has a stumpy, ungraceful appearance, the fish is not bad to look at. The dark spot, flanked forward and back by brilliant cream-white scales, makes an interesting feature. A second black spot near the ventrals is described by Rachow, but our photograph did not pick up any such marking, nor does the writer remember any. Perhaps this occurs in still younger specimens.

The fish has a reddish brown cast, with bluish throat and a white ventral region. With age it loses its redeeming markings.

They build a nest of water plants and twigs, but seldom breed. Temperature range, 68 to 90 degrees.

COLOR PLATE PAGE 579

Colisa fasciàta (BLOCH AND SCHNEIDER)
Pronounced Ko-lee'sa fas'see-ay"ta   *Popular name,* Striped Gourami
MEANING OF NAME: *Colisa,* from a native name; *fasciata,* banded or striped
Also known as *Trichogaster fasciatus*
India   Eastern Location Map o15 to p32 and v23   Length, 4½ inches

*W*HILE the breeding habits of this *Colisa* are in general the same as for the family, there are differences. It does not build a very definitely formed nest, but blows a few scattered bubbles, preferably under a large leaf. The eggs are lighter than water and float to the surface, where they are more or less scattered. For some reason which we are not even able to surmise, the male takes mouthfuls of sand and blows it among the eggs. It is a male shown in the illustration.

In the meantime, both before and after the hatching of the eggs, the male takes several gulps of air in his mouth, proceeds to a point below the surface and expels a fine mist of air bubbles backward through his gills, scattering it with his pectoral fins. For a moment it seems as though the bubbles are coming from all over his body. He busies himself with this procedure in all parts of the aquarium. We believe this is the first record of these facts.

Eggs hatch in 2 days at 78 degrees. Remove female after spawning and male 3 days after eggs hatch. A peaceful, beautiful species, easily fed,

COLOR PLATE PAGE 580

Colisa lália   (HAMILTON-BUCHANAN)

Pronounced Ko-lee'sa   lal'e-a   *Popular name,* Dwarf Gourami
The scientific name is based on two native names
Formerly known as *Trichogaster lalius*
Northern India   Eastern Location Map o15 to r39 and o30   Length, 2 inches

*C*OLISA LALIA is the smallest of the genus *Colisa,* and certainly one
of the most beautiful. A highly satisfactory and interesting aquarium fish with but a single fault. It is apt to be timid and hide away in
the foliage. It is too beautiful a flower to be allowed to blush unseen.
By associating it with more forward fishes that rush to their master for
food, this little beauty soon overcomes its shyness.

In breeding habits this species varies from the type description for
bubble-nest builders in one interesting particular. Bits of plant are
incorporated into the nest, such as the fine leaves of Myriophyllum; also
the female helps build it. In addition to his much brighter colors, the
male may be distinguished by his orange-red "feelers." Temperature
range, 68 to 84 degrees. Breeds at about 80. They are subject to dropsy.
Some males shoot water somewhat like the archer fish.

COLOR PLATE PAGE 580

Colisa làbiòsa (DAY)

Pronounced Ko-lee'sa lay'bee-o"sa   *Popular name,* Thick-lipped Gourami
MEANING OF NAME: *Colisa,* a native name; *labiosa,* thick-lipped
Formerly known as *Trichogaster labiosus*
Burma   Eastern Location Map r33 to w35   Length, 3¼ inches

THIS is the middle size among the aquarists' Colisas. Although a handsome fish when in full color, it is less brilliant than the other two. On the other hand it is not so "scary," which is always an advantage in an aquarium fish.

To the casual observer the lips do not appear to be unusually thick, nor very different from those of the Giant Gourami, *C. fasciata.*

Breeding is practically the same as with *Colisa lalia,* except that the female does not help build the nest. Clear eggs float to the surface.

The apparent difference in the shapes of the above heads is mainly due to a tilt of the upper fish (female), presenting a slightly top view.

COLOR PLATE PAGE 581

Trìchogáster trichópterus (PALLAS)   (Blue type)
Pronounced Try'ko-gas"ter   try-kop'te-rus
MEANING OF NAME: *Trichogaster,* hair-belly; *trichopterus,* hair-fin
Also known as *Trichopodus trichopterus* and *Osphromenus trichopterus*
Popular name, Three-spot Gourami (the third spot being the eye)
Malay Peninsula, Indo-China   Length, 5 inches
Eastern Location Map v37 to 40 to F39; L43; F46

FOR a time the Three-spot Gourami was known in the hobby only as
a silvery fish overlaid with grey markings, and with orange dots in
the fins. The same species, as shown above, was later found in Sumatra,
and has become popular as the "Sumatra" or "Blue" Gourami. When the
two color phases are crossed the blue in the babies is apt to be duller.

The species is one of the most easily bred of the bubble-nest builders,
although the nest itself is scattered and weak. This makes little difference, as both eggs and young float. Lusty fishes with such big spawns
that the young are sometimes used as food for other fishes!

Large specimens are liable to eat other fishes that are much smaller.
On the other hand they are wonderful for destroying that pest which few
other fishes will touch—Hydra. Male (lower) has longer dorsal fin.

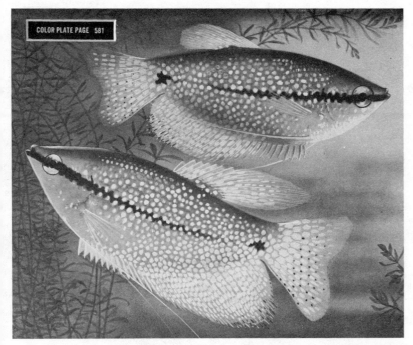

COLOR PLATE PAGE 581

Trìchogáster leèri (BLEEKER)

Pronounced Try'ko-gas"ter leer'eye   *Popular name,* Pearl Gourami

Named for Leer

Siam, Malay Peninsula, Sumatra   Length, 4 inches

Eastern Location Map D36 to F39; F37 to J41

*J*F the male fish maintained its full breeding color as we see it here, it could be fairly called the "Robin Red Breast Gourami," but it doesn't. Instead of being a flashy fish it is one of exquisite refinement. The regularity with which the pearly dots are distributed nearly all over it has given rise to still another popular name by which it is known in Europe—Mosaic Gourami. In England, Lace Gourami.

Breeding is in the typical style of the bubble-nest builders. The male is not very insistent about driving the female away after spawning is completed. Neither of them eats the eggs or young. The eggs float.

Temperature range between 68 to 85 degrees. The species shares hydra-eating honors with the preceding fish, *T. trichopterus.* It is quite gentle and is well suited to community life among fishes of approximately its own size. Imported in 1933. Occasionally this fish develops large, creeping golden areas. They are not permanent, and apparently not a disease.

COLOR PLATE PAGE 582

Photo by Sharad R. Sane, M. Sc.

Colisa Chuna

Pronounced Ko-lee′sa   *Popular name,* Sunset Gourami

Name is based on two native names

Northeast India (Assam, Bengal, Uttar Pradesh, etc.)   Length: 2¼ inches

Eastern Location Map M-23 to N-30

*C*OLISA *chuna* is a relatively newcomer to the aquarium scene. In keeping with its popular name, the male is brick red with a yellow dorsal. A nearly black line passes from the eye horizontally to the base of the caudal, and a blue triangular area fades in obliquely from the eye to the posterior tip of the anal fin, which is edged in black. The female shows a more distinct band running from the eye to the peduncle on a washed silver-brown body. The dorsal and anal fins are edged with orange-red.

Breeding this species is accomplished by bringing the temperature of the water down from a normally 83°F. to 78°F. A ten-gallon tank is large enough, and although plants may be present, the male builds his nest independent of plant fronds. Spawning lasts from an hour to two hours, during which time about 400 eggs are released. Within 24 hours the eggs begin to hatch and in 72 hours the fry are free swimming. First food consists of infusoria, and within three days egg infusion may be offered. Newly hatched brine shrimp is taken five days later. The fry show the dark bands by four weeks. Growth is rapid and the youngsters mature by the time they are four months old, displaying their attractive colors. Edited by H. S.

Helóstoma témmincki   CUVIER AND VALENCIENNES
Pronounced Hel-os'to-ma   tem'mink-eye   *Popular name,* Kissing Gourami
MEANING OF NAME: *Helostoma,* with turn-back mouth, referring to the thick re-curved
lips, which are provided with series of small teeth; *temmincki,* for C. Temminck,
of Leiden

Malay region, Java, Borneo, etc.   Length, up to 12 inches
Eastern Location Map x38; F36; L43; G44, etc.

THIS fish has been publicized both as a "kisser" and as an industrious eater of all kinds of algae. The latter claim is much exaggerated. The purpose of the kissing is not known. Some aquarists say these fishes annoy others by sucking at their sides. The larger ones do persecute the smaller of their own kind. Only one or two in a "community" tank seems best.

Breeding begins at 5-inch size. They embrace like other Gouramies, build no nest and have from 400 to 2,000 floating amber eggs, pin head size. Young hatch upside-down in a day. Parents *may* eat eggs, but will completely ignore young. Babies need Infusoria for a week, followed by newly-hatched Brine Shrimp or sifted live Daphnia. In two weeks, fine floating food. Thereafter they are surface feeders. Adults like powdered oatmeal with ground dried shrimp; also Pablum or crumpled dried spinach. They have few diseases, but decline if kept cool, or not fed several times daily. Prefer a temperature of 75-82. There are two color phases; silvery green and a pinkish, iridescent white. It is the latter strain that does most of the breeding. There are no external differences in the sexes.

Anabas téstudíneus   (BLOCH)

Pronounced An'a-bas   tes'tu-din"e-us   *Popular name,* Climbing Perch
MEANING OF NAME: *Anabas,* climber; *testudineus,* turtle-like
Formerly known as *Anabas scandens*
India, Malay Region and Philippines   Length, 6 to 10 inches in wild specimens
Eastern Location Map u23; r27; C22; I52; G58; w51

cA S surely as a monkey in a window attracts attention, just so surely
does any kind of a "walking fish" at an aquarium show draw the
crowds. Attendants in charge of these pleasant affairs will tell the same
story of panting persons who want to know, "Where is the walking fish?"

The Climbing Perch does the show-off job very well and doesn't seem
to mind. The fish has spiny edges on its gill plates. Note them in the illustration. By extending the plates and using a clumsy rocking motion, it
can make fairly good progress out of water. In its native habitat it is said
to travel overland in search of a new pond if its own dries up.

These are labyrinth fishes, but do not make any bubble-nest. Tiny eggs
float at the surface and hatch in a day. Parents ignore them. The body is
a brassy brown. Fins are brownish and sometimes the tail fin is an attractive dark red. They are ravenous eaters and will take anything, preferably animal food in chunks. One successful breeder conditions them on
canned dog food. Had best be kept by themselves. Temperature range,
65 to 90 degrees.

THE SNAKEHEADS
FAMILY CHANNIDAE
Pronounced Chan'ni dee

The Snakeheads are long, slim, snaky, air-breathing fishes from Africa and Asia, having no spines in the fins. In this they differ from their close relatives, the Anabantids. The Snakeheads are important food fishes in the Orient. They are tough and stand transport in tubs with little or no water. Chinese fishmongers can chop a good many steaks off the end of a fish before it sees fit to expire. Voracious gluttons all!

Chánna àsiática (LINNAEUS)
Pronounced Chan'na a'see-at"i-ka
MEANING OF NAME: *Channa*, meaning unknown; *asiatica*, Asiatic
Incorrectly called *Channa fasciata*

China   Eastern Location Map i48 to p42   Length, 8 inches

*W*HILE the length of this peculiar fish is given as above, it is more apt to average about 5 to 6 inches in the aquarium. Their toothed mouths are enormous; appetites to match. Bad company for other fishes.

The dotted zigzag lines on the sides divide a greenish color above from a gray tone below. Rather attractive. It has no ventral fins, which most other species of the family possess.

Eggs float at the surface and receive no attention, nor are they eaten. They hatch in about 4 days at a temperature of 80 degrees. The young are easily raised on Daphnia. Temperature range, 65 to 85 degrees. Sexes similar. Illustration shows adult and young.

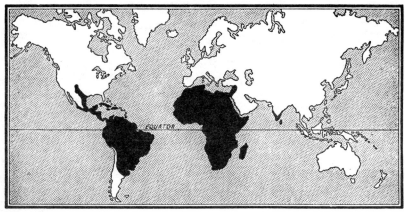

DISTRIBUTION MAP OF THE FAMILY CICHLIDAE

THE CICHLIDS
FAMILY CICHLIDAE
Pronounced Sick'li-dee

The Cichlids (pronounced Sick'lids) are spiny-rayed fishes agreeing with the Pomacentrids in having only one nostril on each side of the snout, instead of the usual two. The Cichlids differ from the Pomacentrids in lacking the shelf of bone which supports the eye socket in the latter group. The Cichlids are found only in Africa, Madagascar, and Tropical America, north of the Rio Grande in Texas, with the sole exception of *Etroplus,* three species of which inhabit southern India.

In general the Cichlids are the big fishes of the aquarium. They are well represented by such species as the Chanchita *(Cichlasoma facetum),* Jack Dempsey *(Cichlasoma biocellatum)* and the Jewel Fish *(Hemichromis bimaculatus).* Rather long fishes with slightly flattened, moderately deep bodies. The head, generally of good size, is armed with a strong, jutting lower jaw and small but sharp teeth, well suited not only to battle, but to the requirements of their remarkable habits in breeding, as we shall shortly see.

While a few of the Cichlids are peaceable citizens, most of them fight, especially with members of their own species, and more especially with those of the opposite sex. These battles mostly occur during courtship— terrific lovers' quarrels, as it were. Occasionally it is between mated pairs, as will be observed later.

No doubt feeling confident of taking care of themselves in open battle, most of the larger species tear out plants as possible hiding places for enemies, especially at breeding time.

Breeding With the unique exception of the mouthbreeders (whose habits will be described under their own headings), the

Cichlids breed so nearly alike that a general description will fit nearly all of them. The few traits that may be peculiar to a species will be noted under its own special text. For example, that popular favorite, *Pterophyllum eimekei* (Angel Fish), requires separate consideration.

The typical breeding actions of Cichlids are certainly the most interesting and highly organized of any known aquarium fishes, especially when the habits of mouthbreeders are added to that which now follows.

Mating itself is with them no hit-or-miss affair. At the very beginning the ancient law of the survival of the fittest is put into practical operation. If left to themselves in a large group, pairs will mate themselves by natural affinity, which is one of the best ways of discovering pairs if one has the room and stock to carry out this plan. The usual procedure in trying to mate a pair with a minimum of risk is to place them in a large aquarium with a glass partition between. That is their formal introduction. One fish is usually ready to mate before the other, and as flirtation through windows is nothing new in the world, one of them makes the opening advances. As again in our world, it may be either the male or the female to make the first move. This consists in a wagging of the body, spreading of the fins and a variety of changes in coloring. When the "party of the second part" returns these salutations and shows signs of approval, it is time to take out the partition and note what happens. Usually the courtship continues and it is not long before the kissing stage develops. This is where one of the uses of strong jaws comes in. They grasp each other by interlocking the lips and then begins the first real test. Each tugs and twists the other, apparently in a test of strength. They may go through the performance several times. If they do this repeatedly without either losing its "nerve," they may be considered to be as well mated as though they have a marriage certificate. But it often happens that one of them takes fright and beats a retreat after one of those vigorous kisses. Fear is fatal, and the victim of it is liable to get killed unless a safe retreat is found, or a kind Fate in the person of the owner separates them.

Sometimes a subsequent trial will prove more successful, but it is advisable to try some other pairing, if substitutes are on hand. Certain fishes will reject or kill several proposed mates before meeting an agreeable affinity.

Owing to the physical tussle which takes place, an effort is usually made by the aquarist to match the candidates in size, but there are many instances of happy unions between fishes where disparity in this respect is great. *Whether or not both fishes are ready to mate is the important thing.* Their courtship promotes the elimination of the unfit.

To return to the actual business of breeding—let us consider the proper conditions which should be provided. Success is more likely in large aquaria. Among the larger species, 3 inches is about minimum breeding size. Such fishes should be bred in an aquarium of not less than 10 gallons. Twenty would be better. As size of the pair increases, follow with proportionate room. It will pay.

Water should be old and at a temperature between 75 and 80 degrees. The best bottom covering is approximately 2 inches of well-washed sand. Any moderately good light is satisfactory. Omit plants for most species. Exceptions in this respect will be noted.

For a few days prior to breeding, the fishes dig holes in the sand. They also start cleaning a surface which they regard as suitable to the reception of their adhesive eggs. This spot may be the side of the aquarium, a large stone, inside or outside of a flower-pot laid on its side, or even a spot on the bottom of the aquarium from which the sand has been fanned away. It has been observed that a light-colored surface is preferred to dark. For this reason some of our fish breeders place a piece of marble or other light-colored stone in the aquarium with mated Cichlids.

The breeding pair takes nothing for granted as to cleanliness. Regardless whether they select a mossy side of the aquarium or a piece of marble fresh from the quarry, the sacred spot to receive their eggs must be painstakingly gone over to insure its absolute cleanliness. They bite, scrape and polish it with their teeth until no flaw can be found. No Dutch housewife could make it cleaner.

A day or two prior to the actual spawning both fish develop from the vent a breeding tube, or ovipositor. It first appears as a very small point or nipple. Whether it is a Cichlid or certain other species which deposit their eggs in a like manner, the appearance of the nipple is regarded as a sure sign that the fish is ripe for breeding. The tube shortly before spawning increases in length. In large specimens it may be as long as a half inch. It disappears within a week after spawning.

In general it is not easy telling the sexes. In older specimens the males often have longer pointed dorsal and anal fins. Where there is any distinctive difference in markings, this will be described in connection with the species. When the females are ripe, they are slightly fuller, but not in a pronounced way. It will be found that the breeding tube of the female is slightly blunt, whereas in the male it is pointed.

All things now being in readiness, the female approaches the prepared spawning spot and touches it lightly with the breeding tube, depositing one or more eggs. The male immediately follows, and with like action sprays the eggs with his fertilizing fluid. This is repeated many times over a period of perhaps 2 hours, when finally there may be from 100 to 2000 eggs laid in close formation. As this whole operation is carried on by a sense of touch and the eggs adhere very lightly, it is quite remarkable how few are lost or knocked off.

The spawning operation being completed, each fish takes turns fanning the eggs with the pectoral fins or tail. They relieve each other every few minutes. It is a popular idea that this fanning is to supply oxygen to the embryo within the egg. We know that bird eggs need oxygen, but with fish eggs there is also another consideration. As fungus is the great enemy of the eggs and the parents go to no end of trouble to have everything immaculate, presumably to avoid this danger, it seems quite likely they are preventing fungus-bearing particles of dirt from settling on the spawn. Sometimes, despite care, fungus develops on a few eggs. It attacks all infertile eggs. Apparently sensing the danger of its spread, the fishes eat the affected eggs. This sometimes ends in all the eggs, good and bad, being eaten.

At a temperature of 80 degrees the eggs hatch in about 4 days. Now begins the next of the several remarkable stages in the breeding habits of these fishes. The parents scrape the eggs off (thus breaking the shell) and the fry are carried in the mouth of either of the parents and deposited in a depression in the sand. It may be newly dug or one left from the home-building connected with the early part of mating. The parents alternate in making the trips between the hatching place and the depression until all are transferred. In some instances the fishes set up a system so that neither end of the line is left unguarded. Each stands guard at one end and as everything is in readiness for the transfer of young, a signal is given in fish language and they dash past each other to the opposite terminus.

The young in the depression look like a vibrating, jelly-like mass not very easy to see. For several days they are moved from one depression to another, gently carried in the mouths of the parents. While it is generally conceded that the lower animals do not reason things out, the result is often the same as though they do. What they do "by instinct" is often wiser than our actions guided by reason. Whether the apparent reasoning in the actions of animals is of their own creation or is a reflection of the Master Mind in Nature makes little difference. Reasons for everything exist. It is interesting to speculate on them, and if we attribute higher thinking powers to our friends the fishes than they actually possess, we are only giving them the benefit of the doubt.

Cichlids have not only the most highly developed breeding habits from the social standpoint, but combine with them a seeming understanding of certain scientific principles which, as far as man is concerned, were discovered but yesterday. These are the recognition of the dangers from bacteria, and of their control through cleanliness. Reference has already been made to the scrupulous care in cleansing the spawning surface and to the eating of such eggs as have been attacked by fungus. Various interpretations may be placed on the practice of moving the young from one hole to another. As this is begun before the babies are old enough to eat anything, it cannot be to provide new pastures. One hole would be as safe from enemies as any other. Besides, in the open places where these fishes breed, they are absolutely fearless in the defense of their young, so the theory of safety may be dismissed. The theory which is in line with their other actions points to cleanliness as the motive—*scientific* cleanliness if you will. The babies are picked up in the mouth, a few at a time, and apparently chewed. They are only rolled around harmlessly and discharged into the next depression. Every last one is so treated. It is the fish's baby bath. Each one emerges perfectly cleansed of any particles. By using a series of depressions for the purpose, the parents are absolutely certain that all babies were "scrubbed," of which they could not be sure if they were kept in one place.

After 4 to 10 days the yolk-sacs of the young have been absorbed and they swim up in a cloud with the parents, usually in formation, headed one way. Stragglers are gathered up in the mouths of the parents and shot back into the school. This family unit is very beautiful to see and gives the aquarist one of his biggest and most last-ing thrills. How long the parents and young should be left together is a question largely of sentiment. In the wild the parents undoubtedly can be of much use to the young by protecting them after they are swimming about, but in the aquarium their usefulness ends at that point. The pleasure of seeing the parents and young together is the only reason for not separating them promptly. No hen could be more solicitous for her brood than are these devoted fish-parents for their fry. In their defense they are the very embodiment of savage fury, no matter what or how large the real or imaginary enemy. The owner himself had better not poke his nose too close to the water when peering into the domestic affairs of a large pair of Cichlids unless he wishes to have it shortened.

The young of the larger Cichlids are a fair size by the time the yolk-sac is absorbed and for the most part can get along without Infusoria if brine shrimp or finely-sifted Daphnia are to be had. For other sugges-tions see items under "Large Fry" on the Menu, page 48.

Theoretically these interesting pairs divide every domestic duty equally. It sometimes turns out that one is a better parent than the other, but resentment is clearly shown by the mate on whom the heavier part of the burden is shifted. An effort is made to drive the negligent parent to its duty. This failing, open warfare is liable to occur, resulting in the breaking up of matrimonial arrangements, the eating of eggs or young and the death of the principal at fault. In other words, these fishes seem to have and to carry out a sense of justice. Otherwise we may look at it as the elimination both of the unfit parent and of its progeny. The eating of the eggs by either fish is, for the same cause, liable to end in the same way. Here, as elsewhere in animal life, defective individuals are eliminated by normal ones.

With many Cichlids it is possible and even advisable to hatch and rear the young away from the parents. This method is described under the heading of *Pterophyllum scalare.*

Some tact should be shown in approaching an aquarium containing eggs or young, as the parents are liable to misinterpret the intentions of the interested owner and eat their young to thwart the imagined enemy.

When the young and parents are finally separated it is well to keep an eye on the old couple, as each may suspect the other of being responsible for the disappearance of the babies, and open an attack in reprisal.

Cichlids all tend towards carnivorous appetites, but few of them insist upon a diet exclusively of meats. While they do very well on worms, flies, larvae, chopped clam, scraped meat, oyster, shrimp or fish (cooked or uncooked), Daphnia, etc., they will take either a mush composed of oatmeal cooked with shredded fish or shrimp, or a dried food containing mixed ingredients. The fishes in a warm temperature—75 to 85 degrees— are heavy eaters, and should be fed not less than twice daily.

Most of them will stand a reasonably wide range of temperature, about 65 to 90 degrees, although with valued specimens it might be unwise to risk anything below 68 degrees.

Cichlid parents, except Mouthbreeders, should be fed while caring for young. Live Daphnia have the double advantage that they drop young for the baby fishes, and are themselves eaten by the breeders.

Large Cichlids live long. It is nothing uncommon for them to reach 10 years, although after 5 years they are likely to develop certain signs of age not connected with feebleness. There are 3 such points which may be noted. The mouth does not close completely in breathing; a spinal hump forms just in back of the head (as in the colored illustration of *Cichlasoma biocellatum*); the colors become more fixed and permanent; the colors do not change so readily under excitement.

Cichlids are commonly not good community fishes, although a number of big ones in a very large tank get along without trouble.

Typical athletic courtship of most Cichlids as expressed by a pair of A. *portale-grensis*. The end may be either murder or a happy marriage which, in Nature, lasts until death do them part.

The above pictures illustrate stages in mating previously described. From them the reader will understand why plenty of room is needed. We are reminded of the song "The Return of the Caballero," made famous by Frank Crummit. The hero asks his inamorata:

Why such big rooms in your castle?
She replies
So in case you get fresh
I'll have room to rassle!

Cichlids like a smooth, hard surface on which to arrange their sticky spawn. Some preference is shown for light colors, but this is not important. Bars of slate are used as spawn support for some species (see plate of *Symphysodon discus*). Flower pots or smooth light stones are good. In this instance an inverted porcelain soapholder was used, largely because of its photographic contrast with the amber eggs; also its convenient size. Unwilling to take cleanliness for granted, the fishes are seen scraping the already immaculate surface that is to hold their sacred spawn.

This turned out to be a spawning of nearly 2,000 eggs. The female squeezes them out of a short tube, temporarily appearing from the vent. The action rather distantly reminds one of a skilled baker putting the last delicate tracery of icing on a wedding cake, but the fish must depend on the sense of touch to make the intricate, compact arrangement of eggs without once placing one on top of another. The male, from a similar tube, sprays and fertilizes each deposit. A spawning such as this may require several hours. The fish are now taking turns fanning the eggs.

Here the eggs have nearly all popped. The parents are most attentively and tenderly placing the hatchlings in their mouths and depositing them in a previously-made depression in the sand. The mass looks like living, vibrating jelly. Transfers are made to new depressions for about two days. Thus every baby is sure to often receive a sort of scouring. Apparently there is never an accident due to this seemingly rough treatment. It is not definitely known whether the parents detach the young from the support just before they hatch, or just after. Infertile eggs are removed.

The problems of a hen looking after her chicks when they first become venturesome are mild compared with the worries of Cichlid parents when several hundred youngsters get out of control and wander into danger. Defense of a concentrated group is effective, but when the babies, as we see in the picture, scatter even for a short time, they give the parents bad moments. But this is something that has to be faced, for babies must learn by leaving the cradle. Enemies may not be present in the aquarium, but animals continue to act on ancestral experience.

Here we see that the youngsters have enveloped their parents as in a cloud. Now there seems to be less worry, but unabated vigilance. Frequently the old pair stands guard facing different directions, the better to see everything. Nervous twitches by the guardians are believed to be signals of real or imagined danger. Now the babies have absorbed their yolk-sac and it is time to think about their next food. Most species at this stage can eat newly-hatched Brine Shrimp, or finely sifted live Daphnia. Infusoria are not of much interest, except certain large rotifers.

Some youngsters are brought through the first stages of fish infancy on powdered dry food, or mashed yellow of hard-boiled (20 minute) chicken eggs, but to get sturdy growth such as this in 10 days' feeding, fresh food is needed. Here they are big enough to tackle adult Daphnia. If they get it, their progress will be fast. They will have a good start. Aquarists unable to secure Daphnia will find fair results from very finely minced and mashed White Worms or the smallest bits of raw shrimp, fish or crab meat rubbed through a fine screen.

This parent is now the embodiment of dauntless fury. Its young are threatened by some unknown giant. Never mind how big; an "all-out" attack must be made instantly. At first the assault was directed against a siphoning hose being used to clean up a bit of debris. When the human hand was substituted, the attack was even more intense. Ordinarily such experiments are not to be recommended. Less excitement than this causes most Cichlids to eat their young, probably rather than having an enemy get them. A death fight between the parents may follow.

From the time the young are free-swimming they gather at night in a school at bottom of tank, with parents hovering over. Picture was taken by flash set off in darkness, camera having been previously pointed at a spot where they had been observed to gather at dusk. These *Aequidens portalegrensis* babies grew to size shown in color plate of the species before separating them from parents, although hundreds were removed from time to time, owing to crowding the small photographing aquarium. All pictures in the series are shown at about half life size.

Hémichròmis fasciàtus PETERS

Pronounced Hem'mee-krow"miss fas'see-ay"tus

MEANING OF NAME: *Hemichromis*, half-Chromis; *fasciatus*, banded

Central W. Africa   Western Location Map x45 to P65   Length, 6 to 10 inches

*W*E sometimes find a Cichlid that is suited to the aquarium only if the fish is not allowed to grow too big. *Hemichromis fasciatus* if kept in an aquarium of 10-gallon size can be held down to 5 or 6 inches, but if in a large tank, it reaches a length of 10 inches. As it is a bad digger, it can do a lot of damage when this size.

Contrary to *H. bimaculatus,* the colors are not bright. A brassy yellow or olive overlaid with 5 to 6 variable vertical bands constitutes the main pattern. Dorsal and tail fins, blue-black with narrow red edge. Ventral fins, clear to yellow; eye, brown. Black spot on opercle. At breeding time the forward part of the body becomes black and the belly pure white. The nose takes on a mahogany-red color, while the anal and tail fins become red. Breeds like *H. bimaculatus.* The fish is inclined to be savage.

The specimen from which the illustration was made had been purchased as *Tilapia nilotica.*

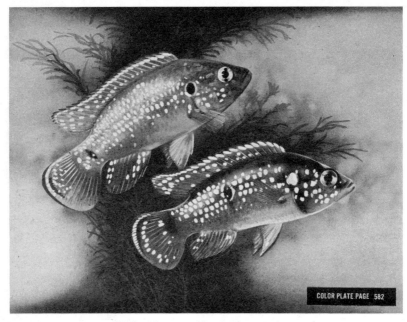

COLOR PLATE PAGE 582

Hémichròmis bimáculàtus GILL

Pronounced Hem'mee-crow"miss by-mak'you-lay"tus   *Popular name,* Jewel Fish
MEANING OF NAME: *Hemichromus,* half-Chromis; *bimaculatus,* two-spotted
Most of Tropical Africa   Length, 4 inches
Western Location Map A56; C59; D64; w70; w45; A52

(O)NE of the typical savage Cichlids. It needs several redeeming traits
to justify being kept, and it has them. A temperamental fish, a good
parent, fairly hardy and at times gorgeously beautiful.

Although the fins and general coloration are the same in male and
female, the sex is easily determined. The male has more and larger jewels
on the gill plate, while those in the tail fin extend farther and form themselves into a crescent. From this it will be seen that the upper fish in the
illustration is the female, but the general difference in body color means
nothing. At other times the male will be brighter. It is true, however,
that in her maximum redness the female is a little brighter than the
male, reversing the usual order of things. During courtship the colors
change rapidly, dark spots become light or disappear altogether, the
jewel facets enlarge.

Out of breeding season both fishes are of a rather dark, nondescript
color, lightly lined with blue jewelled scales and displaying a dark spot

Hemichromis bimaculatus FANNING EGGS

near the centre of the body, one on the gill plate and one at the tail base. It is hard to understand why the specific name of the fish is not *trimaculatus*.

Mating time is difficult and dangerous. Whether the group natural selection method is used or when there are only 2 fishes to work with, it is advisable with this species to have plenty of refuge places for the one getting the worst of it. In addition to the flower-pot for receiving the spawn, there should be heavy plants like Giant Sagittaria or some large stones placed in formation for recesses.

The eggs of this species, if in clean conditions, can be satisfactorily hatched and reared if the parents are removed, but then the aquarist loses one of his greatest pleasures by not witnessing the instructive and touching family life of the fishes.

The young grow rapidly and when about 6 weeks old begin attacking each other. For this reason they should be kept in an aquarium of at least 10-gallon capacity.

Temperature range, 60 to 90 degrees. Breeding at 80.

Tilàpia macrocéphala (BLEEKER)

Pronounced Ti-lay'pee-a mak'row-sef"a-la   *Popular name,* Blackjaw Mouthbreeder
MEANING OF NAME: *macrocephala,* large headed; meaning of *Tilapia* is unknown
Incorrect name, *Tilapia heudeloti* (another species)
Gold Coast to S. Nigeria   Western Location Map B51 to B58   Length, 7 inches

℟HE habits of this fish are very much the same as the preceding, except that the male is the nursemaid. Also he does not hold the eggs with such bulldog tenacity. If caught in a net he will spit them all out and will not pick them up again. Under these circumstances one need not give up hope of hatching the eggs. Place them in clear, shallow water and stir them around a bit with a spoon several times a day. In about a week tiny fish will be found attached to the eggs, much smaller than the eggs themselves. The fry grow by absorbing the egg.

Sexes can not be told before the fishes are about 3 inches long, at which time the gill plate of the male becomes brassy yellow in the centre, whereas in the female it is delicate, translucent pink. Inset shows young.

A large species of *Tilapia,* carrying young, still native in Lake Galilee, may very well have been caught by fishermen of Biblical times.

The two outstanding features of the fish are the very black throat which sometimes develops, and the rosy glow in the fins, especially in the broad tail. The body is silvery, variably marked at times with black.

A gluttonous, good-natured fish. Temperature range, 68 to 85 degrees.

COLOR PLATE PAGE 583

Haplochròmis Múlticolor   (HILGENDORF)

Pronounced Hap'low-krow"miss mul"te-col'or *Popular name,* Egyptian Mouthbreeder
MEANING OF NAME: *Haplochromis,* plain chromide; *multicolor,* many-colored
Also known as *Haplochromis strigigena* and *Paratilapia multicolor*
Egypt   Western Location Map o68; r70; v70   Length, 2½ inches

OUTHBREEDERS! What whim of Nature have we here? It is
not so much a whim as it is one of Nature's most unusual bits of
ingenuity for the protection of the eggs and young of certain species, of
which this happens to be one. There is nothing very unusual about the
first part of the courtship. The male fans a depression in the sand about
3 inches in diameter and induces the female to circle with him over this
shallow pit, during which action a few eggs are dropped and fertilized
from time to time. The eggs of each deposit are quickly picked up in
the capacious mouth of the female and kept there, not only until they are
hatched, but until the yolk-sac is fully absorbed. The whole process takes
about 15 days. As the eggs resemble small mustard seed both in size and
color, and as there may be as many as 100 of them in the mouth of this

small fish, it will be seen that she undertakes quite a burden, even though she is liberally equipped with mouth capacity. The bony structure of the head of the female is noticeably larger in proportion than that of the male. This is somewhat exaggerated in appearance as she approaches the end of her maternal duties, for during the entire period of carrying the eggs and young, she steadfastly refuses food, thus becoming thin and wasted about the body. The lower fish in the photograph characteristically shows the bulged head and shrunken body of a female near the end of her heroic, self-imposed task. It seems that she must say to herself, "Be not weary in well-doing." Young emerge in 11 days.

This aversion to food during the carrying period is no doubt Nature's provision against either accidental or intentional swallowing of eggs, for one of a fish's greatest delicacies is fish eggs. Many of them, as we have numerously noted elsewhere, do not stop at eating the eggs of other fishes, but also consume their own. What self-control the Cichlids must display in order to propagate their own kind, for practically all of them take their eggs or young into their mouths at some time; but especially the mouthbreeders whose temptation is multiplied by hunger!

The tenacity of these small fishes in caring for the eggs and young is remarkable in another way. If caught and roughly handled in a net and exposed to the air, they will not divulge their secret, but will keep their mouths tightly locked.

During the period of incubation and development of the young, all mouthbreeders use a peculiar chewing motion of the jaws to give a circulation of water among their charges. There is, no doubt, also sufficient friction used to keep them clean and free from dirt which might carry fungus. At the same time it can be noted that the lips are not opened as freely as when they are out of the carrying period. By getting a favorably lighted direct view into the mouth, the eggs can be seen.

It is best to remove the male after the spawning is completed.

The male can be identified by the reddish tip on his anal fin.

The young are at first only allowed to leave the mother's mouth for short periods. At the least sign of danger they all rush back. The young emerge in 11 days after the female picks up the spawn. In 4 or 5 days of liberty they are too big to return, and here the maternal care abruptly ends, for she is then likely to eat them. At this point she should be removed.

On account of its comparatively small size this species is sometimes kept in community tanks, but it has been known to attack and kill such fishes as the *Brachydanios*. Perhaps this is in anticipation of defense of its young. A suitable temperature is between 70 and 80 degrees.

Tilàpia mossambíca PETERS

Pronounced Ti-lay′pee-a moss′am-bee″ka   *Popular name,* Mozambique Tilapia
Named for Mozambique, E. Africa
S. Africa and Portuguese E. Africa
Western Location Map X65 to J73   Length, 4 inches

𝒜 MOUTHBREEDING species, the female carrying the eggs, which are said to be fertilized within her mouth as she breathes water just previously inseminated by the male. The babies first emerge from the maternal maw in about 10 days, retreating again as danger approaches, as described for *Pelmatochromis guentheri.*

The species is seen in dealers' tanks only occasionally, but we anticipate a better supply, since they have been introduced into different parts of the tropics as food fish, and have multiplied greatly. We give 4-inches as the average aquarium size, but the bulletin of the Indonesian Veterinary Association claims that specimens in pond culture reach an incredible 6 pounds. This fish is a heavy feeder and takes any food. Male at breeding time shows white (as above) on lower part of head, while the tail tip becomes deep red. Temperatures 70-80.

Later reports indicate that the fabulous poundage expectation from the fish has not always been realized, because their very productivity soon overcrowds a pond, resulting in much smaller fish.

Nowhere have we yet found an exception to the axiom that great growth needs not only heavy feeding, but also liberal water surface per fish.

Tilapia sparrmani A. SMITH

Pronounced Ti-lay′ pee-a spar′man-eye   *Popular name,* Peacock Cichlid
MEANING OF NAME: Named for Anders Sparrman (1748-1820), Swedish explorer
of South Africa

South Africa from Angola and Orange River to Natal and Zambesi
Western Location Map M62 to O72 and T62   Length, 7 inches

THE generic name *Tilapia* is usually associated with mouth-breeding
Cichlids, such as those preceding this page. As *T. sparrmani* are
not mouthbreeders, we again point out that breeding habits have little,
if anything, to do with scientific classification.

This species was imported from South Africa in 1947. In the aquarium
it grows to about 5 inches, but starts breeding at half that length. The
highlights shown in the dorsal fin are pale iridescent blue, tipped with
red. The fin also has an interesting spot. Body color, olive, overlaid with
rapidly changing dark patterns. Upper fish here is the male, but body
shape is the only safe guard as to sex. At the moment he was in one of
the dark color phases.

They breed like other large Cichlids, such as *A. portalegrensis,* but are
more temperamental as to fighting and also as to eating their young.
Easily spawned, and may turn out very large families or none at all.
They are safest kept either singly or with large numbers of their own
kind. Not suited to a community tank. Temperature, 65-85 degrees.

Pelmátochròmis guentheri   (SAUVAGE)

Pronounced Pel-ma'to-krow"miss   gin'ther-eye

MEANING OF NAME: *Pelmatochromis,* Sole-Chromis, referring to a peculiar internal
formation of the gill structure; *guentheri,* after the naturalist, Guenther

Trade name (incorrectly) *Pelmatochromis belladorsalis*

Equatorial W. Africa coastal rivers   Length, 4 inches

Western Location Map F58 to B51

THE dorsal fin on this fish is most striking, and entirely different from
that of any other known aquarium fish. The light portions shown in
the fins are much like applied gold leaf. As the body is a plain drab,
of purplish hue, devoid of pattern, the startling fins have the field to
themselves. The fish is peaceful and will eat anything.

At the time they were introduced (1933) they were believed to be
mouthbreeders. This proved to be the case. They breed like *Tilapia
macrocephala,* and on several occasions have reared their broods in small
aquariums with both parents present. When the young first emerge, they
are large. At the slightest sign of danger, they continue to use the mouth
of the father as a refuge, even after they have reached a length of ⅝ inch.
It is quite an amusing sight to see them scamper in, especially when their
size makes it impossible for all to enter. It is like a hen who is no longer
able to hide all her chicks under her feathers. Temperature, 70 to 82.

Pelmátochròmis annéctens **BOULENGER**

Pronounced Pel-ma'to-krow"miss an-nek'tens

MEANING OF NAME: *annectens,* connecting, no doubt meaning a connecting
link between species

Lower Niger   Western Location Map A to B on 56   Length, 4 inches

*I*N commercial circles this fish has been handled both as *Pelmatochromis
arnoldi* and *Pelmatochromis fasciatus.* The late J. R. Norman, leading
authority on this group of fishes, said that our photograph closely resembles *P. annectens,* as here listed, and as Stoye has an elaborate description
of the species under this name, and that description accurately fits the
fish photographed, we feel reasonably certain it is correct.

A small but distinguishing feature is the bright white spot just above
the vent in the female. This barely shows in the male. There are 6 vertical bars and sometimes 3 horizontal stripes. Dorsal and tail fins tipped
red. The dorsal of the male (upper fish) is not usually as long as shown
in this specimen. Geometric blue dots in ends of dorsal, tail and anal
fins. Gorgeous in mating colors. Not a mouthbreeder.

For breeding, needs a large aquarium and a temperature of about 80
degrees. Does not destroy plants. Temperature range, 68 to 85 degrees.

For some reason it is difficult to induce this species to spawn.

Gèophàgus brasiliénsis HECKEL
Pronounced Jee'o-fay"gus   bra'sil'ee-en"sis   (Gee-off'a-gus   allowable)
MEANING OF NAME: *Geophagus*, earth-eater; *brasiliensis*, from Brazil
Brazil   Western Location Map L37 to ★26   Length, 6 inches

SOME Cichlids might well be the envy of mere man, for they become handsomer with age. *G. brasiliensis* is one of that kind. The picture demonstrates the point. The high lights on the body and fins are electric blue-green and it will be seen in the illustration how much better they are developed in the older and larger fish. The dark central body spot is larger and more showy than the photograph indicates. The base color of the body is a varying shade of olive, while the fins are dark orange. Dorsal edge not as bright a red as in some other Cichlids—for instance, the "Dempsey." Breeds in standard Cichlid manner, but not often.

The fish is rather easily distinguished from the other popular Cichlids by the outline of its body. The head is large and the body tapers off sharply where it joints the tail fin. This end of the body is called the "caudal peduncle." The eye is dark gold and black.

And, by the way, the picture shows a happily mated pair, despite the difference in size, and that the male is the larger. It is a common belief that there is less likely to be trouble if the female is the larger of the two.

COLOR PLATE PAGE 583

Pelmatochròmis kribénsis   BOULENGER
Pronounced Pel-ma'to-krow"miss   kree-ben'sis   *Popular name,* Kribi Cichlid
MEANING OF NAME: *kribensis,* from the Kribi River, Cameroon
French Equatorial Africa   Western Location Map C58   Length, 3 inches

SOMETIMES confused with a similar species, *P. taeniatus,* of which it
may be a geographical race, this spectacular fish is not new to science,
but a popular modern introduction to the aquarium world. We first saw
it in 1952. Its colors are extremely and rapidly variable, especially those
in the fins. The red of the belly, especially in the female, varies only in
intensity, but colors such as those of the prominent spots on the gill
plates alternate instantly between fiery orange and electric blue. In the
cramped confines of a photographic aquarium the male, oblivious of his
surroundings, constantly courts the female, flashing rapid color changes.
Eggs are placed on the inner, upper side of an arch, which can be supplied by a 6-inch flower pot (above), either cut in half or partially
sunken on its side. Guarded mostly by the female they hatch in 2 days
and are easily reared by the usual Cichlid routine.

A peaceful, somewhat shy, quick-moving fish, preferring soft, slightly
acid water and a variety of foods, including algae. Temperature, 68-80.

COLOR PLATE PAGE 584

Etròplus maculàtus (BLOCH)

Pronounced E-tro'plus mac'you-lay"tus   *Popular name,* Orange Cichlid

MEANING OF NAME: *Etroplus,* with armored abdomen, referring to hard fin rays;
maculatus, spotted

India and Ceylon   Eastern Location Map y21; A22   Length, 3 inches

𝒜 VERY individual Cichlid, and a rather touchy one as to living conditions. Some of our best aquarists have given it up in despair, yet others have little trouble.

It is one of our very few Cichlids from India, and can stand plenty of warmth, being happiest in a range about from 75 to 82 degrees. The plate shows breeding colors. At other times the fish is not so deep a yellow, and the central body spot is black. The black in fins is less intense at other times. Upper fish is the male. Out of breeding season the male is just a little stronger in color and has more red in the eye.

Very dark eggs are deposited on the underside of an arch, such as the inside of a large flower pot laid on its side. Each baby is hung by a thread. Both parents fan eggs, but swimming young follow their mother, while father does police duty. One breeder of this species adds 2 level teaspoons of salt of each gallon of their water.

Gèophàgus jùrupäri   HECKEL

Pronounced Jee'o-fay"gus   ju'ru-par"ee   *Popular name*, Jurupari

MEANING OF NAME: *jurupari*, after a native name

The Amazon   Western Location Map A21 to J9 and F29   Length, 5 inches

*T*HIS *Geophagus* is peculiar in the possession of a particularly long, pointed head, and in having a dorsal fin that is quite high along its entire length. The long, downward arching profile of the snout makes the lower line of the head and body seem somewhat flat. The eyes are very large and are placed high. Owing to the long snout they also seem to be set far back, giving the fish an odd look.

Like all other Cichlids, their color and markings vary greatly. The average background is a rather light golden color, while the light pattern on the body and in the fins is metallic blue.

The upper fish is the male, showing a longer point on the dorsal fin.

This is one of the more peaceful Cichlids, and does not tear out plants. It is a peculiar mouthbreeder.

Another species, *G. acuticeps,* is similar, but has extensions on the ends of the ventral fins, similar to those in the adult *Cichlasoma festivum.*

Heríchthys cyanoguttàtus BAIRD AND GIRARD
Pronounced Her-ik'thiss   sy-an'o-gut-tay"tus   *Popular name,* Rio Grande Perch
MEANING OF NAME: *Herichthys,* fish like Heros; *cyanoguttatus,* blue spotted
Incorrectly, *Neetroplus carpintis*
Mexico and Texas   Western Location Map i15 to n15   Length, 7 to 9 inches

IN point of distribution this is the most northerly of all Cichlids. Through the Rio Grande and its tributaries it actually extends into Texas, and is the only member of the family found in the United States.

Although without pronounced coloration, the fish is easily recognized. It is of a grayish tone, thickly sprinkled with small, light, round dots, extending well into the dorsal fin. These dots are smaller and more numerous than in any other Cichlid we know of—"star-scattered," to use one of Omar Khayyam's best phrases.

At breeding season it develops interesting brown markings and patterns.

As may be assumed from its natural distribution, this fish can stand lower temperatures than most of the species, although it likes to breed at about 78 degrees.

The chief objection to the fish is that in a large aquarium it grows to an inordinate size. The species is not troublesome in company with other large fishes. Temperature range, 65-82 degrees.

COLOR PLATE PAGE 584

Photo by Wolfsheimer

Nannacara anomala REGAN

Pronounced Nan'-na-car'-a a-nom'-a-la   *Popular Name*, Golden-eyed Cichlid

MEANING OF NAME: *Nanna*—(Latin) dwarf; *anomala*—(Latin) deviation
from common rule

British Guiana (Western)   Length—male, 3 inches; female, 1½ inches
Western Location Map B20

THIS symmetrical dwarf Cichlid has received considerable attention from aquarists in recent years, and taking into account its many attributes, it can be credited as an ideal aquarium fish. Its elongated, somewhat compressed body is well-proportioned and the high dorsal of the male complements the body, running from the nape to anterior to the peduncle. The rounded caudal and sweeping anal fins make for interesting lines. The head is copper-brown, the sides metallic green, shading sometimes into olive. The sides of the head show shots of bright green and black irregular splotches.

The female is considerably smaller than the male and is not so beautifully colored, usually showing a drab brown.

Spawning procedure follows the Cichlid pattern in most respects. The ideal temperature seems to be in the high 70's and should not be lower than 72 degrees F. The eggs hatch in 3 days and it is very nearly a week before the fry are free-swimming. Newly hatched brine shrimp and micro worms should be offered at this time. Edited by H. S.

Cíchlasòma còryphœnòides (HECKEL)

Pronounced Sick'la-so"ma   ko'ree-fee-no"i-dees   *Popular name,* Chocolate Cichlid
MEANING OF NAME: *Cichlasoma,* thrush-body; *coryphœnoides,* dolphin-like
Near Manaos, Brazil   Western Location Map G20   Length, 4 inches

A SPECIES which has been imported from time to time, but of which we know little. For a year after its introduction it was temporarily labelled Cichlasoma U2, the letter U standing for "unidentified." We are now reasonably sure that the above identification is correct.

Even for a Cichlid the fish is remarkable for its extremes of color changes, and the speed with which they take place. The author, being responsible for the popular name, Chocolate Cichlid, does not feel that this was a very happy choice. Although one of its color phases is a purplish chocolate shade, a better name would have been Marbled Cichlasoma, for the light markings in the illustration, being of a warm ivory shade, often appear in marbled patterns against a most variable dark background, frequently a purplish brown, flushed with rose, if such a combination is thinkable! It is interesting to observe the color changes which take place if a light is turned on these fishes when they have been in darkness.

Efforts at breeding have thus far ended only in killings, but the survivors of the battles remain beautiful and interesting exhibition fishes. Temperature requirements, 70-85 degrees.

Cichlasòma cútteri   FOWLER

Pronounced Sick'la-so"ma   cut'ter-eye

Named for Mr. Victor Cutter, President of United Fruit Co.

Honduras   Western Location Map s23   Length, 3½ inches

THE dominant feature of this fish is its 7 to 8 dark bars against a pale background, faintly suffused with blue. These bars at breeding time become stronger in the female, while her throat and belly take on a brown or black appearance. The third bar tends to extend into the dorsal fin, and at times ends in a peacock spot. Contrary to the female, the male loses most of his bars at the breeding season and his body becomes brown to olive green. The eye is attractively flashed with blue-green.

Unusually good care is provided by the parents, especially by the mother, who seems to be the *charge d'affaires.* One pair of these fishes raised its brood in a community tank without loss either of babies or damage to the other inhabitants, a performance calling for an unusual degree of firmness and tact. Male tears out plants only during breeding.

The species is easily confused with the true *C. nigrofasciatum*, which averages darker and greener in color, and has a golden brown eye.

C. cutteri may be regarded as one of the safe Cichlids, having little or none of the pugnacious qualities common to most of them.

Eggs hatch in 3 days at 80 degrees.

Cichlasòma facètum (JENYNS)

Pronounced Sick′la-so″ma fa-see′tum   *Popular name,* Chanchita

MEANING OF NAME: *facetum,* attractive

Discarded scientific name, *Heros facetus*

Argentina   Western Location Map ● 22   Length, 7 inches

HE Chanchita is one of the older friends of modern aquarists, and one of the most dependable. It will stand a temperature of 60 without trouble, is a sure breeder, an excellent parent, a fish that lives long and is easy to feed. This was the first Cichlid domesticated—1884.

Perhaps not so showy as some other of the large Cichlids, it is a fish of distinction and of interesting variation in color. Usually the background is horn-color overlaid with the black pattern shown in the illustration. The body color sometimes becomes almost black. The eyes are strikingly red, but the depth of their color varies in individuals. This is one of the few Cichlids which does not show any metallic spangles.

Except at breeding time the Chanchita is not a pugnacious fish, although the larger specimens are too big for the average community tank.

In breeding and feeding habits it is typical of the description for the group. It is well suited to summer culture in pools in states of temperate climate. Large broods can be raised with little attention.

COLOR PLATE PAGE 585

Cíchlasòma meèki (BRIND)

Pronounced Sick'la-so"ma meek'eye		*Popular name,* Firemouth
	Named for Prof. Seth Meek	
Yucatan	Western Location Map n21	Length, 4 to 5 inches

NOT every fish has a pronounced individual characteristic marking. C. *meeki* has two: the green-edged spot at the base of the gill plate and a fiery orange color along the belly, and which extends *into the mouth.* This color is present at all times and is brighter in the male, but becomes most vivid during mating, especially in the *female.*

The specimens used in the illustration were about 3 inches long, and up to this size there are no external sex differences, except that the belly coloring on the male may be a shade brighter. Six months later, when the pair had grown another inch, the male developed the usual long point on the dorsal fin, common to most male Cichlids.

It has now been successfully bred many times. The breeding habits are the same as with the other Cichlids. It is surely worthy of a place in any collection of fishes of this type.

Breeding temperature, about 80 degrees.

COLOR PLATE PAGE 586

Cichlasòma séverum (HECKEL.)

Pronounced Sick'la-so"ma sev'e-r-rum   *Popular name*, Deacon

MEANING OF NAME: *severum*, severe

Formerly, *Heros spurius*

Amazon   Western Location Map A21 to I9, and F29   Length, 5 to 6 inches

REFERENCE has already been made to the great changeability in coloring and marking of the various Cichlids. This is particularly true of the *Cichlasoma severum*. The background color in any individual may, in a few seconds, change from pale gray to deep green, brown or nearly black, with any imagined intervening shades. Agitation of one kind or another usually causes the color changes.

While the name *severum* means "severe," it is no more militant than the average large Cichlid.

Undoubtedly this is one of the more difficult Cichlids to breed. It should have a large aquarium, plenty of warmth (about 80 degrees) and be well fed on garden worms in order to induce mating and spawning. Otherwise the methods conform to standard. The sex is easily told. The male has the regular rows of dots on the side, whereas the female has few, if any. When young they show only dark, distinct, vertical bars.

Cíchlasòma féstivum (HECKEL)

Pronounced Sick'la-so"ma fes'ti-vum   Known as *Acara bandeira* in Brazil

MEANING OF NAME: *festivum,* gaily attractive, festive

Also known as *Mesonauta insignis*

Amazon   Western Location Map A21 to O19 and F29   Aquarium size, 4 inches

A FISH of marked individuality. The strong oblique stripe traversing the body from the mouth to the upper tip of the dorsal fin is unique among our aquarium fishes, and makes identification of the species easy. The thread-like extensions or "feelers" seen on the ventral fins are a little longer than we commonly see among Cichlids. These increase with age, but nothing to compare with those on "Scalares." The general color of the body is silvery, with a green cast. The fins have none of the color markings common to many species of the genus. The magnificent upward oblique bar is in itself a sufficient gift from Nature for any one fish. This fish is at its best in a size of about 3 inches. When it gets larger the markings are apt to become less distinct. Breeding temperature, about 82 degrees.

The fish is fairly hardy, especially as it becomes older and larger, but it is difficult to mate. Although not a timid fish, it seems to prefer privacy when mating and caring for its young.

Cichlasòma nìgrofasciàtum (GUENTHER)

Pronounced Sick'la-so'ma ny'gro-fas'see-ay"tum   *Popular name,* Zebra Cichlid
MEANING OF NAME: *Cichlasoma,* resembling Chromis; *nigrofasciatum,* black-banded
San Salvador, etc.   Western Location Map v24; t-u on 21   Aquarium size, 4 inches

HE "Jack Dempsey" fish was for years considered to be *Cichlasoma
nigrofasciatum.* "Dempsey" has been found to be *C. biocellatum.*
Our present subject is a comparatively new introduction to aquarists,
and is sometimes known in the trade by the rather misleading name of
"Kongo Cichlid."

While they breed like other Cichlids, it is more necessary to give
breeding pairs a large aquarium liberally supplied with refuges, such as
flower-pots or large stones arranged in arches or other forms providing
hiding places for the pursued. This is not necessarily the female. The
male sometimes gets the worst of it. It is usually the smaller fish that
beats a retreat. The female assumes most of the care of the eggs.

Cichlids which are high-strung change their colors rapidly. This
species belongs to that type. Our illustration shows 2 color phases.
The one to the right displays brilliant bottle-green in the bars and cheeks.
Tail spot, vivid black. Oddly enough, the *female* has most of the color.
This fact is unique among known aquarium fishes. She has an irregular
pattern of dull orange scales on the posterior part of her body. This
extends into the lower fins.

The species not only fights its own kind, but is unsafe among other
fishes. Its attacks are swift and without much warning.

COLOR PLATE PAGE 586

Cichlasòma bìocellàtum REGAN

Pronounced Sick'la-so"ma   by'o-sell-ay"tum   *Popular name,* Jack Dempsey

MEANING OF NAME: *biocellatum,* with 2 spots, referring to the 2
spots on the sides

South America, probably Brazil   Length, up to 7 inches

*B*EFORE the reign of the Scalare, this fish, popularly and affectionately known as "Jack Dempsey," was the most popular of the Cichlids. Of its own type, with a long body and strong head, it is still the leader, for it has dazzling beauty, it is hardy, a good breeder and parent. A dependable show piece.

Our description of breeding of the Cichlids fits this species perfectly.

It was one of the earlier introductions into the aquarium, and for many years was known as *Cichlasoma nigrofasciatum.*

With the Dempsey it is particularly true that with age the colors become more fixed, brilliant, and less likely to change under the influence of fear or other emotional excitement. Our illustration shows the hump-shaped nape, which in some Cichlids develops with age.

Often a large individual fish is kept as a pet in an aquarium by itself, where it soon learns to beg, in fish language, for morsels of food from its master. Lives for 10 years or longer. Temperature range, 65-90 degrees.

Æquidens làtifrons (STEINDACHNER)

Pronounced Ee′kwi-denz lay′te-frons   *Popular name,* Blue Cichlid

MEANING OF NAME: *Æquidens,* with teeth of same length; *latifrons,* broad forehead

Also known to aquarists as *Acara cœruleo-punctata, Acara pulchra* and
Cichlasoma coeruleopunctata

Panama and Colombia   Western Location Map x10   Length, 6 inches

A LONG established favorite of mild disposition. A prolific breeder. "Blue Acara" is a widely accepted name for the fish, but there is nothing distinctly blue about it. The body color is rather greenish, with the usual sprinkling of blue-green spangled scales and irregular markings on the head. Central body spot on the third bar is large. In strong, direct light, 3 purplish or plum-colored stripes show along the body. The scales on the upper part of the body have blue centres with brown edges, while the lower scales are exactly the reverse—brown centres with blue edges. Fins, dull orange, with blue-green markings. Sexes colored alike.

Temperature range, 70 to 85 degrees. Breeds at about 78.

COLOR PLATE PAGE 585

Æquidens cúrviceps   E. AHL

Pronounced Ee'kwi-denz kur'vi-seps   *Popular name,* Blunthead Cichlid

MEANING OF NAME: *curviceps,* with dome-shaped head

Commonly but incorrectly known as *Acara thayeri,* a fish not yet imported

Amazon   No exact locality known   Length, 3 inches

HERE are several points about this fish which destine it to remain among the aquarists' choice selections. It is not large, it is both beautiful and different in color, it is not savage and may be used in a community aquarium. Lastly, it can be bred, but not too easily.

This is one of the Cichlids which does not tear out plants. Otherwise there is no difference from the breeding habits described at the beginning of this section. They are prone to eat their eggs. It is believed that the eggs should not be exposed to direct sunlight. This is a rather shy fish and needs privacy. One aquarist devised a plan by which he places a card in front of the aquarium, perforated by a peep-hole for observation.

The illustration shows the breeding tubes just emerging. Sexes are very similar. There is often a dark spot in the centre of the dorsal fin where it joins the body. This does not indicate sex. Temperature, 74-78 degrees.

COLOR PLATE PAGE 588

Æquidens portalegrénsis (HENSEL)

Pronounced Ee'kwi-denz por'tal-e-gren"sis

Named for Porto Alegre, Brazil   *Popular name,* "Port"

S. E. Brazil   Western Location Map ★26 to ‡21 and Q22   Length, 4 to 5 inches

USUALLY considered to be the most kindly of this general type and size of fish. Quite easily bred, even in aquaria that are too small. That is, it will manage in a 7-gallon aquarium, when it ought to have a 15 or larger. Owing to its easy disposition and sure-fire breeding qualities the species was chosen for the series of eight pictures appearing in the introduction to the present section on "The Cichlids," in which the progressive steps in the care of spawn and eggs are shown. Although there were in all 20 of these pictures made at extreme close-up (with 4 flash-bulbs to each exposure) covering a period of several weeks, the breeders never lost their poise nor relaxed in their duties. Few Cichlids would have gone through this ordeal without destructive reactions.

The sexes are not easily told, but the male has more spangles, especially in the tail fin. The species is easily recognized by its blunt face and the peculiar pattern in the tail.

The accompanying color plate is life-size. It presents the proud father with a few of his boys and girls, never having been separated from them up to the time this picture was made.

Æquidens marònii STEINDACHNER

Pronounced Ee′kwi-denz ma-roe′nee-eye   *Popular name,* Keyhole Cichlid

Named for the Maroni River, Venezuela

British Guiana and Venezuela   Length, about 3 inches

Western Location Map A21 to A15

HE reason for the popular name of this fish is in evidence only part of the time. Luckily it was quite plain when the photograph for the illustration was made. The wedge-shaped, vertical bar, topped by a rounded end, looks much like a big, old-fashioned key hole. Present at most times, in either dark or light color, is the upper round spot, or "ocellus," common to many Cichlids, although occurring at different places in other species. Various dark blotches shown in the illustration are extremely variable, the most constant being the brown-to-black one from the upper head, through the eye, and to the lower gill plate. Base color of the fish is cream to light brown. Upper dorsal and tail fins are edged with white in mature specimens. The developed male has more pointed dorsal and anal fins. Upper fish in picture is the male.

The fish is unusually mild-mannered and kindly for a Cichlid.

Breeding and other habits conform to description under "Cichlids."

Æquidens tetramèrus (HECKEL)

Pronounced Ee'kwi-denz tet'ra-mee"rus   *Popular name,* Saddle Cichlid

MEANING OF NAME: *tetramerus,* in four parts, referring to the color

Amazon and Guiana   Length, 7 to 8 inches

Western Location Map A21 to H14 and G28

ONE of the rarer Cichlids, imported only occasionally and probably never bred in the United States. The distinguishing characteristic marking is the body spot, high on the side and usually going all the way across the back, forming a dark saddle. The scales on either side of the spot are somewhat golden. Regularly-spaced green-gold spots form lines along the lower sides. Not so many blue markings in the fins as in most Cichlids. Large eye is brown and gold. The fins of this species do not seem to develop flowing lines with age. The dorsal and anal rather get to curve inward at the ends as the fish attains size. Ultimately it reaches a length in the aquarium of about 7 inches, and is then a showy fish. Striped metallic markings about the head are particularly vivid. A fish worth cultivating when opportunity offers. Temperature, 70-85 degrees.

Astronòtus ocellàtus (AGASSIZ)

Pronounced As'tro-no"tus os'el-lay"tus   *Popular name,* Oscar

MEANING OF NAME: *Astronotus,* marked with stars; *ocellatus,* with eye spot on tail

Guiana, Amazon and Paraguay   Length, up to 8 inches

Western Location Map H12 to G28 and U22

*A*LLOW us to present a strange Cichlid, of such odd appearance and ways that one could well believe it to belong in another family. The scales are not very visible, the fish seeming more to be clothed in a sort of olive suede leather, handsomely decorated by a few fiery orange markings. These are represented in the photograph by the white areas, including the stunning ring of that brilliant color in the tail, which is further set off by an outside edge and a centre, both of black. The body markings are lighter shades of green-gray, or the fish may become nearly black. The fins are opaque.

When alarmed they have a peculiar habit of assuming a close head-to-tail position and doing a sort of slow roll. These fish will accept live food, but can be raised just as well on washed canned shrimp or small pieces of lean raw beef. Given a large tank (50 to 100 gallon capacity), they spawn readily. They are excellent parents.

Edited by H. S.

These large eggs look like strings of tiny pearls. Hatching time, 3 days.

COLOR PLATE PAGE 587

Pterophyllum scalare (LICHTENSTEIN)

Pronounced Ter'-o-fill"lum ska-la're   *Popular names,* Angel Fish and Scalare

MEANING OF NAME: *Pterophyllum,* winged leaf; *scalare,* like a flight of stairs, referring to the dorsal fin.

Amazon and Guiana   Length, 5 to 6 inches

Western Location Map A21 to I11 and F29

THREE "species" of *Pterophyllum* have been recognized, although *P. altum,* from Venezuela, has not been seen by us. It is probable that all three represent only subspecies or geographical races of one species.

The bluish color of the points shown on the lower fins is quite natural, but the upper edging of blue on the body and dorsal fin is somewhat misleading. It is really not present. The effect is due to back lighting.

To the untrained eye, *Pterophyllum* does not look like a Cichlid, but nevertheless it *is* one. The typical Cichlid shape is seen in the younger stages in our illustrations on a later page, particularly in figure 4. It is also different from the ordinary Cichlid type in nature and habits.

Except that it will eat small fishes of suitable size, it is quite a good "happy family" member. While the breeding habits are much the same as we look for in Cichlids, there are two distinct points of difference.

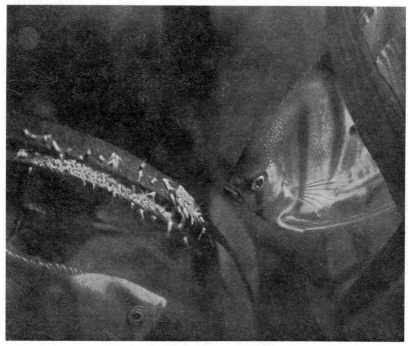

THE ANGEL FISH NURSERY

The babies are in process of transfer from one leaf to the other. Those being examined so intently by the upper fish (male) have been sprayed where they are from his mouth. One is slipping off, but will be retrieved by the female.

Instead of depositing the spawn in or on such objects as flower-pots or stones, they prefer for this purpose a firm aquatic leaf, such as Giant Sagittaria, or some substitute that will approximate it. The color plate shows the beginning of a spawn on a leaf of Giant Vallisneria. They will accept a heavy glass tube for the purpose, especially if something is inside it. They seem to have no confidence in the clear glass. Sometimes a glass tube is slipped over the aquarium drain pipe. The tubing should be about an inch in diameter. An excellent article for this purpose is a strip of one quarter-inch slate, two to three inches wide and 8 inches long. It is placed against the aquarium side, sloping a few degrees off vertical. The chimneys of oil lamps have been successfully used, but here again they should be filled or else painted inside with a waterproof material. These mechanical substitutes have their advantages and are mentioned here at some length because the big producers of Scalares use

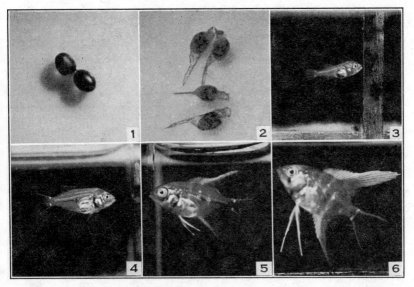

THE ANGEL FISH, FROM EGG TO FISH

1. Eggs, light yellow in life, magnified 6 diameters. 2. Alevin at 3 days, same magnification. Shows attached yolk-sac. As with all baby fish, this is slowly absorbed, furnishing the first nourishment. 3, 4, 5 and 6, at 2-diameter magnification, represent ages, 12, 20, 28 and 36 days. Note how figure 5 resembles the more usual Cichlid form, like *Tilapia macrocephala*.

them. How it is done will be described after pointing out the following other important differences in breeding habits.

Unlike the great majority of Cichlids, the "Scalare" does not place its young in prepared holes in the sand. Wherever the baby Scalare hatches, there it adheres suspended from the head by a sticky thread, vibrating its tail vigorously. The mass of young produces an appreciable current in this way, thus getting both exercise and a rapid change of water. During this period the parents pick up mouthfuls of young, retain them a few moments and gently spray them on another leaf, repeating the operation at intervals of perhaps an hour, until the babies can swim freely, which is in about 2 days. One observes that the parents are most solicitous, and use great care to pick up any of the young which did not adhere to a new location. Babies seldom reach the bottom before rescue arrives.

As to how long to keep the parents and young together—if at all—is a matter for each aquarist to decide. Leaving them all together is a most interesting procedure if successful. The family of Scalares shown

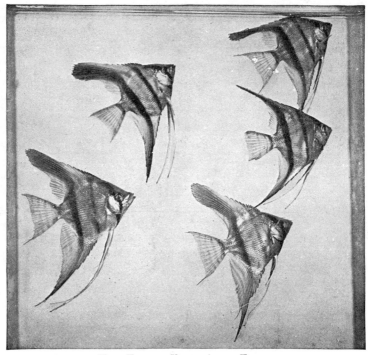

FULL-FLEDGED YOUNG ANGEL FISHES
They "sail like swans asleep."

in the pictured nursery remained together 6 weeks, apparently without a loss, and were only separated because of signs of a new spawn. This new spawn, under apparently identical conditions, was eaten.

If the main object is to rear fish, and one is willing to forego the pleasure of witnessing their interesting family life, then the best thing to do is to remove the eggs to a hatching tray or aquarium containing water not over 8 inches deep. The container and water should be perfectly clean, for the babies are not to be freed of dirt particles in the laundry-mouths of their natural parents. The water, of course, should be seasoned. If fungus appears, boil the water next time and add 2 drops of 5% Methylene Blue solution per gallon after spawning. (This is bad for plants.)

Returning to the subject of artificial spawn receivers, it will now be apparent where their use is a practical convenience, for they are easily lifted out of the aquarium and laid sloping, egg side down, in the hatching tray. A light current of water about the eggs and young, produced by the mechanical liberation of air, is important. By the time the young have absorbed all of the yolk-sac and become free-swimming, they are able to eat newly hatched brine shrimp. Re-read page 32 in reference to food for the babies.

A number of other Cichlids may be reared in this way. It is worth trying when parents persistently eat eggs or young.

Newly hatched Scalares look nothing like their parents, but in a few weeks there is no mistaking their identity. Growth is rapid under the influence of liberal feeding and warmth.

Peculiarities of Scalares   Several things about Scalares require special consideration. Perhaps the most outstanding one is an unaccountable loss of appetite. Try a change of food. They are particularly fond of live mosquito larvae, Daphnia, Water Boatmen (for large fishes), small or chopped earthworms, white worms and canned shrimp. If these fail to tempt, then try baby Guppies. Pretty bad case if these morsels fail to bring back the appetite. The only thing then left to do is to try a change of aquarium or of water in the present aquarium. Scalares seem to do best in slightly acid water, about pH 6.8. See paragraph on pH under "General Management." They seldom really starve.

There should be plants in the aquarium with Scalares. These tend to prevent dashing themselves to death against the glass when frightened.

Ordinarily when a fish lies over on its side on the bottom of the aquarium it is preparing to enter Fish Paradise. The Scalare is liable to do this from shock, fright or chill, and is quite likely to regain its equilibrium.

This fish is not very susceptible to Ichthyophthirius, but it is liable to a disease which causes the eyes to protrude. This sometimes leads to blindness and usually ends in death. See "Popeyes," under Diseases.

Under identical conditions some individuals will have brilliant black bars, while others are gray. Cause unknown. It is no indication of a state of health.

Sex in Scalares   This remains difficult to distinguish, but we can make a shrewd guess. Even mating is not a certain sign, for two females sometimes mate and have infertile eggs. In THE AQUARIUM for September, 1949, an illustrated article points out seven methods of discovering the sex in Scalares. Several of these are of doubtful value. The one in use by practical breeders has reference to the space at the lower edge of the body between the "feelers" and the beginning of the anal fin. In the female this portion of the body outline is longer and straighter. As with other Cichlids, the breeding tube, which appears in both sexes just before egg-laying, is more pointed in the male, and is carried at a more forward angle. This is well shown on the color plate, the fish in the rear position being the male. Also the female when filling with eggs looks fuller from an overhead view.

New Black Angels

STARTING as a "sport" or mutation in the Scalare ponds of Mr. Woolf of Florida, in 1948, showing only a little excess of black at first, it has, through long selective breeding by several experts at scattered points, been brought to a brilliant black, usually breeding true. Those not coming solid black are known as "Black Lace," and are apt to prove both more disease-free and fertile than the blacks. Lace angels produce some pure blacks.

Considering the great popularity of other black fishes, such as the Mollienesias, big things seem to be in store for this entirely new race.

Crénicíchla lepidòta HECKEL

Pronounced Kren'i-sick"la le'pi-do"ta   *Popular name,* Pike Cichlid

MEANING OF NAME: *Crenicichla,* Cichla with teeth; *lepidota,* with scales
on ear region (gill covers)

South America Western Location Map U22 to •22 and ★26 Length, 4 to 5 inches

"**B**AD ACTOR" is a term applied by aquarists to fishes which are unneighborly in the community tank. Unfortunately it fits all the Crenicichlas, of which there are a number of species.

They follow the usual Cichlid method of breeding, but only the male looks after the eggs and young. He is a strict disciplinarian and requires the flock of young to follow him closely. Those that fail in this pay with their lives, for he eats them—his way of eliminating the unfit.

Although lacking brilliant coloring, they are decidedly attractive. The anal and lower part of the tail fin are shaded red, while all of the unpaired fins are interestingly dotted and lined with various shades of gray. The irregular markings on the back, observed in the photograph, are variable in their intensity. In this species it is the *female* which has the longer rays on the dorsal and anal fins. (Upper fish.)

None of the species of *Crenicichla* is often in supply commercially. They like a temperature of about 68 to 80 degrees, and do not tear out plants.

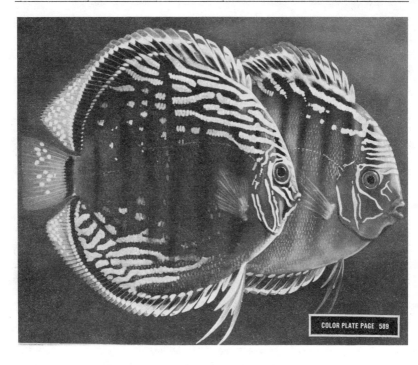

COLOR PLATE PAGE 589

Symphysodon discus (HECKEL)

Pronounced Sim-fy'so-don dis'kus

MEANING OF NAME: *Symphysodon,* with teeth at middle (symphysis) of jaw; . . . . *discus,* like a disc

Amazon　　　　　　Western Location Map G17 to F29　　　　Length, 5 to 6 inches

ONE of the spectacular introductions of 1933. It is of the "pancake" type, flattened like the Scalare. A show fish. Something that even the uninitiated remember. Its showy quality is increased by its large size.

Our illustration presents the fish in breeding colors, although sometimes the blue color pattern extends more over the body. At such times the male rivals the gaudy beauty of the most brilliant marine fishes. Occasionally the female is a more brilliant golden yellow than pictured.

A considerable study has been made of various possible indications of difference in sex, but the only dependable point is that the blue pattern on the male is more pronounced and more extensive than on the female. Perfectly peaceful, but unexpected battles may occur between mated pairs.

Minimum breeding size, about 3-inches. The best way of securing a pair is to have say 6 in a 30-40 gallon aquarium and let them select their own mates. They are fussy feeders and should have a variety of live foods, including, if available, the shrimp-like Gammarus (see index). The new young have extremely small mouths. Many appear to die of starvation, due no doubt to our former failure to learn that their first food is the slime they pick from the bodies of their parents. The adults at this time

New Babies Feeding on Parental Slime (*Wolfsheimer photograph*)

seem to secrete a heavier slime on their bodies, an odd provision of Nature, akin to the fact that pigeons develop a "milk" in the crop as first food for their squabs. This recent discovery makes it clear that young should be tended by parents, even at the risk of their eating the spawn. Thus we may hope for greater numbers and wider distribution of this great beauty.

The species is subject to a few peculiar diseases, particularly abscesses about the head. Their water, especially for breeding, should be slightly acid and at a temperature of about 78 degrees.

There are three closely related species known popularly as the green, blue, and brown Discus. Edited by H. S.

Apistogramma agassizi (?) (STEINDACHNER)

The Dwarf Cichlids

The *Nannacara* and the *Apistogramma* species

THERE are a number of interesting dwarf Cichlids which are puzzling to correctly name, because ichthyologists have done so little work with them and we do not know the locations from which commercial specimens have been collected. The accompanying illustrations give a good idea of the general types and their sizes. We use the names under which they are sold, which will have to serve for the present.

It is the belief of the writer that the merits of these charming little fishes have largely been overlooked by aquarists. Many persons will not keep the ordinary types of Cichlids because of their large sizes and a general propensity to fight and to tear out the plants. The dwarfs have neither of these faults. They are beautiful, but a little shy.

Their breeding methods, so far as we know them, are like those of their larger cousins, except for the fact that the female takes charge of the eggs and young, and assumes all domestic obligations, driving the male away. If the male is taken out, the female may be depended upon to take excellent care of her young family, and at no time to eat them.

One great advantage about these little Cichlids is that they can be successfully bred in an aquarium of about 3-gallon size.

As to temperature they are very well satisfied within a range of 70 to 80 degrees.

One of the best known and probably the handsomest of these miniature cichlids is the one sold in the trade as *Apistogramma agassizi*. It is
also the largest of the dwarfs, so to speak. There are at least 2 species
passing under the same name, the other one being deeper of body than
our illustration, especially about the fore part, while the dorsal, although
handsome, is not as high in proportion to the depth of the body. However, the colors of both species are the same, so far as a description goes.
The outstanding feature is the interesting color design in the tail fin.
The illusion of a white spearhead is increased by the almost bloody
streak along its lower half, indicated by the dark portion in the photograph. The lower fins are rich orange, while the dorsal is brilliantly
topped off with blood red. Typical blue-to-green spangles ornament the
body. Seen with its fins spread in the sun, this fish is a rare sight.

*Apistogramma per-
tense* is a high-spir-
ited, aggressive little
fish. Female often
kills male, but by good
management can be
bred. The high-lights
seen about the head
are blue. The black
pattern changes rapid-
ly. The species is one
of the more available
of the dwarf cichlids.

Apistogramma pertense (?) (HASEMANN)

Until comparatively recently no *Apistogramma* had been seen having a
double-pointed or lyre-shaped
tail fin. Now there are 2
known species. When the first
of these arrived, rather than
saddle the fish with a name
that must later be forgotten,
and at the same time to give
it a better identity than one of
the many "*Apistogramma* species," the writer proposed giving it a temporary symbol
"Apistogramma U2," the letter
U standing for "unidentified."

Apistogramma "U2"

COLOR PLATE PAGE 588

Apistográmma ramírezi MYERS AND HARRY

Pronounced A-pis'toe-gram"ma rah-meer"ez-eye

MEANING OF NAME: *Apistogramma,* in reference to peculiar lateral line; *ramirezi,* after Sr. Manuel Vicente Ramirez, of Caracas, Venezuela. *Popular name,* Ram

Western Venezuela   Western location map B13 to z14   Length, 2 inches

ONE of the outstanding importations of 1947, this strongly individual little fish with a saddle-shaped dorsal, seems to have attained permanent popularity. It is not only beautiful, but is easily bred and is free of that aggressiveness which marks most Dwarf Cichlids. While courting, males challenge and chase each other, but no harm is done.

The strong violet hue seen in adults is variable. It shows best in direct sunlight. Female (upper fish) shows rosy spot on sides when ready to spawn. She takes the lead in breeding and care of young. The tall spike at front of dorsal fin is not always peculiar to the male, but his is the darker. Temperature 70-80 degrees.

Eggs are usually placed on a flat stone, but in the above picture the sand was fanned away, exposing the slate bottom on which they spawned. Male fans eggs. Female guards young. Eggs can also be hatched in a separate container as described for Angel Fish. Soft, slightly alkaline water preferred.

Crenicara maculata (STEINDACHNER)

Pronounced Kren"ih-ca'ra mack-you-lay'ta   *Popular name,* Checkerboard Cichlid

MEANING OF NAME: *Crenicara,* scalloped acara, from the little spines on the
preopercular bone, and the generic name, *Acara; maculata,* spotted.

Lower Amazon River   Western Location Map G20 to G29   Length, to 2½ inches

THIS unique species can be ranked among the Dwarf Cichlids, the
pair reproduced here at a trifle less than life size being the largest
and best developed we have seen. Usually they are not only smaller, but
the head markings and fin patterns are not so clear, nor the fins of the
males quite so flowing. Trade circles report that males are scarce. The
main characteristic of the fish is the striking geometric arrangement of
rows of dark islands, giving rise to the "checkerboard"effect. The pattern
seen in the fins is pale orange. Top of dorsal is finely edged white and red.

Imported only occasionally. Although taking easily to life in captivity
and eating various foods, reports indicate that they do not live long and
have never bred. One large dealer who previously gave them Tubifex
worms changed to dry foods and occasional live Daphnia. His losses ceased.

This attractive little fish is quite peaceful. It moves forward in a series
of jumps and takes its food with a downward, bobbing motion. Temperature, 72-78 degrees.

THE POMACENTRIDS OR DAMSELFISHES

FAMILY POMACENTRIDAE

Pronounced Po ma sen'trid ee

The Pomacentrids, or Demoiselles, are like the Cichlids in having only one nostril on a side but differ in having an internal bony shelf to support the eye socket. Most of the species are marine coral reef fishes, but it has recently been found that at least some species can be acclimated to nearly or wholly fresh water. It is, however, very doubtful that they will ever breed or hatch their eggs in fresh water.

Dascýllus trimáculàtus (RUEPPELL)
Pronounced Das-sill'us tri-mac'you-lay"tus   *Popular name,* 3-spot Damsel Fish
MEANING OF NAME: *Dascyllus,* meaning not known,
trimaculatus, three-spotted (banded)
Red Sea to East Indies and Hawaii (Marine)   Length, 2 inches

THE description and remarks regarding *Dascyllus aruanus* fit this variety very well, but it is not considered to be quite as durable. The intense white enamel spots on the sides and forehead are very vivid against the dark background. The 3-spot damsel fish has been successfully bred by Dr. J. Garnaud, of the Monaco Aquarium.

It is best to keep marine aquaria out of strong daylight, as the water under the influence of sun is apt to rapidly turn green. Recently synthetic sea salt preparations have been developed that make a satisfactory substitute for sea water.

Dascýllus aruànus (LINNAEUS)
Pronounced Das-sill'us ar-oo-ay"nus   *Popular name,* Black-and-white Damsel Fish
MEANING OF NAME: *aruanus,* from the Aru Islands, E. Indies
East Indies to S. Pacific Islands (Marine)   Length, 2 inches

*A*S a marine fish to be kept in salt water in a home aquarium, this
fish, considering all points, is unsurpassed by any that we know.
It lives as well as the more dependable fresh-water fishes, is easily fed,
is flashy in appearance and is always "on the go." Unfortunately it
sometimes fights with those of its own kind. To what extent it can be
brought to fresh water is not known to the writer.

Although the markings are striking, they are extremely simple. They
are just black-and-white, exactly as the picture shows. The white is
brilliant. With fright the black parts become gray or nearly disappear.

This fish may commonly be seen in large public aquaria, but there is
no reason why it cannot be kept privately in small space. Aeration
desirable but not imperative.

Nearly all small sea-fishes enjoy and are benefited by a fair proportion
of meals consisting of chopped clam.

Pomacéntrus fúscus CUVIER AND VALENCIENNES

Pronounced Po′ma-sen″trus fus′kus   *Popular name,* Blue Devil

MEANING OF NAME: *Pomacentrus,* with spiny gill cover; *fuscus,* dusky

Florida and West Indies (mostly Marine)   Length, up to 4½ inches

Western Location Map j25 to o37

☞HERE is considerable difference in the adaptability of those marine fishes which can be kept in the fresh-water aquarium. Our subject here is one of those which can be brought to the changed environment by care—and it is worth all the patience that may be necessary. It is a sparkling, vivacious little individual, darting about in a most sprightly way, flashing its yellow rear fins and the geometric rows of deep sapphire-blue scales on the body. These scales and the head markings of the same brilliant coloring are indicated by the white portions of the photograph. The smaller fish, believed to be the male, displays more rows of the sparkling scales. The body background is dark gray to purplish.

In Nature they deposit their eggs on the inside of large empty shells, fan them and care for the young in the same manner followed by the Cichlids.

Those which were received were in 50% marine water. Some died, but others were slowly changed to straight fresh water in about 6 months, and are living happily after nearly 2 years. They had best be kept singly, or where good retreats are provided. (One should not attempt to keep plants in brackish water.) Once established this fish should be moved about as little as possible. Easy to feed. Temperature requirements, 70 to 80 degrees.

COLOR PLATE PAGE 589

Amphiprion percùla   (LACÉPÈDE)

Pronounced Am-fi-pry'on per-kew'la   *Popular names,* Clownfish, Anemone Fish
MEANING OF NAME: *Amphiprion,* both saws (referring to rough edges on sides of head); *percula,* little Perch
On coral reefs   Eastern Location Map y35 to T71 and C82   Length, 2 inches

O F the several small marine fishes suited to the small home aquarium this is one of the best, and is probably the most brilliantly colored. Also the coloration is so different from any of our fresh-water fishes that it is nothing short of startling. There are several closely related species with slight variations in color pattern and depth of shade, from lemon yellow to orange. Also individuals vary in intensity of color.

It is very lively, always busily on the move. In Nature it hovers about Sea Anemones, ready to take shelter among their poisonous tentacles. Probably the Anemone receives some benefit from this strange partnership, but what it is, is not known at least to this writer.

The Clownfish eats Brine Shrimp eagerly, also baby Guppies. It will take bits of raw scraped fish, and some ordinary prepared fishfood.

It needs marine water at a temperature of 70-75 degrees. Not bred.

We have seen oval fertile eggs placed on flat stone, but none hatched. Photo by Woodbridge Williams.

THE SUNFISHES
FAMILY CENTRARCHIDAE
Pronounced Cen trär'ki dee

This family contains the North American Sunfishes and Black Basses. They are found nowhere else. They are related to the Sea Basses but differ in various internal characters. Two nostrils on each side are present.

Elassòma évergladei   JORDAN

Pronounced El'as-so"ma ev'er-glay"dee-eye   *Popular name,* Pigmy Sunfish
MEANING OF NAME: *Elassoma,* small body; *evergladei,* of the Everglades
North Carolina to Florida   Western Location Map f25 to i26   Length, 1 inch

𝒯HE male is rather smart-looking, with his big dorsal fin and vivacious manners. In the breeding season he becomes enveloped in velvety black, through which sparkle flecks of green and gold, a beautiful sight. Our illustration is slightly enlarged.

Out of breeding season the sexes can be distinguished by the male's larger fins. The dorsal is arched higher. All his fins are a darker gray.

The fishes build a simple nest of bits of plants at the bottom of the aquarium, into which the eggs are placed. These are guarded by the male, but he is so fond of his young that he may eat them.

The species seems to thrive only on living food. It is usually best to keep these little fishes by themselves.

Another species, *E. zonatum* Jordan, is sometimes shipped north. It is very similar to *evergladei.* Temperature range, 65-80 degrees. A new species of pigmy sunfish, named *E. okefenokee* by Dr. James Böhlke, was discovered in 1956. It is smaller than *evergladei* and more beautifully marked. A native of southern Georgia and northern Florida.

THE CHANDIDS
FAMILY CHANDIDAE
(Formerly Ambassidae)
Pronounced Chan'di-dee

The Chandids are small, brackish and salt-water fishes of the Indian Ocean and Western Pacific. They are very much like the salt-water Cardinal Fishes but differ in having the spiny and soft dorsals connected at the base. Most of the species are translucent, this characteristic reaching its highest development in the little Glass-fish, *Chanda lala*.

Chánda buroénsis (BLEEKER)

Pronounced Chan'da boo'ro-en"sis   Old name, Ambassis buroensis

MEANING OF NAME: *Chanda*, a native name; *buroensis*, inhabiting the island Boeru or Buru in the East Indies

Boeru in East Indies   Length, 2¼ inches
Eastern Location Map J57; H53; W49; x73

L ONGER and not quite so translucent as *C. lala* and lacking the blue edges on fins. It has been demonstrated that this species can be trained to eating shredded dried shrimp. Incidentally, this is one of the best foods for weaning live-food eaters over to prepared foods. It originally came in under the title of *Ambassis agassizi*, a name unknown to science.

Breeding habits are similar to those of *C. lala*. Although the species has been with us only a short time, it is found to be a very free breeder.

COLOR PLATE PAGE 590

Chánda lála (HAMILTON-BUCHANAN)

Pronounced Chan'da la'la   *Popular name,* Glassfish
MEANING OF NAME: After native name, laal-chandee   *Old name,* Ambassis lala

India   Eastern Location Map s27; x22; t31; w32; y35   Length, 1½ inches

THIS translucent little beauty, like a crystal suspended in the water sometimes catches the light in such a way as to reflect prismatic colors. Far from being as delicate as it might seem, it is, under suitable conditions, tough and long-lived. Must have live food, such as Daphnia, Brine Shrimp or White Worms cut in two.

Breeds occasionally. Males more yellowish and have brighter blue fin-edgings. Illustration shows 2 males. Riccia is an ideal plant for receiving the eggs, which are projected upwards from an upside-down position. They hatch in 8 hours at 82 degrees. Young require finest infusoria and should be separated from parents.

This species is found in salt, brackish and fresh waters. A heaping tea-spoon of sea salt to each gallon of their aquarium water is desirable, and will not injure plants. Temperature 70-82, but have been known to survive 45 degrees, where other fishes died.

THE THERAPONIDS
FAMILY THERAPONIDAE
Pronounced Ther a pon'i dee

The Theraponids are spiny-rayed salt-water fishes of the East Indies which frequently ascend rivers into fresh water. They have 2 nostrils on each side, but differ from most related families in the absence of the small scale-like flap at the base of the ventral fins.

Thérapon järbua (FORSKAL)

Pronounced Ther'a-pon jar'bua   *Popular name,* Jarbua

MEANING OF NAME: *Therapon,* shield-bearer; *jarbua,* a native name

Red Sea, E. Coast Africa to China, N. Coast Australia   Length in nature, 10 inches

THE drooping concentric lines on a ground of shining silver are dark gray to black. In fact all the dark parts of the photograph are, in life, black or nearly black. The large spot in the dorsal is particularly intense, and adds to the already strange aspect of the fish.

Like the Chandids, to which it is closely related, it is a marine fish which enters fresh water.

Unlike *Chanda lala* and *Chanda buroensis,* it has never been bred in captivity. It is one of the things to be hoped for.

The fish seems to be rather quarrelsome. Although a marine fish, it is easily kept in fresh water at a temperature of about 73 to 78 degrees. Seldom imported.

THE ARCHER FISHES
FAMILY TOXOTIDAE
Pronounced Tox o'ti dee

The Archer Fishes are a small family of 4 or 5 species from the East Indies. The head is flat above and pointed, the dorsal is set far back, and the soft dorsal and anal fins are scaly. Some of these scales can be seen in the illustration, especially on the anal fin.

Natives in Asia have long known that the Archer Fishes shoot water at insects above the surface, but ichthyologists long doubted it, even ascribing the habit to a different fish *(Chelmo)*. Early in the present century, European aquarists first saw captive imported Archers shoot, but it was not until the experiments of the late Dr. Hugh M. Smith, in Siam during the 1920's, that the shooting was fully proved. In 1934 Dr. George S. Myers, while collaborating with Dr. Smith, worked out the struc ture of the shooting apparatus in the Archer's mouth. We here present the best-known species of Archer. Long, colorful articles by Dr. Smith on this extraordinary fish appeared in "The Aquarium" (July, 1939 and August, 1944), also by Commander Alfred Marsack in January, 1952. Extinguishing distant lighted cigarettes at night by a pellet of water is one of their famous acts.

Toxòtes jáculàtor   (PALLAS)

Pronounced Tox-o'tees jack'you-lay"tor   *Popular name,* Archer Fish

MEANING OF NAME: *Toxotes,* archer; *jaculator,* hurler

East Indies   Eastern Location Map r28; v33; w37; t48; N68   Length, 5 inches

*H*ERE is one of the unique showmen among aquarium fishes, and with the correct properties and settings supplied, it can be depended upon to do its act.

This is one of a few fishes that, from written descriptions, appealed to the author many years ago, and it was only recently that he had the thrill of seeing it in natural action. The weird statement that a fish could accurately aim a mouthful of water as a missile with which to bring down a fly seemed to border on the fanciful. Aside from the mechanical difficulties of such a feat, anyone with a slight knowledge of optics knows that, due to surface refraction, objects do not appear in their true positions when looking into or out of water, unless, as might rarely happen, the line of vision or aim is vertical. A bullet from a rifle aimed at an angle to the water and apparently pointed at a small object below the surface could not hit it unless allowance were made for the optical "bend." The same thing is true from the *under* side of the surface, looking out, but the Archer Fish has learned to compensate for this and will accurately splatter its prey from a distance of a foot or more, and usually brings it down.

It shoots a few drops at a high speed, capable of carrying 10 feet. If the first shot does not bring down the prey, it is followed by a rapid series until the insect falls. Few escape. The mouth is quite large, and the shooting is done while the lips are just above the surface of the water.

We are told that *Toxotes* varies considerably in color. Those shown here were silver with a slight overtone of yellow. Dorsal and anal fins are edged black. The 6 dark bars are gorgeous black, making the fish easy to remember by its striking appearance, as well as its original way of gaining a livelihood. It will eat live food which it has not knocked into the water. Meal worms seem to be particularly relished.

Nothing is known as to sex distinctions or breeding habits. A temperature of 75 degrees proves satisfactory. This is one of those species coming from salt, brackish and fresh waters, and we believe a mixture of sea water is advisable. They get along well together and even prove themselves sports by not quarreling, when the shooter's victim is gobbled by another fish! Several species occur from India to northern Australia.

Like the various Electric and Walking Fishes, the Archer Fish is a star attraction at a public fish show, for it will "knock off" live flies as long as the spectators choose to supply them.

THE "SCATS"
FAMILY SCATOPHAGIDAE
Pronounced Scat'o fag"i dee

The "Scats" differ from the salt-water Butterfly-fishes, to which they are most closely allied in various technical internal features. They cannot be confused with any of the other groups of fresh-water aquarium fishes. The "Scats" are all from brackish water in the East Indies.

COLOR PLATE PAGE 591

Scátophàgus ärgus (PALLAS)
Pronounced Scat'o-fay"gus ar'gus (Scat-off'a-gus allowable)
MEANING OF NAME: *Scatophagus,* offal eater; *argus* thousand eyed (from the spots)
Popular name, Spotted Scat
Salt, brackish and sometimes fresh water of the East Indies
Length—Aquarium sizes, from 2 to 5 inches; in Nature, 10 inches

ALTHOUGH we are told that in Nature this fish comes in 10 and even 12 inch lengths, the usual size seen in the aquarium is from 2 to 4½ inches.

The fish is rather flat in form, or "laterally compressed," as it is called.

In markings it is so variable that one would easily get the impression that the different patterns indicate various species. There are 3 principal types. Our color plate shows two of them. The upper fish, more or less striped with orange and black, is known as the "Tiger Scat," and is sometimes recognized as a variety called *rubrifrons*. The end of the tail fin, as shown here, is lightly tinted with pale red or pink. This is not always present. Some aquarists believe these tiger markings denote the male fish. While we believe this to be a mistake, we can offer no other evidence of sex. The subject is not important anyhow, as we have little prospect of breeding the species.

The lower fish shows a second and much more common type or variety. The third variety has a dark coffee-colored background, no bright colors and more numerous dark dots of smaller size.

Of the three varieties the "Tiger Scat" has the most striking appearance and brings the best prices. None of the species is cheap.

A renewed interest in marine household aquariums finds a considerable number of Scats doing well in ocean water at full strength.

There has been much discussion as to whether the species can be successfully kept in fresh water. The answer definitely is that it can, although the addition of a moderate amount of sea water or sea salt (as described for Fundulopanchax) is advisable. If this is not done, the water should at least be kept in an alkaline condition—say a pH reading of 7.4 or a little higher. This is a good fish to be kept in localities where the water is hard.

In Nature the fish is one of the real scavengers of the sea, inhabiting the mouths of rivers and the docks of various tropical seaports. It is therefore not surprising to find that it will eat anything, although it is hard to account for the fact that it is extremely fond of Riccia and Nitella, plants entirely strange to their native brackish and marine waters. Temperature, about 70-78 degrees. In common with most marine fishes, it should not be subjected to high temperatures. If the water unavoidably goes above 80 degrees, aeration should be employed.

Owners are usually very fond of the active and harmless fish, for it has "personality." It is a heavy feeder, and always has a hopeful eye open for the appearance of the master. Quite a pet.

Sélenòtoca pápuénsis FRASER-BRUNNER

Pronounced Sel'een-o"toe-ka pa'pu-en"sis   *Popular name,* Moon "Scat"

MEANING OF NAME: *Selenotoca, selene,* the moon and *tocus,* offspring—born of the moon; *papuensis,* living in Papua (N. Guinea)

New Guinea   Eastern Location Map L67   Length, 4 inches

A FEW aquarium fishes can live in either fresh or salt water. This is one that can. Of course, if a change is made from one to the other, it should be gradual.

The light portions in the illustration are brilliant, mirror-like silver, showing to especial advantage under strong light. The darker portions of the fish are black. No bright colors, nor even tints. Body flat, like that of a Scalare. A similar species, S. *multifasciata,* occurs in Australia.

Altogether it is a very satisfactory aquarium fish; certainly a showy one. In the several years since the introduction of quite a shipment of them, we have heard of no deaths.

Eats anything. Never bred. Suited to living with other fishes of about its own size. Swims about the aquarium industriously, always on the move. There is no known method of distinguishing the sexes. Temperature range, 70 to 80 degrees.

THE MONODACTYLIDS
FAMILY MONODACTYLIDAE
Pronounced Mon o dak ty'li dee

The deep form and the scaly fins will distinguish the Monodactylids from other aquarium fishes. They are brackish and salt-water fishes of the Old World.

Monodáctylus argénteus (LACÉPÈDE)

Pronounced Mon'o-dak"ty-lus ar-jen'tee-us (Mo'no-dak-ty"lus allowable)

MEANING OF NAME: *Monodactylus,* with one finger, referring to appearance of dorsal and anal fins; *argenteus,* silvery one

Indian Ocean   Vacated scientific name, *Psettus argenteus*   Length, 4 inches

NOT knowing that this is a marine fish, one would hardly suspect it. It is beautiful, but not with that gaudy display we have come to expect of marine tropicals.

The fish is extremely silverly, while the dark portions of the upper and lower fins represent a beautiful, rich yellow. Preference in purchase should be given to the younger specimens. They will grow rapidly in a large aquarium, *but should not be unnecessarily disturbed or moved about.* Salt water unnecessary. Never bred. Temperature, 75 degrees.

THE GOBIES

Three families of Gobies contribute species to our list.

FAMILY ELEOTRIDAE

Pronounced El e o'tri dee

These have the ventral fins entirely separate from one another, and *not* connected into a sucking disk.

Dòrmitàtor màculàtus (BLOCH)

Pronounced Dor'mi-tay"tor mac'you-lay"tus   *Popular name,* Sleeper Goby

MEANING OF NAME: *Dormitator,* sleeper; *maculatus,* spotted

Coast of Tropical America, Atlantic side, brackish water

Length—Aquarium size, 3 to 4 inches; in Nature, 10 inches

Western Location Map from d26 to w30 and y8 to F30

*A*LTHOUGH the species in color is a pattern of browns and grays, it is not lacking in character. The light spot in back of the gill plate is a sparkle of blue. The anal fin is ornamented with brown and blue spots, and is crisply edged with electric blue. A peculiarity is that in certain lights the center of the eye is a blind-looking stony blue.

Peaceful and seldom bred. Many small eggs are attached to cleaned stones. Tiny young are hard to rear. Temperature, 65-85 degrees.

Oxyéleòtris märmoràtus (BLEEKER)

Pronounced Ox'ee-el'e-o"tris mar'mo-ray"tus   *Popular name,* Marbled Goby

MEANING OF NAME: *Oxyeleotris,* sharp Eleotris; *marmoratus,* marbled

Malayan Region   Eastern Location Map w36 to F51   Grows to nearly 3 feet

NATURE in providing for everything has not forgotten to give aquarists a few cannibal fishes which may be used for the disposal of small, diseased or surplus specimens. This species performs the gruesome task with considerable satisfaction to itself, thus relieving the aquarists of a problem. Our subject here, with the aid of a very spacious mouth, will soon dispose of a fish almost half its own size.

Its pectoral fins are much larger than the photograph shows. We happened to get an edge view.

The marbled ivory markings against varying shades of brown are quite attractive. Most of the time the fish rests motionless, on or near the bottom, waiting for victims. Will eat earthworms or a porridge containing a large proportion of shrimp. Very hardy. The specimen here photographed has, at this writing, passed through 7 known ownerships in 2 years, and is in the best of health. Like most Gobies, it has not been bred, which will be good news to other aquarium fishes. Temperature range, 68-85 degrees.

That this species is perhaps the largest goby in the world, growing to nearly a yard in length, is probably the reason our smaller aquarium specimens do not breed.

Mogúrnda mogúrnda (RICHARDSON)

Pronounced Mo-gurn′da mo-gurn′da   *Popular name,* Purple Striped Gudgeon

MEANING OF NAME: *Mogurnda,* native name in N. W. Australia

Formerly known as *Krefftius adspersus*

Australia   Length, 4 inches

A PRETTY Australian fish and quite lively for a Goby; in fact, too
lively in one respect, for it tears the fins of other fishes. As a community fish, it is one of the world's worst, being comparable in this
respect to the much better known *Gambusia affinis.*

The spots on the body and fins are black and dark red, while the
3 light stripes on the cheek are purple, giving the fish its popular
name.

Larger fins identify the male. Eggs are deposited on the glass of the
aquarium in a space free from plants, usually on the near side where
the aquarist may conveniently watch them. At a temperature of 72
degrees they hatch in 9 days. The male fans the eggs, but he should be
removed after the eggs hatch.

Our friend, the late Wm. A. Poyser, first illustrated the species as
Krefftius adspersus in "Aquatic Life" in 1918. There have been subsequent importations.

Temperature range, 60-80 degrees. Food preferably carnivorous. A
desirable fish if kept only among its own kind, and rather pretty.

FAMILY GOBIIDAE
Pronounced Go bee'i dee

The true Gobies have the ventral fins united into a more or less perfect sucking disk by which the fishes adhere to solid objects.

Bràchygòbius nùnus (HAMILTON-BUCHANAN)

Pronounced Bray'kee-go"bee-us noo'nus   *Popular name,* Bumble Bee Goby

MEANING OF NAME: *Brachygobius,* short goby; *nunus,* from a native name

Formerly called *Brachygobius doriae*

India to Java and Borneo   Eastern Location Map r28 and x22 to L44 and I46

Length, 1½ inches

LIKE so many of the Gobies this little fish spends most of its time on the bottom of the aquarium, hopping about in a droll way. It can scarcely be called a scavenger fish, for scavengers eat anything, whereas this species has a distinct preference for Daphnia and white worms, although it will take dried food containing a large portion of shrimp or other animal matter.

This little fish is often but not always to be had from the stocks of dealers. In common with most specimens from the Far East which have not been bred, it is never low-priced. Temperature range, 72-85 degrees.

This is the commoner of the two species of Bumble Bee Gobies in our tanks. It is more chunky than *B. xanthozona* and has much larger scales. Both are butter-yellow with dark brown to blackish blotches. This one is more variable in the blotching than *xanthozona*. In habits and breeding the two appear to be similar. However, few are usually bred in captivity and imported stock is never cheap. A calm, bold and rather "picky" fish among other kinds of its own size.

COLOR PLATE PAGE 590

Bràchygòbius xánthozònus (BLEEKER)

Pronounced Bray'kee-go"bee-us   zan'tho-zo"nus   *Popular name,* Bumble Bee Goby
MEANING OF NAME: *Brachygobius,* short goby; *xanthozonus,* with yellow zones or
bands
Malaya, Borneo, Sumatra, Java   Eastern Location Map E36 and E38 to I48 and M47
Length 1¾ inches

THE remarks regarding *Brachygobius nunus* apply to this species, except to add that this is a somewhat larger and less common fish.

They have rarely been bred. The breeders are conditioned on chopped earthworms and grown Brine Shrimp. Eggs are laid on upper side of an empty flower pot laid on its side. Female takes an upside-down position in the pot while applying strings of eggs that adhere to the upper side. She drops to the bottom while the male does a "loop-the-loop," fertilizing the eggs as he passes them. Spawn hatches in 5 to 6 days at 75 degrees. Male fans spawn and does not eat young. They must be fed on fine Infusoria for 3 days after their yolk-sac has been absorbed.

The species prefers live food and they are apt to be fin-nippers.

Evorthodus breviceps GILL
(Upper, male, lower, female)
Pronounced E'vor-tho"dus brev'ee-ceps
MEANING OF NAME: *Evorthodus*, very straight tooth; *breviceps*, short head
Freshwaters of Trinidad   Length, as shown
Western Location Map x19

*A*N INTERESTING and useful importation of 1952. Most of the
Gobies demand live food, but these little oddities readily take anything of a size they can swallow. They are bottom feeders and have a cute
way of seeming to bend the neck (which they do not have) when peering
about for morsels to gobble. The effect is enhanced by their hopping movements. Desirable "scavengers," as they do not roil the water by disturbing
the sediment. For health they should have a reasonable amount of live food.

The ventral fins are formed into a suction plate capable of taking hold
anywhere on a smooth surface, such as the glass of their tank.

The front section of the dorsal fin of the male is very long and is
occasionally erected impressively. Ordinarily the fins of the species are
not expanded as shown here. The top streak in the tail fin of the male is
gold dotted black; centre, pale blue; bottom, pale gold. Quite peaceful.
Not yet bred. Temperature 70-78.

FAMILY PERIOPHTHALMIDAE
Pronounced Pe'ree off thal"mi dee

These fishes differ from the Gobiidae in their projecting, movable eyes.

Périophthálmus bärbarus LINNAEUS

Pronounced Pe'ree-off-thal"mus bar'ba-rus   *Popular name,* Mud Skipper

MEANING OF NAME: *Periophthalmus,* looking in every direction; *barbarus,* foreign. Not found in Europe, it being one of the few foreign Gobies known to Linnaeus

Also known as *Periophthalmus kaelreuteri*

Tropical Asiatic coastal waters from India Eastward; also Polynesia

Length, 4 inches

*B*IOLOGISTS are pretty well united in the belief that life on the land crawled out of the water. The habits of this extraordinary fish make that very easy to believe. It is not only equipped with an efficient air-breathing mechanism, but the strong, muscular base of the pectoral fins enables it to use those fins as sturdy legs, while the eyes are finely adapted to vision above the water. It is easily conceivable that with a little further specialization of equipment many of these water animals could have permanently left their original environment to rove the land and undergo all manner of further changes.

Many importations have been made, but it is only recently that we learned how to keep them. They need ample space, not less than 3 feet square, and sandy flats rising from shallow, half-marine water, so that the fishes can be in any depth from 2 inches to nothing. Provisions should be made for them to climb to still higher levels and perch on rocks or sections of gnarled wood. The temperature ought to be at about 80, and it is important that their atmosphere be entirely enclosed, so as to keep it moist, as well as warm. The importance of moisture can be seen in their actions. They like to stand for long periods in about a quarter inch of water, but frequently they will roll over, somewhat like the action of a dog, to moisten themselves. Also using a pectoral fin like a paw they will wet their faces, no doubt in order to keep the eyes moist. They may be seen kept under ideal conditions at the Shedd Aquarium in Chicago, where they have even been taught to take dried food. They take meal worms readily.

The following extract is from a most interesting article in THE AQUARIUM (November, 1932), by Henry W. Fowler, of the Academy of Natural Sciences in Philadelphia: "About the extensive mud flats of the Indo Australian Archipelago, Mud Skippers are met with in perhaps their greatest profusion. This is usually near lagoons or tidal estuaries, especially about or near mangrove flats. My first acquaintance with it was in the coral reef islands in the Java Sea. Though only a few were found at first, I saw perhaps more of its ability to skip about on land and over the water, than most any place visited. Its method of skipping over the surface of shallow pools, by leaping a foot or more, was most interesting. Each time it alighted on the surface of the water with a little splash and soon progressed from about 5 to 20 feet. Its objective was nearly always toward some goal above the water. Often it would finally alight on a mangrove root and then crawl or wriggle up until well above the water line. Sometimes it would jump from one root to another, often with fins expanded, though its movements through the air are so difficult to follow I was not always sure of this. On the soft, wet mud it would crawl, wriggle or skip about with apparent abandon, though doubtless in search of minute insects or crustaceans which were scarcely visible. Here it was found in numbers of a dozen or more, though appearing scattered and not in schools. About the mangrove roots it is usually impossible to catch any."

In color the fish is an olive brown with irregular, light blue markings, especially about the head. The colors of the front dorsal, beginning at the bottom, are blue, white and black. The rear dorsal is gray. A dark blue stripe, edged white, traverses it. The tail fin, usually being closed, looks unnatural spread as it is shown in our illustration.

THE SCORPION-FISHES

FAMILY SCORPAENIDAE

Pronounced Skor-peen'i-dee

This very large family of marine fishes is well represented in practically all temperate and tropical seas. They belong to the order Cataphracti (or Scleroparei) which differs from the perch-like fishes (Percomorphi) in the enlargement of one of the cheek bones under the eye. Most of the tropical species have venom glands at the bases of the fin spines and a venom-duct running along each spine. Pressure on the spine (as when a man's hand is punctured) injects the venom. Many of the species are dangerous to handle and a few are deadly.

COLOR PLATE PAGE 591

Ptéroïs vòlitans (LINNAEUS)

Pronounced Ter'o-iss vo'le-tans   *Popular name,* Lionfish or Turkeyfish

MEANING OF NAME: *Pterois,* from the Greek word pteroeis, meaning winged or feathered; *volitans,* flying (which the fish doesn't!)

Tropical Central and Western Pacific Ocean; Indian Ocean   Length up to 10 inches

THE Lionfish is perhaps the *fanciest* fish alive, so far as fins and general appearance go. The relatively few individuals that are imported find a ready sale at fairly high prices to marine aquarium enthusiasts. Unfortunately, the fish will not live in fresh water.

This is a dangerous fish if one's hands come in contact with the fin spines, for even small ones can give a sting far worse than a hornet, and with large fish the sting may be as serious as a venomous snake bite.

The Lionfish seems to be aware of its powers for it is a slow-moving, self-possessed and fearless aquarium fish, giving it a distinct grandeur and dignity. Movement nearby does not frighten it, but serves only to attract its attention and make it spread its dangerous fins—hence the name Turkeyfish.

Requires small fishes as food (of which it can swallow fairly large ones), or small pieces of lean meat or fish dangled before it on a stick or toothpick. Best kept alone. Temperature 75 to 80 degrees. Color photograph by *Ernest Palinkas*.

Other related species, with smaller fins, are sometimes imported as the Lionfish. The most outstanding of these is *Dendrochirus barberi* from Hawaii. It is surprising that this fish is so seldom imported, as it has several points in its favor. Most obvious, of course, is the fact that its location is much nearer to the United States than that of *Pterois,* which must be imported from the South Pacific or Indian Ocean. *Dendrochirus* is a much more desirable aquarium fish, as it does not grow to more than three or four inches. Because of this small size, it can be kept in smaller aquariums than *Pterois*.

Dendrochirus is not so strikingly colorful as *Pterois,* but it is attractive nonetheless. The predominant color ranges from greenish to salmon. The pupil of the eye is bright green, surrounded by a reddish iris.

Shedd Aquarium, of Chicago, reports their Hawaiian divers collected *Dendrochirus* by bringing pieces of coral to the surface. Every third or fourth coral head would contain a small specimen.

A Dwarf Lionfish, *Dendrochirus barberi*

THE BROAD-SOLES
FAMILY ACHIRIDAE
Pronounced A ky'ri dee

The Broad-Soles belong to the order Heterosomata or Flatfishes, all of which lie on one side and have both eyes on the upper side. The Soles differ from other Flatfishes in having a very twisted mouth. There are several families of Soles. The broad-soles are salt-brackish, or fresh-water fishes.

Upper Side   Lower Side

Trinéctes maculàtus (BLOCH)

Pronounced Try-neck'tees mac'you-lay"tus   *Popular name,* Fresh-water Sole

MEANING OF NAME: *Trinectes,* with 3 "swimmers" (fins); *maculatus,* spotted

Also known as *Achirus fasciatus,* Common Sole

Coastal waters from Cape Cod southward   Length, aquarium specimens, 2 inches

*W*E hesitated to include this fish in our list, but as there is a mild, persistent interest in it, we did so. It is really the young of a 5- to 6-inch fish related to the Flounders. Interest in it lies chiefly in its method of swimming. This is accomplished by an undulating movement of the fins at the edges of the body as the fish glides in a horizontal position, like a pancake being propelled through the water. All fishes of this type—and there are many of them—at first have eyes normally on each side of the head. At an early age, one of them moves over to the other side, so that eventually we see a fish blind on one side and with 2 raised eyes on the other. They lie in wait in the mud for small passing victims. In the aquarium they can be fed Daphnia or bits of chopped clam. They can stick quite firmly on the sides of the aquarium by body suction. Temperature, from 60 to 72 degrees.

In the aquarium they are not very active, spending much time either on or in the sand. On the whole we would say that they are more novel than satisfactory. Not safe with other fishes. They are fin-nippers.

THE SPINY EELS
FAMILY MASTACEMBELIDAE
Pronounced Mas'ta sem bell"i dee

The Spiny Eels are not true eels. They are elongated tropical Old World fresh-water fishes with numerous spines preceding the dorsal fin.

Mácrognàthus aculeatus (BLOCH)
Pronounced Mack'rog-nay"thus a-kew'lee-ay"tus
MEANING OF NAME: *Macrognathus*, big-jawed; *aculeatus*, sharp
Formerly known as *Rhynchobdella aculeata*

India and Burma (in river mouths)   Length, 7 inches
Eastern Location Map O15 to r28 and F45

*A*N odd creature, seldom imported. We include it here because of its interesting appearance and the fact that it is the only member of this order which we have to show. It is one of the "spiny eels."

Like the Weatherfish, it spends much of its daytime buried in the sand, head peeping out. Probably the Weatherfish does this for protection, but with *Macrognathus* it is more likely a camouflage for attack, as it is a strictly carnivorous fish. At night it swims about the surface of the sand. In common with most nocturnal fishes it can be taught to eat in daytime, but as soon as it has had its meal of chopped earthworms it quickly returns to its sandy hide-out. Not interested in Daphnia or in raw meat. It will gladly take worms.

These fishes seem to like a temperature of about 78 degrees. After 2 years in the Shedd Aquarium, at Chicago, none of them have died. Neither have they bred.

Similar species to the above, but belonging to the genus *Mastocembelus*, have been imported from tropical Africa and Asia from time to time.

495

THE PUFFERS
FAMILY TETRAODONTIDAE
Pronounced Tet'ra o don"ti dee

The Puffers are comical fishes. They can blow themselves up with air or water into a veritable balloon. No other fishes possess this remarkable ability. Like some other families in the order Plectognathi the fused teeth (2 above, 2 below) form a beak with which the larger species can give a dangerous nip. Most of the species are of good size and inhabit salt water throughout tropical and semi-tropical regions, but a few small ones inhabit fresh water.

Tétraodón flùviatìlis   HAMILTON-BUCHANAN
Pronounced Tet'ra-o-don flu'vee-a-ty'lis   *Popular name,* Blow Fish
MEANING OF NAME: Tetraodon, four-toothed; *fluviatilis,* of the river
Most of India, Burma, Malay Peninsula   Length, 2 to 5 inches
Eastern Location Map y19 to F40

"BLOW FISH" in different species have a wide distribution throughout marine waters. This one occurs principally in fresh and brackish locations, and in aquarium trade circles is known as the Freshwater Tetraodon.

The background color is light, with a vivid sheen of green, interspersed with large, dark blotches and spots. Belly white, or nearly so.

Although a fish of clumsy, thick appearance, it is extremely active, never still a moment. It is also quite aggressive towards its own kind, but seems to do little harm.

The outstanding feature of these Blow Fishes is their ability to puff themselves up with air or water, balloon-like. They do this when fright-

496

ened. Most but not all specimens will do it when removed from the water, placed on the hand and tickled. Air is taken in at the mouth in about a dozen noisy gulps, until the belly is fully inflated and hard. As the internal pressure increases, little hollow spines are projected from the scale spots. Even the vent is blown inside-out into a point. The fish is able to maintain this balloon form only about half a minute. When placed back on the water the inflation soon collapses and the fish quickly drops to the bottom of the aquarium like a punctured balloon.

With ordinary care it will live well in the aquarium, preferably with its own kind. Eats anything. In Nature it is a scavenger. Never bred. Temperature, 70-80 degrees.

THE LUNG FISHES
FAMILY LEPIDOSIRENIDAE
Pronounced Le pid'o sir en"i dee

These peculiar fishes, which breathe by means of lungs, are much more primitive in their general make-up than the other fishes in this book, but their specialized breathing apparatus shows that they sowewhat approach the amphibians. This family is found in Africa and South America. Another family, consisting of one species, inhabits Australia.

Protópterus annéctens (OWEN)
Pronounced Pro-top'te-rus an-neck'tens

MEANING OF NAME: *Protopterus,* before a fin, *i.e.,* with fins of primitive type; *annectens,* connecting (with reference to similarity to South American Lung Fish)

Tropical Africa   Length, 3 feet

Western Location Map (for 3 species) x46; z47; H69; B58; E71, etc.

*W*E include the species here on account of its extraordinary life habits, and the prominence it has been given in literature. It is a real "lung fish," encases itself deeply in mud as its pond dries, and can remain in this condition, breathing atmospheric air for a year or more, if necessary, awaiting the return of the rainy season.

Dr. Homer Smith, of New York, wrote a book called "Komongo," describing his search in Africa for this remarkable fish. It is so truly an air-breather that the first ones collected *drowned* in a container that was not deep enough for them to reach the surface with their mouths at the proper angle to enable them to take new air. Other lung fishes also occur in South America and in Australia. A few of 6-inch size are kept in small aquariums.

The fish is gray. The rope-like extensions on the sides are pectoral and ventral fins, which they use in a circular rowing motion.

Limia nigrofasciata x *Limia melanogaster* hybrids

HYBRIDS AND HYBRIDIZING

HYBRIDS among aquarium fishes, as is generally known, occur mainly among live-bearing or viviparous fishes. This seems to be due mainly to the fact that these males in their amorous ambitions have little of that reserve which nearly all the egg-layers display in ignoring females except those of their own kind.

The fact that lively males of some of the viviparous species are often seen paying court to strange females—sometimes even to egg-layers— gives rise to a mistaken belief that *any* species of live-bearers can cross. As with other animals, fertilization cannot take place unless the species are closely related. The farther apart they are in that respect, the less likely is success. If it does occur in distant relationships, the young are more apt to prove sterile, to be physically defective, and to die early.

Crosses within the bounds of a genus are the most apt to be successful. Cases in point would be between species of *Mollienisia,* or between species of *Limia,* or of Platies. Such matings are called inter-specific. In nature *Mollienisia latipinna* crosses freely with *M. sphenops* to produce an inter-specific hybrid. The offspring are perfectly healthy, but they appear all to be females of a type intermediate between the parents. They once erroneously received the scientific name of *Mollienisia formosa.* These females, strange to say, when mated with a male *M. latipinna,* produce only females like themselves.

Occasional results may also be had when two genera (indicated by the first name of the fish) are closely related. These are called inter-

499

generic hybrids. Before Platys were recognized as members of the Swordtail *(Xiphophorus)* genus we believed we had many intergeneric crosses between "Platys" and Swordtails, but as a matter of fact, such crosses are very rare, the one recorded here between Guppies and Mollies being a true example. The young of such crosses, especially those being wholly or partially black, are likely to develop fatal tumors, mostly manifested as swellings about the base of the tail, and in progressive deformity of the tail fin.

Guppy x Mollienisia hybrid
(Lower figure)

Crosses between such distantly related Poeciliids as Guppies and Mollienisias have occasionally been made. The one in our accompanying illustration had a swelling under the gill plates at the time the photograph was made. It died about 2 months later, but lived long enough to be displayed at several exhibitions. Dr. Carl Hubbs examined the preserved fish and confirms the claim of its strange parentage.

Our illustrations also show 2 of the newer and more successful crosses between live-bearers.

It is not uncommon for hybrids to be larger than either parent. Such seems to be the case with the hybrid red Swordtails, the hybrid Montezuma (a 5-inch monster sometimes) and, to a lesser extent, with the *Xiphophorus variatus x Xiphophorus montezumoe* hybrid shown following.

A comparison with the parents of these 2 kinds of hybrids will prove interesting. They are illustrated under their own headings.

Reference has been made to the promiscuous character of male live-bearers. This should be qualified. They prefer their own females, and, as a rule, will not mate with other kinds if females of their own species are present. That answers a question often raised by owners of aquariums containing several species of live-bearers.

This brings us to the point of first importance in making crosses. It is the use of virgin females. As one fertilization lasts for from 4 to 6 broods of young, it is obvious that results of a cross would be uncertain if the female had previously been with developed males of her own species. Therefore it is best to take young fishes intended for hybridization and

Xiphophorus variatus x *Xiphophorus montezumæ* hybrid

The dark bars, the tail point and extra development of the dorsal
fin as shown here all became well developed only after two years.

place them in individual jars a little before it is time for the sexes to
become apparent. After the sexes are known, all females can be placed
in a large aquarium by themselves for further growth, and for eventual
breeding to selected males.

There is a difference in the shape of the gonopodium, or male fertilizing organ, of the various species of live-bearers. This is one of the characteristics noted by ichthyologists in recognizing species.

Certain egg-layers can also be hybridized, as will be seen on the page
following the Brachydanios. Nothing of much interest to the aquarist
has ever been produced by those crosses. One of the rather rare ones is

Xiphophorus variatus HYBRID

Except for short spike on tail fin, this fish might be taken for a
giant *X. variatus*. Dorsal fin is yellow, tail deep red. It is a hybrid, said to be produced by mating a *variatus* male to the daugh-
ter of a *Limia nigro-fasciata* x green *hellerii* cross.

the illustrated *Colisa labiosa* x *Colisa lalia* cross. This pair is about intermediate in all ways, and so far has proved sterile. The females of the egg-laying fishes, of course, need not be virgins for hybridizing.

The fixing of colors or color patterns in a given species is most interesting, and is also of commercial value. This is popularly referred to as "line breeding" as differentiated from the rule-of-thumb scheme of merely discarding undesired types and breeding from desired ones. It is an effort to put into practice the laws of inheritance as revealed by Mendel. Usually it is confined to the simple plan of breeding together either parents and offspring or brothers and sisters of such individuals as show the desired characteristics. While this sometimes produces favorable results, it is by no means taking full advantage of possibilities.

Colisa lalia x *Colisa labiosa* hybrids
The pair has so far proved infertile.

THE LOWER MALE DELIVERED YOUNG

SEX CHANGES IN FISHES

*I*T is almost as difficult convincing a confirmed aquarist that a fish can change sex as it is to persuade the uninformed that some fishes have their young born alive. Yet observations of sex change are becoming more frequently recorded, especially among the live-bearing species. With them, however, one should be very careful about jumping at conclusions, because males are sometimes very late in developing sex, and unless they are known to have had young and later turned to males, such cases are open to doubt. We were recently in receipt of a letter from a lady in Florida who said that most of her female Black Sailfins had turned to males, and wanted to know whether we could suggest any way of preventing the balance of them from changing!

A case in point was experienced by the writer. Receiving some of the first of the orange-tailed *Mollienisia sphenops*, he bred them rapidly. When the young were 1½ inches long, he sorted them in order to set aside those having the best colors, and was astonished to find only about 10 per cent males. Some time later, in an article he stated that only a small proportion of the strain are males. They continued to be kept in a large aquarium, where they were fed heavily, grew rapidly and bred freely. In a year most of the grown fish were *males*, and among these were noticed two that surely looked "loaded." Mr. Frederick Stoye impressed on us that they ought, as a matter of record, to be photographed. The result is the accompanying illustration, in which the upper fish, an ordinary male, with the usual male outline, is placed for comparison. The print was not retouched. After being photographed, the heavy males were placed in an aquarium containing no other livebearers. Next morning one of the two was much more slender, and there appeared a flock of little baby black-spotted *Mollienisia sphenops* swimming about. The other one also lost much of its girth, but no more young were found. We cannot say whether either of these fish had previously delivered young. They can scarcely be expected to do so again.

Ordinarily when the change takes place the ova present in the female at the time are absorbed.

There are numerous authenticated instances of *Xiphophorus helleri* changing sex after bearing young. No case has ever, to our knowledge, been recorded in which a male became a female. It seems that even among animals none prefer the lot of the lady!

Microscopic examinations of *X. helleri* embryos in their early stages indicate that all of this species are for a time neuter, and that when delivered they are invariably females. While there is an average period for each species as to when the anal fin of the female becomes the gonopodium of the male, it is far from fixed. Indeed it seems that it is never too late for the transformation to occur.

As elsewhere stated, males grow little after their external sex characteristics appear. It is believed by some that all very large males have been females during the period of their principal growth, and that most of them have delivered one or more broods of young.

There are instances, recorded on good authority, of Bettas and of Paradise Fish in which females spawned normally one year and next season they had turned to males and functioned perfectly as such.

Among wild fishes, Fowler has found that about one in 20,000 shad are double-sexed, having both roe and milt. These are no doubt purely freaks, and have no bearing on sex changes as we define the subject.

Our Editor, Dr. Myers, cautions us that change in the external sexual features of a fish is no proof that a fish can act as a parent of a sex opposite from that it had at first. The most rigorously controlled scientific experiments would be necessary to prove such a case. Either sex usually possesses both male and female hormones, which, when unbalanced, may cause an external appearance of sex change. Certain genetic factors make true sex change in some fishes exceedingly unlikely.

Marine Aquariums

The salt-water aquarium opens a door to an exciting phase of fish-keeping which can bring much satisfaction if the hobbyist is willing to accept a somewhat different set of rules than that which he has used in the fresh-water hobby.

Most failures stem from a lack of knowledge of the medium itself, i.e., salt water. Salt water must be handled meticulously in that it must never come in contact with materials it breaks down such as metals and some aquarium cements. Equipment must be chosen with this in mind. Plexiglas tanks are the best containers for salt-water. If tanks are used that have been carried over from the fresh-water hobby, it must be understood that water changes will have to be frequent. Toxicity builds up in salt water that is in contact with standard aquarium cements, and the only way to keep ahead of it is to change the water. We recommend that a third of the water be discarded each week and that freshly collected sea water be used to replace it. If artificial salt water is being used, the same schedule may be used, the replacement water being freshly mixed and no change in the formula made. Always use the same brand or formula of water in the tank. If you have several tanks, you may wish to use several brands, but never mix two brands or formulas in one tank.

Glass covers should be used to cover tanks. Reflectors should be placed on top of such glass covers so that water resulting from evaporation will collect on the glass rather than on the inside of the metal reflector. Water that has collected on a metal reflector is contaminated with metal salts, and when it drops back in the aquarium, it contaminates the aquarium water.

Salt water will not support as many specimens in a given amount of water as will fresh water. A rough rule might be for fish measuring less than three inches from head to tail to allow five gallons of water per specimen. For fish measuring more than three inches from head to tail, but not more than six inches, allow 15 gallons of water per specimen. Larger fish are not desirable in the home aquarium.

Acquaint yourself with the various temperaments of species before purchasing a selection. *Amphiprion percula,* mentioned earlier in this book, is an excellent aquarium subject. Two pairs of this species, however, will quarrel over territories. *Dascyllus trimaculatus* and *D. aruanus* are both apt to be scrappy and do best in tanks of their own.

Salt-water aquariums are best decorated with coral that has been boiled and allowed to weather for several months. Staghorn coral and coral rock may be used. Not only does coral add beauty to a tank, but it is functional as well. It provides hiding places for fish which are necessary to all salt-water species. It also serves as a water conditioner as it has a tendency to keep the water alkaline. Only a sprinkling of coral sand is used on the floor of the aquarium. A handful of fine beach sand might be piled in one corner of the aquarium for specimens that like to dig.

A TAME "HORSE"

Sea horses are not very "scary" and soon learn that their feeder is their friend. This one has cultivated an expensive appetite for live baby guppies, which it either gobbles as they pass within striking distance, or daintily takes one from the fingers of his lady. Minus the ornamentation of the tropical kinds, this is our Atlantic Coast species, *Hippocampus hudsonius.*

Constant aeration is necessary in the salt-water aquarium. Standard aeration is adequate but power filters serve a double purpose. Not only do they create a current in the water but they filter out solid waste materials also. Many experienced hobbyists use an airstone and a power filter. Whatever one's preference may be in this matter, constant aeration should be supplied. Although tropical marine fishes are subjected to temperature changes in their natural habitat, avoid such changes as much as possible in the home aquarium. During the winter months heaters are not necessary if the room in which the aquarium is kept is maintained at approximately 78°F. If the room is not thermostatically controlled, however, a heater should be employed. Keeping the salt-water aquarium cool in the summer time is probably more difficult. An air-conditioned room is ideal, but if this is not available, a plastic screen over the aquarium will help. The reflector should be removed from the tank when such a screen is provided to prevent water that has collected on the metal from returning to the tank. Salt-water tanks should not be allowed to read more than 80°F.

Feeding salt-water specimens is not difficult. Most species will eat tiny pieces of lean beef, or scrapings of raw shrimp. A supply of both may be kept in the freezer. Newly hatched brine shrimp is ideal for most species. Algal growths should be allowed to grow on corals and on the rear and side glasses of the aquarium. Most marine species require some vegetable matter in their diet. Salt-water fish should be fed at least twice a day, and very small specimens as many as four times a day if possible.

The most ideal scavenger for the salt-water aquarium is the hermit crab. These little creatures do an excellent job of cleaning up.

Of all marine animals the sea horse seems to be the most popular among fish fanciers, and probably no other creature of the sea has been more unknowingly abused by hobbyists. The dwarf sea horse is the best species for the aquarium because its needs are less demanding. A steady diet of newly hatched brine shrimp will keep it in good condition, and it can be kept in a five-gallon tank. Constant aeration should be supplied. Only a limited number of the fry should be kept (eight or nine at the most), as the amount of food the fry first take is limited in a small tank. Larger sea horses are not so successful in the home aquarium as they will only take live food and brine shrimp does not seem to be adequate.

If artificial salt is to be used in the home salt-water aquarium, follow the distributor's directions carefully. Do not mix brands in one tank, and have your tank set up with the artificial mix properly diluted (according to the distributor's directions) several weeks before you purchase your fish.

The salt-water hobbyist should not try to operate without the aid of a hydrometer. This instrument permits the aquarist to determine the amount of dissolved material his aquarium water contains. Sea water collected in southern waters usually reads 1.025 approximately. If all the water was allowed to evaporate from a gallon of such water, about a quarter of a pound of salts would be found in the container. Because water evaporates, the salt-water aquarium would become more dense as time went by unless fresh water were added to make up for the water lost through evaporation. The hydrometer is used to determine how much water is lost, or how dense the remaining water has become. As pointed out above, water collected in the south reads about 1.025. The aquarist with safety can allow the salinity to be less. A reading of 1.020 can be reached gradually, and salt-water specimens will get along very well in water having this reading. Hydrometers can be purchased for less than $5 in well-stocked aquarium shops.

Salt-water fish are beautiful, entertaining, and in time become very tame. Give yourself a chance to keep these lovely creatures by limiting the number you keep. The more room these fish have, the better is their chance for survival. Before you set up your tank read at least one book devoted solely to the maintenance of salt-water fish.

"Community Tank" Combinations

In response to many requests for "happy family" selections for different sizes and kinds of aquariums, we present, with some hesitation, the following suggestions. Not only do tastes vary greatly, but opportunities for securing the different species do not always present themselves in accordance with our wishes. Care has been used, as far as possible, to list fishes which are usually in stock. No dealer, however, should be thought lacking in enterprise who does not constantly have on hand all of the species mentioned.

The most that can be expected of the lists is that they will furnish practical ideas which each aquarist may modify to suit his own preferences, conditions, opportunities and resources.

Calculations have been made on the basis of using well-planted aquariums of ordinary proportions, located in a good light and comfortably but not excessively heated—say fairly close to 73 degrees. Cooler aquariums are given separate consideration. Aeration is not counted on. As elsewhere stated, it would materially increase the number of fishes that might safely be used.

Almost any combination of the ordinary live-bearers can safely be made. Different species will seldom cross if mates of their own kind are present. Color varieties of the same species will cross freely. If this is not desired, they should not be placed together in the same tank.

The community tank presents an interesting and varied spectacle, but it is not usually suited to the propagation of fishes. That being the case, some aquarists use only male fishes in mixed collections, as their coloration is usually more brilliant, and conflicts due to mating are eliminated.

In our listings we have kept in mind not only temperaments, but sizes and similar food requirements. Some thought has also been given to the selection of species which furnish interesting color contrast and which otherwise look well together.

Possibly due to different conditions and feeding, certain fishes do not always act as harmoniously as we would like. For instance, *B. tetrazona*, one of our most spirited and showy aquarium fishes, sometimes works off its excess vitality by chasing or even nipping its neighbors. Yet for some it does not do this, and it is too good a fish to exclude from the "happy family" without a trial. This and other questionable species have been marked with a star (*).

Some good fishes have been omitted because they will eat nothing but live food, a luxury few of us can supply in sufficient quantity for all. *Chanda lala* represents this type. Other desirables have been left off just because there are too many of them to be included. The author is really "sticking out his neck" in proposing these various combinations, but it is all in a good cause.

Names have been used by which the fishes are generally recognized, whether popular or scientific.

5-gallon: liable to become cool (about 60 degrees)

17 smallish mixed-sized fishes

6 Bloodfins
2 Medakas
1 2-inch Paradise*
1 1¾-inch *Corydoras paleatus*
2 Platy variatus
3 White Clouds
2 *Brachydanio rerio*

15- to 20-gallon: liable to become cool (about 60 degrees)

46 mixed-sized fishes

10 Bloodfins or White Clouds
4 Medakas
1 2-inch Paradise*
2 2½-inch *Corydoras paleatus*
6 Platy variatus
4 *Mollienisia sphenops* (plain, spotted, or orange-tail)
6 *Brachydanio rerio*
2 *Ctenobrycon spilurus*
2 Australian Rainbow Fish
1 Weatherfish 3- to 4-inch size
4 2-inch Chanchitas*
4 *B. semifasciolatus*

5-gallon: normal temperature

19 small-sized fishes

2 *Brachydanio rerio*
2 *Brachydanio albolineatus*
2 Glow Lights
2 *Hyphessobrycon flammeus*
2 *Pristella riddlei*
2 *Hemigrammus ocellifer*
1 small Corydoras (1¾-inches)
2 White Clouds
2 *B. oligolepis*
2 Neon Tetras

5-gallon: normal temperature

12 fishes a little larger

2 Scalares (body size of half dollar)
2 *B. tetrazona* or *conchonius**
2 Dwarf Gourami

2 Blue platys
2 Platy variatus
1 Male Betta
1 Corydoras (2-inches)

7-gallon: normal temperature

8 fishes, still larger

2 Scalares (body size of dollar)
2 *B. conchonius*
2 *Danio malabaricus*
2 Australian Rainbow Fish

10-gallon: normal temperature

31 small fishes

4 Scalares (body size of half dollar)
2 Rasbora or White Clouds
4 *Brachydanio rerio*
2 *Brachydanio albolineatus*
4 Neon Tetras
4 *Hemigrammus ocellifer*
2 small Corydoras
1 Male Betta
2 *Pristella riddlei*
4 Guppies
2 Bloodfins

10-gallon: normal temperature

15 fishes a little larger average size

2 Scalares (body size of a dollar)
2 Platys
2 *B. conchonius* or *cummingi*
1 Male Betta
2 medium-sized Corydoras
2 *Brachydanio albolineatus*
2 *X. hellerii* (pair)
2 *Trichogaster leeri* (2½-inch size)

20-gallon: normal temperature

60 fishes, mostly smaller sizes

6 Scalares (body size of half dollar)
4 *Brachydanio rerio*
2 *Brachydanio albolineatus*
4 *Pristella riddlei*
4 *Hemigrammus ocellifer*
2 *Hemigrammus unilineatus*
3 Corydoras (medium-sized)

1 Male Betta
4 *Hyphessobrycon flammeus*
2 *Colisa lalia*
2 *B. tetrazona* or *conchonius*°
2 *Copeina arnoldi*
2 *Esomus danricus*
8 Guppies
4 *Rasbora heteromorpha*
4 *Platy variatus* or *maculatus*
2 *Nannaethiops unitaeniatus*
4 Bloodfins

20-gallon: normal temperature

37 larger fishes

4 Scalares (body size of a dollar)
2 Portalegrensis or 2 Blue Acaras°
2 *Ctenobrycon spilurus*
2 *Trichogaster leeri* (3-inch size)
2 *Barb. everetti* (3-inch size)
2 *Barb. conchonius* or *Barb. ticto*
2 Kissing Gourami
2 *Aplocheilus lineatus*
3 *Corydoras*
2 *Chanchitos* (2½-inch size)°
2 *Moenkhausia oligolepis*°
2 Black Mollienisias
4 Large Platys
2 Blue Gularis
2 Helleri or Helleri hybrids (pair)
2 *Danio malabaricus*

40-gallon: normal temperature

78 fishes, mostly medium sizes

6 Scalares (body size of a dollar)
2 *Ctenobrycon spilurus*
1 large male Betta
1 large male Paradise°
4 *Barb. everetti* (3-inch size)
2 *Barb. conchonius*
2 Black Mollies
2 *Copeina guttata*
4 Spotted or Red-tail Mollies
2 2½-inch Scats
4 *Corydoras*
2 Kissing Gourami
6 *Platy variatus*
6 *Platy maculatus* (color to suit)
4 *Danio malabaricus*
2 *Hemigrammus caudovittatus*°
2 *Aequidens curviceps* (*thayeri*)°
2 *Trichogaster leeri*
2 Blue Gularis°
2 *Colisa fasciata* or *labiosa*

4 Red Helleri ⎫
4 Green Helleri ⎬ only 1 male
4 Orange Helleri ⎭
2 *Aplocheilus lineatus*
2 *Limia vittata*
2 *A. maronii*
2 Blind Cave Tetras

40-gallon: normal temperature

65 mostly large fishes

4 Scalares, large size
4 *Barb. everetti* (4-inch size)
4 *Moenkhausia oligolepis* (3-inch or larger)°
2 *Ctenobrycon spilurus* (3-inch size)
4 Black Sailfin Mollies (large)
2 *Portalegrensis*°
2 *Aequidens latifrons* (Blue Acaras)°
1 Dempsey (4-inch size)°
2 *Trichogaster leeri* (4-inch size)
4 Mollies, spotted or Red-tail
4 *Hemigrammus caudovittatus*°
4 *Danio malabaricus*
4 Rainbow Fish
2 *Colisa fasciata* (large)
6 Swordtails (large) ⎫
4 Red Helleri (large) ⎬ only 1 male
4 *Corydoras*
4 Blue Gularis (large)
2 *Cichlasoma severum* (*Heros spurius*)°
2 Three-Spot Gourami°

For any of the last group there may be substituted equal numbers of Chanchito, Kissing Gourami (large), Schreitmülleri, *Tilapia macrocephala* or *Barb. binotatus* or *Barb. lateristriga*.

Some of the fishes particularly well suited to making a group display exclusively of their own species are: Bloodfins, *Brachydanio rerio*, Neon Tetras, Black Tetras, *Hemigrammus ocellifer*, *Rasbora heteromorpha*, White Clouds, male Guppies, and *Barbus sumatranus*. (*Tetrazona*)

Ctenobrycon spilurus is mentioned in several places, but it should be noted that it tends to eat plants, especially Vallisneria.

Two of the worst fishes for a community tank are *Gambusia affinis* (fin rippers), and Black Line Tetras (chasers and nippers).

Easiest Fishes for Beginners

Among the livebearers we unhesitatingly select the Guppy. It is the surest to please and to succeed under a wide variety of conditions. Second choice, Platies.

Egg-layers; White Cloud Mountain Fish, especially if chilly temperatures are anticipated. Given plenty of room, good feeding and small-sized food and let alone they are dependable producers. Breed mostly in spring and early summer. Second choice, Zebra Danios. The Medaka is probably the easiest egg-layer to spawn and raise, and it will stand lower temperatures than either of the two preceding. However, it is much less colorful than either.

Cichlids; Chanchita and Portalegrensis.

Bubble-nest-builders; Paradise and 3-spot or Blue Gourami.

Most Profitable Fishes for the Small Breeder

Occasionally we receive a request from some ambitious beginner wanting to know the names of fishes that are easily bred and for which there is a ready market at good prices. As a farmer said on first seeing a Giraffe, "There ain't no such animal."

As surely as water seeks its own level, fishes easily produced bring low prices. The difficult kinds seldom pay adequate returns for the time and effort required. The amateur breeder had best find his profit in success for its own sake.

"Once in a blue moon" a new, attractive, easily-bred fish importation appears on the horizon of aquarists. A few early breeders enjoy a short harvest, but soon the price sinks to the level of everything that comes easily.

WHOLESALE BREEDING

*W*HILE the principles governing the breeding of any fish must always depend upon the nature of the fish itself, there are special methods employed in quantity production. Again, the methods of whole-sale breeders vary according to climatic conditions, as well as personal ideas. What follows refers only to Exotics. *Not* to Goldfish.

A number of our very large breeders are in the Gulf States, for the obvious reason that heating expense there is reduced to a minimum. Whether this counterbalances the disadvantage of having to ship by a 3-day express haul to the main market (New York) is, and probably will remain, an open question. However, we are not so much concerned here with that commercial problem. What we are rather trying to do is to give our readers some idea of how and where the big producers carry on.

Regardless of location, one principle applies to nearly all of them. They specialize in only a few species, usually those for which there is the greatest popular demand. Ordinarily this comprises not over 5 or 6 species per establishment, and more likely not over 2 or 3.

The majority of Southern fish farms (they can scarcely be called establishments) consist of a series of large pools in which breeder fishes are placed and fed, and from which several crops a year are netted. In many of them, especially those in the lowlands of Florida, it is impossible to drain off the pools except by the use of power pumps. This is owing to the high natural water level in the surrounding soil. Those pools that can be drained have a sloping bottom, so that the fish concentrate at the low point when the water is nearly out. Here they are easily caught.

The majority of these plants have no buildings, except perhaps a rude sort of shipping shed. This is a disadvantage, because it leaves the fish farmer with no control over excessive sun nor the chilly weather which is sometimes prevalent. In the Gulf States some pools have an enormous supply of water from warm springs, a most valuable asset when the frost king pays one of his rare visits to the South.

Little or no effort is made at these simple farms to protect the fishes in ground level pools against their natural enemies. The idea seems to be to breed the fishes faster than they can be consumed by enemies.

In such places the fishes are left to breed as best they can. Nature takes its course, with very little assistance. The only help they receive is enough food so that cannibalism is reduced to a minimum, and a reasonably good supply of plants in which the fishes can hide from each other and from their enemies. After all, this state of affairs approximates

Nature, and when Dragonfly larvae and Water Tigers are not too plentiful, the fish farmer harvests fairly large crops.

Most wholesale breeders have large pools in which they raise Daphnia. Mosquito larvae are also important as food, especially in the South, where their natural season is very much longer.

Not all of the Southern fish-producing plants are conducted on the "let-Nature-do-it" scheme. There are a number of large and beautifully

SECTION OF BREEDING HOUSE WITH PARTIALLY SOLID ROOF
This is the generally approved design, especially in the South where there is an excess of light. A live-bearer section is shown here with aquariums for breeders and globes for deliveries of baby fish. The central section (below) contains large storage pools.

conducted establishments in which the pools, tanks and aquariums are housed over, assuring control of light and temperature. Scientific methods are in use. In such places a number of good strains of fishes have been developed by selective breeding.

In general, the wholesale breeding plant is *not* a greenhouse, especially in the South. The sides of the houses are solid and contain no glass. Openings in the roof comprise about one-third of the area. This admits sufficient light. Some houses are glazed where the roof openings occur, and others are merely screened to keep out fish enemies, particularly Dragonflies and the flying bugs whose larvae are Water Tigers.

The principle of using solid sides and roof, with all illumination coming from overhead openings is one that is well for all those to remember who consider building a fish house or *aquiary,* as it has been well called, especially where there is an abundance of light. Excess light and heat can be a great detriment. Small greenhouses or "lean-tos" may be best for city dwellers who are nearly or completely closed out of direct sun. In the North the walls should not only be solid, but well insulated and

NORTHERN FISH AND PLANT PROPAGATING HOUSE

The side tanks are for propagating, while the big central ones are for increasing size. In these are seen tall wooden dividers to separate species and to prevent their leaping into another compartment. The fishes may jump into the alleys if they wish, but a careful wholesale breeder would rather lose a fish than have it mixed with other species or varieties. Although glass is whitewashed, this house admits too much light and heat.

air-spaced, for the saving in fuel will soon offset the slight extra expense in construction.

In reference to heating, let us repeat that nowhere, either in home or fish house, should any system be employed in which the product of combustion is discharged indoors. This applies particularly to gas and oil, and more especially to "gas-water" heaters that do not take the burned gas out through a flue. Modern grills looking somewhat like automobile radiators, heated by steam or electricity, with air forced through by a fan, are highly efficient. They are usually placed high in a room. A heating specialist should be consulted regarding capacity and installation.

Besides the primitive principle of allowing the fishes to breed unattended, as it were, well-managed establishments have certain established and carefully followed procedures suited to different species. In a large Northern hatchery, for instance, all live-bearers and a number of species of egg-droppers are bred in wooden trays having ¼-inch mesh wire

BREEDING TRAYS WITH SCREEN BOTTOMS

bottom, through which eggs or young are dropped by the breeders. The trays are partially submerged and are supported on small inverted flower-pots. The tanks in which these breeding trays stand are shallow and very large. Our illustration pictures the general idea. To prevent loss of efficiency the wire screen must be occasionally scrubbed.

In other establishments, especially in the South, the live-bearing species are kept in large observation tanks, and as a female shows signs of early delivery, she is placed in an ordinary globe aquarium containing a sprig of Anacharis and more Mosquito larvae than she can eat. A very small percentage of young is lost.

Thousands of globes are also necessary for the rearing of Bettas in wholesale quantities. The females may be placed in tanks together, but as soon as the males are nearly an inch long, each must have his own globe if he is to develop and retain perfect fins. This practice sometimes gives rise to the belief that a small globe is necessary to the growth of very long fins. Such is not the case, but those using little containers for that purpose are "doing the right thing for the wrong reason." The real point is protection from other males, as well as the saving of space.

Northern breeding establishments as a rule are not so large and are conducted more intensively. The Scalare is very important commercially. While many young are bred in Europe and sent to the United States and elsewhere, we produce great quantities of them here, mostly in one-man establishments within 100 miles of New York.

As to wholesale breeding of Scalares, a number of large ones are kept together in a big aquarium, and are allowed to mate naturally. Spawning is induced by frequent partial changes of water. Breeding pairs are not removed, but the eggs are taken out as soon as spawning is completed. Thousands of young can be reared to sufficient size for market in a small fish house in a few weeks if given aeration, room and plenty of live food, For details as to rearing, see *Pterophyllum scalare.*

A recent development among large breeders is the use of refrigerator linings as tanks. These are "seconds" from refrigerator manufacturers, but to the breeder they are perfects. All they need is a piece of glass set in the open end. This is easily done and makes an extremely cheap tank of about 50-gallon capacity. Being a brilliant white inside these tanks tend to keep the fishes pale, thus reducing their market value. This does not prevent their later assuming normal colors when placed in darker surroundings. White surfaces of these tanks can be darkened by a coating of asphaltum varnish.

Feeding methods used in wholesale establishments are described under "Wholesale Feeding" in the section on "Feeding."

Our opinion is sometimes asked as to the advisability of going into the commercial raising of fishes. With money-making the sole objective, it is pretty sure to prove a disappointment. A natural love of the hobby, plus successful experience, plus business sense, are all needed. The transition from amateur to professional status had best be gradual, remembering the shrewd couplet of Benjamin Franklin:

> *"Little boats should keep to shore,*
> *Larger craft may venture more."*

COLLECTING AND TRANSPORTING EXOTIC AQUARIUM FISHES

*I*T IS quite natural that those who find interest in our various aquarium fishes should wish to know more of their origin than can be told by the use of maps. As we have found much curiosity, but little knowledge on the subject, we present a brief outline of those happenings which cause fishes to eventually find themselves in the hands of friends thousands of miles removed from their native waters.

Among people not actively in contact with the trade it is commonly supposed that "importers" are domestic firms who send out collecting expeditions to different parts of the world. Ordinarily that is not so.

Let us go back a little. In the beginning of the Exotic fish hobby sailors and petty officers of boats touching tropical ports were paid by aquarists to bring back what small fresh-water fishes they could gather in distant waters. This soon developed into a system of having people at foreign ports collect the fishes between boat calls and delivering them to the sailors on their next visit.

Enterprising men of foreign lands gather large numbers of fishes and acclimate them to tank life before the arrival of the boat. The actual gathering is done by natives, either on their own account or under the direction and management of the exporter. Realizing the extra value of rare species, many of these people have become discriminating, and make extra efforts to bring in fishes that are out of the ordinary.

Since 1953 two important developments in the technique of shipping fishes have occurred. The first is in placing the fish in a large double plastic bag, knotted at the top and in turn enclosed in a firm double fibre shipping box, or one of wood, or in a tin can. A big bubble, preferably of oxygen, imprisoned when the bag is knotted, furnishes enough oxygen to last several days. Hard to believe, but true. For additional insulation against temperature change, the box is stuffed with torn newspaper or other inert material.

The second revolutionary idea is to "dope" the shipping water with mild sodium amytal, ½-grain to the gallon. In an hour this greatly slows down all the life processes of the fish, so that they need much less water (or can be more crowded); they do not bruise themselves nor fight; male Bettas or other fighters need not be shipped singly, but should be placed in the treated water an hour before being placed together. Recovery of fishes in fresh water is prompt and complete. A prescription may be needed to get the drug.

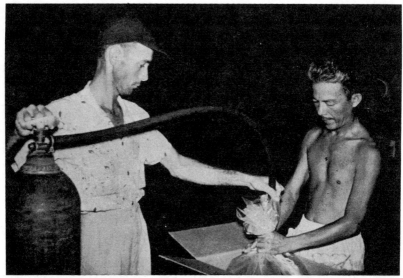

Fishes were formerly shipped in bulky metal cans, equipped with aeration facilities. Today they are placed in sealed plastic bags, which are in turn put into corrugated cartons. Here famed British Guiana collector Louis Chung (right) inflates a bag of fishes with pure oxygen in preparation of a shipment to the United States. **Photo by Alan M. Fletcher.**

Loaded interior of the plane illustrated on the opposite page. With the plastic-bag-and-carton method, several times more fishes can be carried than by former methods. They also arrive in better condition. Photograph by Alan M. Fletcher.

Large shipments by plane are now a reality. Many thousands of Neons and other choice fishes are flown from South America to Florida and New York at frequent intervals. Large privately-owned planes, equipped with temperature control, are mostly used for these interesting errands.

Photograph by Alan M. Fletcher

"THE FLYING FISH," REGULARLY FLYING BETWEEN SOUTH AMERICA AND FLORIDA
This plane, loaded in the fuselage with fiber cartons, is capable of successfully transporting 100,000 fishes of Neon size. Between trips to S. A., it makes deliveries all over the U. S. The plane is owned by Paramount Aquarium, Inc.

Owing to equatorial weather conditions, some fishes can be collected only at certain seasons. In order to make them available at other times, most shipments are routed through Florida to be held in live storage until wanted. This serves to both rest and acclimate them. Air shipments are also made from the Orient and Europe. Air shipments have not only reduced immediate losses, but have resulted in delivering fishes in better condition. Two Florida breeders use planes for domestic deliveries.

Hamburg, prior to World War II, had become the center for the importing, breeding and exporting of Exotic fishes, but with Germany's loss of its merchant marine and great ocean liners, together with the advent of reasonably-priced air transportation, the business became more decentralized, the principal focus now being New York and Florida. Most South American fishes are distributed by American importers. Many Asiatic fishes are brought into Ceylon and Singapore; then shipped east, west and south.

As to the methods employed by natives in catching fishes, they vary according to conditions and custom. The most successful general principle for catching fish alive and uninjured is by the use of a net called a seine. It is a long, narrow strip, weighted at the bottom, corked at the top, and is drawn from the ends by two men wading in the water.

Various native traps are used where seines cannot be worked. Among the most interesting of these are cast nets, circular affairs, weighted at the edges. When thrown they sink, parasol-like, and are then pursed by being drawn up from the centre, thus trapping the fishes, which have previously been drawn to the spot by bait thrown on the water.

When the base of operations is not a boat, it is often necessary to place the carrying cans on pack animals, for many of the roads are mere crude paths, impassable by automobiles.

Considering that the fishes pass through at least 4 sets of hands, many changes of water and of temperature, it is really very wonderful that so many of them survive the ordeal. Quite a number of attractive species cannot stand the handling, and we never see them. We get only the comparatively hardy ones, which is proof enough that with fair care our Exotic aquarium fishes ought to do well.

SKILLFUL THROW OF A CAST NET

SHOW RULES AND PRACTICES

It would be very desirable to have national standards for judging competitive aquarium exhibitions. Efforts to organize societies so that this would be possible have so far not met with success. In the absence of nationally accepted standards, we publish the rules of two prominent societies which cover most points, over a period of years, and which have been found generally acceptable.

The point system in use by The Pennsylvania Fish Culturists Association in judging fishes is as follows:

Condition and style	40 points
Color	40 points
Relative size, male and female	20 points
	100

Pairs always have precedence over single fish. Where sexes are difficult or impossible to recognize, 2 fish constitute a pair.

This society's practice with reference to household aquarium competitions is to have a committee of 3 examine the aquarium at the home of the owner. Awards are made on this basis:

AQUARIUM. Design, appearance and location	25 points
FISH. Condition and beauty of individuals	25 points
PLANTS. (Must be in growing condition.)	
Arrangement, condition, varieties	40 points
GENERAL APPEARANCE	10 points
	100

The aquarium competitions of the Boston Aquarium Society are held in conjunction with a large public exhibition. This to some extent changes their specifications, which follow:

Arrangement of Plants and Accessories	20 points
Variety and Rarity of Fish	20 points
Variety of Plant Material	15 points
General Artistic Effect	15 points
Design of Aquarium	10 points
Quality of Plant Material	10 points
Other Aquatic Fauna	10 points
	100

Competition in the show is confined to amateurs, but there is a special award for dealers. They are allowed to placard their aquariums, but the names of the owners in the amateur competition are not placed on the tanks until after the judging is completed.

There is also a competition for home-made aquariums. While they must be fully planted and equipped, the awards are based on workmanship.

It is a general practice at all shows that no fish are allowed to be sold nor removed before the close of the exhibition, unless approval is secured from the committee in charge.

Another general practice is that owners feed their own fish.

Shows should never be held in a place where the temperature is liable to drop below 70 degrees, unless controlled electrical heating equipment can be installed in aquariums.

Personally the author believes that it is best to keep exhibition on a non-competitive basis. In this he usually finds himself in the minority.

AQUARIUM SOCIETIES

Association with others interested in the same hobby is of inestimable value. Through friendly comparison of notes many a rough spot is made smooth, or some bit of knowledge is picked up that is not found even in the best book. No author can think of everything.

There are many places in which there is sufficient interest to support a society, but where no effort at organization has yet been made. If a few will take the lead, others will follow. The most effective way of doing this is to put on a public exhibition, even though it be modest in size. Newspapers, if approached, will give publicity in news items. Those of like tastes will attend and some of them will no doubt wish to join.

In building a society it should always be remembered that a congenial membership is more important than numerical strength.

Some societies have found themselves lacking a back door for the banishment of members who prove objectionable. This is a convenience that should not be overlooked.

Enlisting the interest of boys and girls in aquarium fishes has proven to be a very fertile source of recruits to our hobby. Among ways of achieving that end are talks and demonstrations at schools and clubs, setting up junior membership or encouraging the formation of independent youth societies.

Some far-sighted dealers make their shops available at stated times as radiating centers for such activities.

Aquarium Construction

ALTHOUGH there is a great variety of well-made aquariums to be had at lower cost than they can be constructed by the amateur, nevertheless there are those who enjoy making their own, perhaps creating something that expresses individual ideas, or that fits, tailor-made, into some odd space for which no suitable tank can be found in stock.

The aquarist located far from any source of supply would have still another reason for trying his hand at building what he otherwise finds difficult or impossible to obtain.

In any case, this chapter is addressed mainly to those having fair mechanical ability and the limited facilities found in an average household, including a vise, a hack-saw and either a small alcohol blow-torch or soldering iron. A carpenter's square, too. Those rather numerous fellows who nowadays make a hobby of operating elaborate home machine shops need no help, except perhaps a hint as to sources of a few supplies and a formula for cement. They are the ones to tackle the big jobs with heavy slate bases and stout iron frames to be machined, welded, drilled and riveted. The more modestly equipped amateur can find fun and a degree of success in building himself a metal-framed aquarium up to say 25-gallon capacity, although about half that size would be more likely to turn out well.

Proportions   In deciding this important consideration, thought should be given to the points laid down on page 2 of the opening chapter of this book. Few will want to totally sacrifice appearance by making a squatty tank like the lower illustration in order to gain the utmost in fish capacity. The usual decision is to combine beauty with utility, so that the result gives something which is compact, with liberal water surface and enough depth for the plants to develop agreeable height. Such an aquarium will give a good view of its contents and prove easy to work in. A proportion meeting these requirements is approximately a double cube, say 10 x 10 x 20 inches, although most people prefer a little more depth, say 12 inches. If there is no object in saving space, a front-to-back thickness, also of 12 inches, adds materially to that valuable water-surface, without detracting from appearance. A 12 x 12 x 20 size, filled to within 2 inches of the top, gives an actual water volume of slightly over 10 gallons.

Materials   Brass is the easiest metal to work. Angle brass, ⅝ inch, is suited to posts and top frame of tanks up to 20 gallons. Base frame, ¾ inch material. From 25 to 40 gallons,

¾ inch posts and top frame, with 1-inch bottom frame. Beyond that, 1-inch angle iron throughout. That is the job for the well-equipped mechanic.

Small tanks can be made rather simply after a bit of practise. The main skill required is in accurately making the oblong upper and lower frames. This can be reduced to a simple system by which the top and bottom frames are each finished in one piece.

Directions　　　First determine the inside measurements of the length and thickness. Cut a nicely squared board form of just that size, taking off the corners as shown in accompanying illustration. If tank is planned to be more than a foot wide it will probably be necessary to get plywood for the form, or to join two boards.

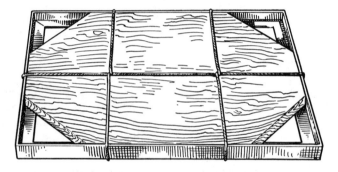

FORM TIED IN FRAME MAKES SOLDERING EASY AND THE RESULT ACCURATE

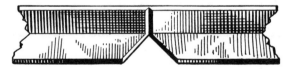

ANGLE BRASS CUT READY FOR BENDING INTO RIGHT ANGLE

Now add together the total length of all four sides. Cut the angle material to a one-piece corresponding length, allowing just a trifle over to compensate for the thickness of the metal at the bends. Bevel both ends, using hack-saw. Then make three marks on the metal, dividing it off into the proper lengths to make the four sides. Again with the hack-saw cut a right-angle V from the inside to the outside of where the material is to be bent. This cut should be a bit scant, so that it can be finished by a *square* file, which is applied until the outside of the angle material is rubbed nearly all the way through. To do this so that the material can be bent and yet not accidentally broken is the only delicate part of the operation. First try a practise cut and bending on a waste short length. If a section breaks, it is of no great consequence, except that the corner will not finish quite as neatly. The risk of breaking these corners is increased on account of having the rather long bar in one piece. This danger can be removed by temporarily bracing each finished V point by lashing a stick of wood on the inside.

After the three V cuts have been made and neatly filed to the proper depth, the whole bar is laid on the floor or a large table, the braces removed and the metal bent at each point so that a neat oblong is formed. This is the upper or lower frame. They are alike, except that the lower frame ought to be of heavier material.

Soldering   All surfaces to be soldered must first be made bright and clean. Then apply flux. Hardware stores have it. It can be made by dissolving as much zinc in hydrochloric acid as it will take. Solder in the form of thick wire is best for the amateur.

Now tie one frame firmly around the board form and solder the two open ends and the three bends. Then remove the board form, transfer it to the prepared material for the other frame and repeat the soldering. With the top and bottom frames thus completed, the finishing of the whole job is simple. Cut four straight lengths of ⅝ inch angle metal to serve as corner posts. Take the top frame and lay it upside down on the work table. Attach the four

C-CLAMP FIRMLY HOLDS PARTS
WHILE SOLDERING

corner posts in position by clipping them to the corners of frame with spring clothespins. Now reverse the position so that the top frame is at the top, and stand the unattached ends of the posts into the corners of the bottom frame. An extra set of clips to hold the bottom corners firmly also is a help, but not absolutely necessary. One small metal C-clamp, however, is very desirable for firmly holding together each post to the corner of the frame while it is being soldered, especially if a blow-torch is being used. Now solder each of the posts to the bottom frame, then turn upside down and finish the top. It is much easier and better to work in a position where the solder runs *downward* into the cracks.

Two refinements of construction are mentioned at this point. It will be seen that the upright posts, being inside, bear virtually all the pressure of the glass; the top and bottom frames none, as the soft cement gives little or no support where there is no contact with metal. That leaves the glass to carry its own strain on the long edges. This is considerable on the back and front sides but not so much on the ends. It can easily be relieved by soldering supporting spots of metal of suitable thickness at central points inside the frame.

The other suggestion is in reference to soldering thin metal right-angle braces in the inside of the corners as shown in one of the illustrations. This is done easily, and adds considerably to the strength. It is only suited to the upper frame, however, as on the lower it would impair the contact between the aquarium floor and the frame.

Bases   A heavy extended slate base is not only a much more difficult job mechanically, but is unnecessary in the style of tank here considered. In medium and small tanks the bottom is placed *inside* the frame. Choice of materials for the bottom usually lies between thin slate (about quarter inch) and heavy glass, preferably wired. In either case it should be purchased cut to size. Slate may be had from makers of blackboards or from other slate specialists advertising in business directories. It should fit snugly but not tightly. Furnishing the dealer a cardboard pattern of the exact size and shape of the inside bottom frame is a good way of meeting any slight irregularity. The glass sides should rest *on* the bottom, not between it and the frame. That makes possible future replacement of glass much simpler. Bargains in heavy glass can usually be had from plate glass insurance companies, and from automobile junk dealers.

Assembling   Use either of the following described formulae for cement. Good prepared ones are on the market at slight cost. Spread liberally in the bottom edge of the frame and slowly press the base into it as far as it will go. Scrape away surplus that squeezes out and repeat the operation on the four glass sides. Cement should cover all metal so that it cannot contact water. Place lengths of thin sticks across the aquarium from glass-to-glass so as to exert a moderate pressure while the cement is setting. With the last described formula this should be not less than a week. Finish according to taste. If nickel or chromium plating is to be used, it naturally must be done before sides and bottom are placed in the frame. Duco or other paint finish is best done last.

If, like professional aquarium builders, one wishes to make a number of uniform tanks, it is best to construct a removable inside wooden form (jig) around which to build the entire frame. This requires a bit of ingenuity, but it pays in the long run, and assures accuracy.

Aquarium Cements

There are on the market several aquarium cement preparations that are superior to anything the hobbyist can make himself. In spite of this, and in spite of the fact that mixing a home-made cement is a messy job, some will want to try it.

Aquarium cements, in addition to being water-resistant, should be firm, tacky and harmless to fishes. They should also remain slightly elastic, so as to reduce the strain caused by the unequal action of temperature on glass and frame. A cement meeting these requirements, and now in use by leading manufacturers, has a base of pure asphalt, usually put up in fine broken sizes under the trade name of Gilsonite. This is thoroughly heated and mixed 50-50 with heavy-bodied linseed oil, so that when only moderately warm it has the consistency of putty. If used in this condition it will be quite firm when chilled by contact with the aquarium, which will be ready for immediate use. A little whiting may be added if desired. It is rather difficult using this cement in tanks of over 10-gallon size. Doing the work where the air is hot prevents the cement from firming too quickly on contact with the frame.

Heavy linseed oil is difficult to purchase. It can be made by slowly boiling and stirring the ordinary raw kind until it is reduced about 25% in volume. This is an unpleasant 15-minute job, and should be done in the open if possible. The smoke is acrid, but the result is superior.

After setting glass, especially on a large aquarium, cut thin small wooden wedges to place permanently at intervals in the cement between the frame and the glass in order to insure the glass firm, even support.

Surfaces intended to bind permanently with cement should be cleaned before applying it. Traces of oil or fingerprints can be removed by rubbing with a bit of clean cloth dipped in any quick-drying solvent, such as alcohol.

A durable, quick-drying cement suitable for use by the amateur is made by mixing red lead in half spar varnish and half raw linseed oil. This varnish is highly water-resistant, and costs more than linseed oil, but in the small quantity used by the amateur it is a wise investment. If one objects to the rather brilliant orange-red of this cement, it can be toned down to brown by the addition of a little lamp black.

A cheaper but still satisfactory article can be made by mixing commercial boiled linseed oil with three parts of whiting and one (by weight) of litharge.

Except with cements applied hot, allow the finished job to stand about two weeks before using. The first filling should be gradual, taking perhaps a week, and using preferably cold water.

Estimated Amounts of Aquarium Cement Required

Size	Width Frame Edge	Cement Thickness	Lbs.	Size	Width Frame Edge	Cement Thickness	Lbs.
Less than 5 gals. ¾″		⅛″	1	15 gallons .... ¾″		¼″	5
5 gallons .... ¾″		⅛″	1½	20 gallons .... 1″		¼″	6½
5 gallons .... ¾″		¼″	3	25 gallons .... 1″		¼″	6¾
10 gallons .... ¾″		⅛″	2	30 gallons .... 1″		¼″	7
10 gallons .... 1″		⅛″	2½	40 gallons .... 1″		¼″	7½
15 gallons .... ¾″		⅛″	2½	50 gallons .... 1″		¼″	8
15 gallons .... 1″		⅛″	3				

Thickness of Glass for Aquaria

Assuming an aquarium to be of ordinary proportions, the principal factor of strain is in reference to its depth.

Up to 14 inches deep, use double thick window glass
From 16 to 18 inches deep use ¼ inch plate glass
" 18 " 22 " " " ⅜ " " "
" 22 " 30 " " " ½ " " "

Tanks that are both long and deep should be reinforced by a crossbar at the top, regardless of the thickness of the glass, unless the frame is extra heavy.

Cutting Glass

Nearly everybody knows how to split glass by first cutting it with a wheel cutter, but there are "tricks in all trades," and this is no exception.

First, lubricate the wheel axle with turpentine to make sure that it turns easily. Next, try it on a spare piece of glass to see whether it makes an even, continuous cut. If not, the wheel may be a poor or dull one, which is often the case. The fault may be in the pressure applied, which should be firm but not heavy. A continuous, light cut is better than a deep one, which is more like a gutter. The cutting should give a sharp, singing sound. Make the practice cut first.

Short marking scratches by the cutting wheel on the glass at measured points at the beginning and end of the proposed cut are helpful guides.

The cutting table should be quite flat. It is important that the side of the straight-edge used in guiding the wheel cutter be smooth, flat and held firmly. In making a long cut, it is desirable to have an assistant hold the far end of this stick. Do not press the cutter hard against it.

If there are gaps in the cut, turn glass over and try the other side, perhaps with a better wheel. Never go over a previous cut.

To split ordinary glass, take hold of it at one end of the cut with thumbs and fingers and bend upwards, while slightly pulling apart. If it shows no signs of breaking under reasonable force, tap along the under side of the cut with the end of the cutter until a series of light splits can be seen the entire length. It then ought to break easily. If not, take a chance on bending it down (under the cut) over the edge of a table, or over a stick *on* the table.

In cutting off a thin strip of glass, either use a slot on the cutter for the breaking, or, preferably, a pair of parallel-jawed pliers, grasping the strip at about the center of the cut, pulling away *and* bending down. Such pliers are handy for breaking off any irregular projections due to a faulty break. Bad edges or unpleasant sharpness can be easily rubbed down with a wet carborundum or other abrasive stone.

Plate or wired glass is cut by the same method, the break being made as previously described over a table-edge, or a stick laid on a table. This valuable glass, however, had best be cut by a professional.

To Find Gallon Capacity

To find capacity, in gallons, of any regular rectangular container, multiply the length, height and width in inches together and divide by 231. For example, an aquarium 20 x 16 x 15 would be: 20 times 16=320. 15 times 320=4800, which, divided by 231, gives almost 21 gallons.

A gallon of water weighs about 8-3/10 lbs. English gallon, 10 lbs.

To find the capacity, in gallons, of a cylindrical container, measure the outside dimensions, calculate as though for a straight-sided container and subtract 1/5 from the result.

The area of a circle can also be approximated by multiplying the diameter by itself and subtracting 1/5 from the result.

Approximate Number of Drops of Water in Gallon

American gallon, 75,000 drops
English gallon, 90,000 drops
Liter (a little over an American quart) 20,000 drops

The strengths of water germicides are usually expressed in proportions involving high dilutions. By being able to roughly measure any large number of drops, it is a simple matter to add one grain of chemical (or one drop of 100% solution) to produce any desired dilution, as a drop is about equal to a grain by weight. Thus a 1-to-300,000 solution would be made by dissolving one grain by weight into 4 gallons of water (300,000 drops).

MISCELLANEOUS INFORMATION

Water Quality

Chlorine   As stated in our opening pages, the average water supplied by the public systems of cities and towns is generally suited to aquarium use. As a matter of public health it must contain a very small amount of chlorine, which is fatal to germs of typhoid, but harmless to humans, even though it tastes and smells unpleasant. Except where running water is used with fishes in it, chlorine is easily removed, for it slowly leaves when the water is exposed to air. That is the main reason for "ripening" or "seasoning" tap water for at least 24 hours before using in an aquarium. The process may be much shortened by the addition of a small amount of photographic "hypo"—say about 3 grains to the gallon, a quantity harmless to fishes. Dealers sell tablets for the purpose.

There are, however, districts where the natural water is too acid, too alkaline or too hard, and the hardness is not fully corrected at the pumping station. Such defective water may cause trouble with certain plants and fishes that are not able to adjust themselves to it. Where general aquarium conditions seem to be good, but some plants and fishes repeatedly fail, it is time to consider the water as the source of trouble. *However, if other aquarists succeed with the same water, one needs to look elsewhere for the cause of failure.*

There are two main qualities in water to be considered, acid-alkaline and hard-soft. These characteristics are not related to each other (except that hard-alkaline and soft-acid conditions often go together) and require different tests for detection.

What is pH?   Under usual conditions water is either acid or alkaline (seldom exactly neutral). The term of pH has reference to those opposite factors and their degree of intensity. A scale has been set up by chemists in which 7.0 represents neutral. Higher is alkaline,

Acid	Neutral	Alkaline
6.0, 6.2, 6.4, 6.6, 6.8	7.0	7.2, 7.4, 7.6

lower, is acid. The accompanying scale indicates the degrees of intensity. Readings are arrived at by taking a small specimen of the water to be tested and placing in it a few drops of a sensitive dye called "indicator solution." The color to which it turns is compared with a standard comparison scale consisting of several numbered shades. Readings are determined by finding the shade most nearly matching the water into which the dye was placed. Testing sets are sold by aquarium dealers and by scientific instrument firms. Those in which the matching shades are on printed cards are only approximately correct. The best are the ones using diluted dyes in sealed tubes. In either case the matching standard colors should be kept out of long exposure to light, especially daylight.

The indicator solution commonly used for aquarium water is made up from the dye, bromthymol blue, and covers the range from 6.0 to 7.6, generally considered inclusive enough for our purposes. Other dyes, if needed, cover ranges above and below those figures.

Corrections in pH are made by the use of "buffer" solutions. Aquarists are urged to make pH changes only as a last resort. It is much better to attempt to gradually adjust fishes to the prevailing local water. For reducing acidity or building up alkalinity, use dissolved bicarbonate of soda.

Reducing the alkaline and increasing the acid side is not quite so easy. The standard "buffer" is a chemical not generally available—acid sodium phosphate (monobasic). A comparatively large quantity is needed to produce the desired effect, and this is liable to cause an insoluble white precipitate, easily siphoned off. Quick but not permanent reductions of alkalinity can be had by the use of vinegar or dilute hydrochloric acid.

Fish Adjustments As before inferred, fishes must make internal adjustment to the chemical qualities of their surrounding waters. Moderate changes (like moving a fish from one tank to another), are made without trouble if the pH difference is slight, such as five-tenths (.5), but a jump of two full points involving the crossing of neutral (7.0), such as 5.5 to 7.5, is liable to prove fatal. Great quantities of shipped healthy fishes are often lost soon after receipt by being jumped from the water of shipment to local water of a very different pH. For that reason, as well as temperature equalization, experienced dealers and aquarists slowly mix seasoned local aquarium water with that in the can of shipment before making the final transfer. As an added precaution, that mixed water is poured into the final receiving tank. The saving of water of shipment is important. An aeration line run into a can of newly received fishes is helpful.

In Nature there are many wide changes of pH in the same place, mainly due to rains and sunlight, but they are *slow* and therefore harmless. Also it will be found that the same kind of fishes are found prospering in waters of different qualities. Those facts should dispose of any idea that certain species must require water of a critically exact pH. True, there are a few broad generalities. The live-bearers, for instance, generally do best in alkaline, slightly hard water. Rasboras and other Malayan families prefer soft water. pH is elusive. A specimen bottled in Nature changes in a few hours before a true test can be made.

Hardness Housewives approximate the degree of hardness of water by the ease or difficulty with which suds are formed in it. Hardness is mainly caused by compounds of calcium and magnesium. Unlike pH, there is no neutral point between hard and soft water. It is just a question of *how much* of the hardening minerals are present. From 0 to 50 parts per million it is considered soft. From 50 to 100, moderately hard. From 100 to 200, hard. Above 200, very hard. (One grain per gallon equals 17 parts per million.)

Contact with limestone formations mainly causes hardness. Deep wells have higher hardness content than open streams in the same locality.

Here again, similar fishes are found prospering in either moderately hard or moderately soft water. However, hardness has certain effects on both fishes and plants. It has been found that some of the hard-to-spawn fishes, such as Neons and the Fundulopanchax group are stimulated to breeding when changed from hard to soft water. This seems to carry out what happens in Nature. A long dry season concentrates the mineral content of the water, thus making it hard. Spawning comes with the rainy season and consequent softening of the water.

There is no safe chemical that can be placed in water to remove its hardness. The addition of distilled or clean rain-water will correct too much hardness. Also there are resinous filters that reduce hardness as long as they are not overworked. Nature's waters such as those of the dark cedar streams of New Jersey and elsewhere are used in whole or part by some breeders of Killifishes, such as *Aphyosemion, Aplocheilus, Epiplatys,* etc.

There are hardness testing sets to be had from the same sources mentioned in the paragraph on *p*H. Boiling removes some hardness. The water is allowed to cool and settle. Then only use the top part, or the bottom can be carefully siphoned off and thrown away. (However, boiling causes marked changes in *p*H toward the acid side.)

Due to concentration by evaporation, hardness increases in an aquarium over a period of months if no water is drawn off. As elsewhere stated, it is advisable to siphon away about 10% of the bottom water occasionally.

Hardness is increased by the presence of a large number of shells from dead snails; also by sand or gravel containing much lime. This can be removed, if desired, by placing it in commercial hydrochloric acid until bubbling stops. It must then be thoroughly washed before use.

Hardness has varying effects on different plants, but we are not yet able to list all of their individual preferences. Like fishes, some have wide tolerances, and do well almost anywhere. One of our famous Florida aquarium plant specialists grows most plants in moderately hard, aged shallow well-water. The list includes most of the Cryptocorynes, Anubia, Aponogeton, all Sagittarias, all Vallisnerias, all Swordplants, Didiplis, Hygrophila and Ambulia. Evidently the Cryptocorynes are among the plants enjoying a wide tolerance, for qualified travellers tell us that they grow in profusion in their native acid Malayan waters.

Most of the algae fail in soft water. Anacharis likes hard water. This may account for the occasional claim that a heavy growth of Anacharis clears green water. It probably exhausts most of the minerals, thus starving the algae. Nitella and Hornwort act the same as Anacharis.

Renewal of hardness supply may account for another well-known fact regarding green water. When the water in an aquarium has become fairly green, many beginner aquarists attempt to clear it by the addition of fresh water. To their amazement this only speeds the green growth, no doubt by the addition of a fresh supply of the hardening minerals. If left alone the suspended green water algae will presently starve itself by exhausting its needed minerals, and the water will then remain clear for a very long time. Local water works on request will give their latest chemical analysis, including pH and hardness.

Facts About Oxygen

The importance of oxygen to all life, and especially in its bearing on the welfare of fishes, has been stated in a general way in the fore part of this volume. To those who wish to consider the subject in more detail, the following facts should prove of interest.

Air is composed approximately of 4 parts of nitrogen to 1 of oxygen. However, when water dissolves air into itself, it does not take the 2 gases in that proportion. It takes 2 parts of nitrogen to 1 of oxygen, a ratio of oxygen which is twice as rich as we breathe. The amount of oxygen as a part of air which pure water is capable of absorbing by volume at different temperatures is as follows:

At 50 degrees Fahrenheit, 7.8 parts per 1000 by volume
60	"	"	6.9	"	"	"	"	"
70	"	"	6.3	"	"	"	"	"
80	"	"	5.7	"	"	"	"	"
90	"	"	5.0	"	"	"	"	"

The value of this table is to point out how rapidly the oxygen content diminishes as the temperature increases.

Actually in ordinary aquarium conditions the amount of dissolved oxygen present is about half that shown in the table. This is due to the unavoidable presence of certain gases (displacing the oxygen). These are generated mostly by the decomposition of organic matter (aquarium settlings, dead leaves, etc.) and the carbon dioxide due to the breathing of the fishes.

While the theoretical capacity of water to hold free oxygen at a temperature of 75 degrees F. is about 6.0 parts per 1000, as a matter of fact, fishes are fairly comfortable with an oxygen content of 3.3, which, as has been pointed out, is what they get in an ordinary good aquarium at 75 degrees. It will therefore be seen why we advocate temperatures averaging about 75 degrees, where, with cleanliness, growing plants in good light (or the use of artificial aeration) and not too many fish, the dissolved oxygen content can be kept between 3.3 and 5.0 parts by volume, per 1000, which is good.

Contrary to popular belief, fishes are injured or killed more by an excess of carbon dioxide than by any lack of oxygen. However, the air contacts which dissolve oxygen into the water also (but more slowly) liberate the poisonous carbon dioxide.

Comparison of Temperature and Measurement Scales

In practically all aquarium literature, except that written in English, Centigrade measurements (often abbreviated as C.) are used to designate temperature. They translate into these Fahrenheit equivalents:

From this it becomes apparent why, in foreign literature on aquarium fishes, the temperature figures range between 20 and 30, but more usually between 22 and 26, equivalent to our Fahrenheit 72 to 78.

It will be noticed that Centigrade zero is the freezing point (32) in Fahrenheit. On the higher part of the scale, not shown, the Centigrade boiling point at 100 equals Fahrenheit 212.

In most foreign aquarium literature we find measurements expressed in the metric system, which is gradually coming into general use. For those who have not been reared to think in those terms, we give a few of the most important equivalents. There are 3 principal measurements of this kind which foreign aquarists use.

Two of the measurements met with most often in our foreign publications are the *centimeter* and the *cubic centimeter,* abbreviated respectively as cm. and c.c. For all practical purposes there are 5 centimeters to 2 inches, as shown on the accompanying parallel scale. The 10 subdivisions to be seen in the centimeters are *millimeters.* These are uni-

Inches ➤➤➤

Millimeters ➤➤➤

Centimeters ➤➤➤

Cubic Centimeter

versally used by scientists to designate the lengths of smaller fishes, such as we keep in aquariums, and of small objects, like fish eggs.

The third measurement we often read is the *liter*. It expresses capacity, and is just a trifle over a quart, so that this is easily kept in mind. It comprises 1000 cubic centimeters, and is the same as a cubic decimeter.

The great advantage of the metric system, is, as most of us know, that it is based on the decimal system. The denominations are in multiples of 10, so that multiplication or division, within the range of those multiples, is accomplished by merely moving the decimal point forward or backward.

Paints and Waterproofing

Water given enough time is a powerful oxydizer. Few substances can stand up against it indefinitely.

Aquarists sometimes inquire as to what kind of paint may be used on the inside edges of an aquarium or on a tin container. We have yet to find one that long endures.

For some years makers of tin cans have been using a wonderful water-resisting baked lacquer on the insides of their cans. Such tins need no further treatment, unless one wishes to do the outside. Plain tin may be painted or rinsed with asphaltum varnish. It lasts about a year in use, and may then need another coating.

Asphaltum varnish applied to inside surfaces of concrete tanks discourages growth of algae.

A durable waterproofer, previously mentioned, well suited to pails, is made by melting together 3 parts of paraffine and 1 part of automobile grease. Apply hot. As this mixture never becomes fully firm to the touch, its uses are limited. Cans already rusty and treated with it have lasted for years.

Glycerine-litharge Cement

Litharge mixed with glycerine to the consistency of putty becomes stone-hard in ten minutes. Contrary to a persistent belief, it is *not* waterproof, and is not suitable as an aquarium cement. Plumbers use it in making temporary repairs to leaks.

CROSS INDEX OF GENERAL SUBJECTS

(Index of Fishes follows)

INDEX OF FISHES

(Cross Index of other subjects is on the preceding pages)

The names to the right are of those persons and firms who owned
selected specimens used for the photographic illustrations.

INTRODUCTION TO THE INNES COLOR PLATES

*T*HE pictures in the following section are, for the most part, original Innes photographs. In cases where fish have recently become popular, we have had to use new photos, but we have tried to keep them on the same high level as the Innes originals.

We feel that one of the most beautiful things about tropical fish is their coloration. Accordingly, we have spared no expense in giving you the best possible color reproductions. The color photographs in this book are on a par with those in costly art folios.

The index of color plates begins on Page 542. Fish are listed according to both scientific names and up-to-date popular names. From this index, you can tell at a glance which fish are represented in the color section.

Each color photograph is cross-referenced with the text proper. In the corner of each picture there is a page number. All you have to do is turn to this page to read about the particular fish.

May we say in closing, that it gives us great pleasure to share these famous color photographs with a new audience of tropical fish hobbyists.

The Publishers

Rasbòra heteromòrpha DUNCKER   **TEXT PAGE** 221
Pronounced Raz-bo'ra het'er-o-morf"a   *Popular name,* Rasbora, or Red Rasbora

Phenácográmmus interrúptus (BOULENGER) TEXT PAGE 135

Pronounced Fee-nack"o-gram'mus in'ter-rup"tus *Popular name,* Feathertail Tetra

Hyphéssobrỳcon flámmeus MYERS TEXT PAGE 138

Pronounced Hy-fess'o-bry"kon flam'me-us *Popular names,* Tetra from Rio, Red Tet

Hyphéssobrỳcon ínnesi MYERS   TEXT PAGE 141

Pronounced Hy-fess'o-bry"kon   in'nis-eye   *Popular name,* Neon Tetra

Cheirodon axelrodi   TEXT PAGE 143

Pronounced Ki'-ro-don   *Popular name,* Cardinal Tetra

Hyphéssobrỳcon púlchripinnis AHL
Pronounced Hy-fess-o-bry'kon pul'kre-pin"niss

TEXT PAGE 145
Popular name, Lemon Tetra

Hyphessobrỳcon rosàceus DURBIN
Pronounced Hy-fess'o-bry"con   rose-ay'see-us

TEXT PAGE 146
Popular name, Rosy Tetra

Hyphessobrycon callistus BOULENGER   TEXT PAGE 147
Pronounced Hy-fess′o-bry″con   cal-lis′tus   *Popular name,* Serpa Tetra

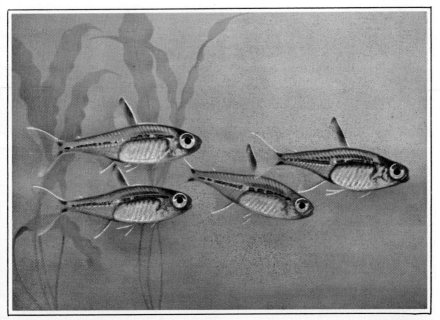

Hemigrammus erythrozonus DURBIN   TEXT PAGE 148
Pronounced Hem′i-gram″muss   er′y-throw-zo″nus   *Popular name,* Glowlight Tetra

Hyphéssobrỳcon heterorhábdus (ULREY)   TEXT PAGE 149
Pronounced Hy-fess'o-bry"kon   het'er-o-rab"dus

Hemigrámmus rhodóstomus AHL   TEXT PAGE 152
Pronounced Hem'-i-gram'muss   row-dos'to-muss   *Popular name*, Rummy Nose

551

Hemìgrámmus océllifer (STEINDACHNER) TEXT PAGE 155
Pronounced Hem'i-gram"muss o-sell'if-er *Popular name,* Head-and-tail-light Tetra

Hemigrámmus caudovittàtus AHL TEXT PAGE 156
Pronounced Hem'i-gram"muss cau'do-vi-tay"tus *Popular name,* Tet from Buenos Aires

Pristélla ríddlei (MEEK)   **TEXT PAGE 159**
Pronounced Pris-tell'a   riddle-eye (not riddley-eye)   *Popular name,* Pristella

Aphyochàrax rubripínnis **PAPPENHEIM**   **TEXT PAGE 170**
Pronounced Af'ee-o-kay"rax rub'ri-pin"niss   *Popular name,* Bloodfin

Serrasálmus spilopleùra KNER

Pronounced Ser′ra-sal″mus spy-low-plu′ra

TEXT PAGE 180

Popular name, Piranha

Copeina arnoldi REGAN

(Showing eggs above water on sanded glass)

TEXT PAGE 185

Pronounced Ko-pie′na ar′nold-eye

554

Copeìna guttàta (STEINDACHNER) TEXT PAGE 188
Pronounced Ko-pie′na gut-tay′ta

Anóstomus anóstomus (LINNAEUS) TEXT PAGE 192
Pronounced An-os′to-mus an-os′to-mus

Nannóstomus margìnàtus EIGENMANN   TEXT PAGE 198
Pronounced Nan-os′to-mus   mar′jin-ay″tus

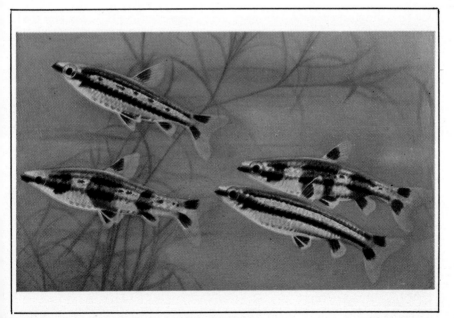

Nannóstomus trifasciàtus STEINDACHNER   TEXT PAGE 199
Pronounced Nan-os′to-mus   try′fas-see-ay″tus

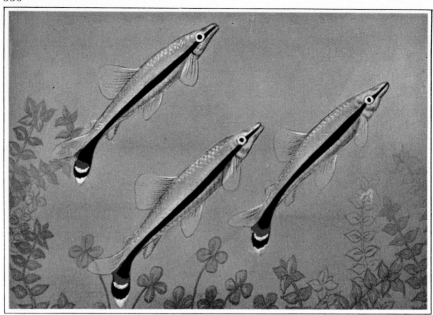

Nannobrỳcon unifasciatus (STEINDACHNER)   **TEXT PAGE 200**
Pronounced Nan'o-bry"con u'ni-fas'sec-ay"tus   *Popular name,* Spot-tail Pencilfish

Bärbus conchònius HAMILTON-BUCHANAN   **TEXT PAGE 234**
Pronounced Bar'bus kon-cho'nee-us   *Popular name,* Rosy Barb

Dànio malabáricus (JERDON)   TEXT PAGE 214

Pronounced Dan'e-o mal'a-bar"i-cus   *Popular name,* Giant Danio

Tanichthys albonùbes LIN   TEXT PAGE 215

Pronounced Tan-ick'thiss al-bo-new'bees   *Popular name,* White Cloud Mountain Fish

Brachydanio rerio   *Brachydanio nigrofasciatus*

Bráchydànio   *Brachydanio albolineatus*

TEXT PAGE 210

Bärbus cummingi   GUENTHER   **TEXT PAGE 235**

Pronounced Bar'bus cum'ming-eye (not cum-ming'-eye)

Bärbus nìgrofasciàtus GUNTHER   **TEXT PAGE 243**
Pronounced Bar'bus ny'grow-fas'see-ay"tus   *Popular* name, Black Ruby Barb

Bärbus éveretti BOULENGER   **TEXT PAGE 238**
Pronounced Bar'bus ev'er-et-eye   *Popular name*, Clown Barb

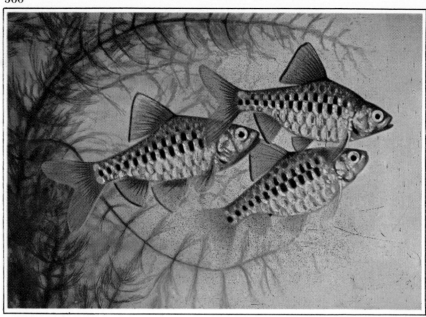

Bärbus oligolèpis (BLEEKER) **TEXT PAGE 244**
Pronounced Bar'bus ol'i-go-lee"pis *Popular name*, Checkerboard Barb

Bärbus tetrazòna BLEEKER (incorrectly *B. sumatranus*) **TEXT PAGE 246**
Pronounced bar' bus tet'ra-zoe' na *Popular name*, Damsel Barb

Bärbus tícto (HAMILTON-BUCHANAN)
Pronounced Bar'bus tick'toe

TEXT PAGE 248
Popular name, Ticto Barb

Bärbus tittèya DERANIYAGALA
Pronounced Bar'bus tit-tay'a

TEXT PAGE 251
Popular name, Cherry Barb

Bòtia mácracántha BLEEKER   TEXT PAGE 258

Pronounced Bo'-tee-a mac'ra-can"tha   *Popular name,* Clown Loach

Còrydòras rabauti LAMONTE   TEXT PAGE 280

Pronounced Ko'ree-doe"rus ra-boat"-eye

Jordanélla flòridae GOODE AND BEAN

Pronounced Jor'dan-el"la flo'ri-dee

TEXT PAGE 293

Popular name, Flag Fish

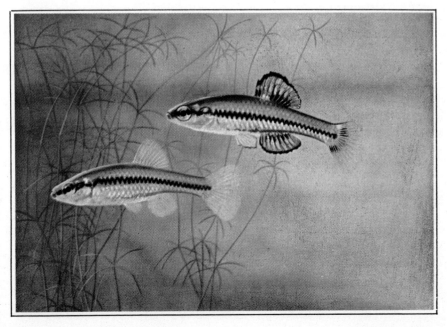

Chriòpeops goodei (JORDAN)

Pronounced Kry-o'pee-ops good'eye

TEXT PAGE 296

Popular name, Bluefin Killy

Aplocheìlus líneàtus　(CUVIER AND VALENCIENNES)　　TEXT PAGE 301
Pronounced Ap'low-kyle"us　linn'e-ay"tus　　*Popular name,* Malabar Killy

Aplocheìlus pánchax　(HAMILTON-BUCHANAN)　　TEXT PAGE 304
Pronounced Ap'low-kyle"us pan'chax　　*Popular name,* Panchax

Epiplàtys chápери (SAUVAGE)   **TEXT PAGE 305**
Pronounced Ep'ee-play"tiss chap"er-eye   *Popular name,* Redjaw Killy

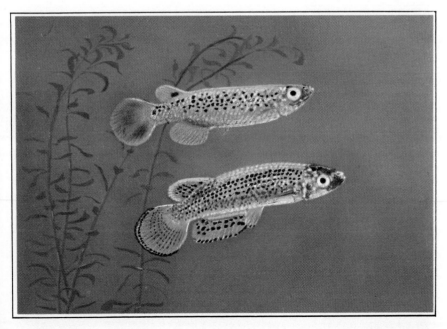

Pachypanchax playfairi (GUENTHER)   **TEXT PAGE 308**
Pronounced Pay'ky-pan"chax   play-fair'-eye   *Popular name,* Rough-back Killy

Rívulus cylindràceus POEY   TEXT PAGE 309
Pronounced Riv'you-lus   sill'in-dray"see-us   *Popular name,* Cuban Rivulus

Rívulus urophthálmus GUENTHER   TEXT PAGE 312
Pronounced Riv'you-lus   your'off-thal"muss   *Popular names,* Red Rivulus
                                                     Blue Rivulus

Aphyosèmion austràle   (RACHOW)   TEXT PAGE 314
Pronounced Aff'ee-o-see"me-on aws-tray'lee   *Popular name,* Lyretail

Aphyosèmion cognàtum   MEINKEN   TEXT PAGE 317
Pronounced Aff'ee-o-see' me-on cog-nay" tum   *Popular name,* Red-speckled Killy

Aphyosèmion bìvittàtum   (LOENNBERG)   TEXT PAGE 319
Pronounced Aff'ee-o-see"me-on by'vi-tay"tum   *Popular name,* Two-striped Killy

Aphyosèmion cœrùleum   (BOULENGER)   TEXT PAGE 322
Pronounced Aff'ee-o-see"me-on see-rue'lee-um   *Popular name,* Blue Gularis

Aphyosèmion sjoestedti (LOENNBERG)   **TEXT PAGE 325**
Pronounced Aff'ee-o-see"me-on shuss'ted-eye   *Popular name,* Golden Pheasant Killy

Nothobranchius rachovi   AHL   **TEXT PAGE 326**
Pronounced No'tho-brank"ee-us ra-kov'-eye   *Popular name,* Fire Killy

Pterolèbias peruénsis MYERS   TEXT PAGE 327
Pronounced Ter'o-lee"bee-as pe-ru-en'sis   *Popular name,* Peruvian Longfin

Cỳnolèbias bellóttii STEINDACHNER   TEXT PAGE 328
Pronounced Sy'no-lee"be-ass bel-lot'ee-eye   *Popular name,* Argentine Pearl Fish

Nothobranchius palmquisti (LOENNBERG)   TEXT PAGE 329
Pronounced No'tho-brank"ee-us palm'quist'eye

Lebistes reticulàtus   (PETERS)   TEXT PAGE 364
Pronounced Le-biss"tees re-tik'you-lay"tus *Popular names,* Guppy and Rainbow Fish

"Wagtail" Platy   TEXT PAGE 369

Xiphophòrus variatus (MEEK)   TEXT PAGE 371
Pronounced Zi'fo-fo"rus vay'ree-ay"tus   *Popular name,* Variatus

Xíphophòrus hélleri HECKEL   TEXT PAGE 372
Pronounced Zi'fo-fo"rus hel'lereye   *Popular names,* Swordtail and Helleri

Red Swordtail Hybrids   TEXT PAGE 375

574

"Orange Tail" variety of *Mollienisia sphenops*
(CUVIER AND VALENCIENNES)

TEXT PAGE 361

"Liberty" variety of *Móllienísia sphènops*
Pronounced Moll'le-en-iss"ee-a sfee'nops

TEXT PAGE 362

Black Mollienisias or Midnight Mollies   TEXT PAGE 363

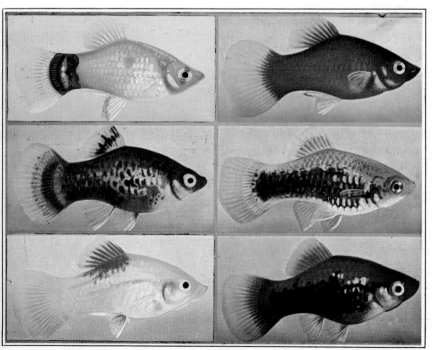

Blue — Variegated — Golden   Red — Black — Berlin

Xíphophòrus maculàtus (GUENTHER)   TEXT PAGE 367
Pronounced Zi'fo-fo"rus mac'you-lay"tus   *Popular names,* Moonfish, Platy

Variegated Hybrids

TEXT PAGE 376

Red Wagtail Swordtails

TEXT PAGE 377

Gásterósteus acùleàtus LINNAEUS   TEXT PAGE 379

Pronounced Gas′ter-os″tee-us ak-you′lee-ay″tus   *Popular name,* Three-spined Stickleback

Mélanotaènia maccúllochi   AHL   TEXT PAGE 383
Pronounced Mel′an-o-tee″nee-a mc-culloch-eye

Badis badis   (HAMILTON-BUCHANAN)

TEXT PAGE 385

Popular name, Badis

Mácropòdus operculàris   (LINNAEUS)

TEXT PAGE 392

Pronounced Mak'ro-po"dus oh-per'ku-lay"riss   *Popular name,* Paradise Fish

Bétta spléndens REGAN   TEXT PAGE 404

Pronounced Bet'ta (not bay-ta) splen'dens   *Popular name,* Siamese Fighting Fish

Colisa fasciàta (BLOCH AND SCHNEIDER)   TEXT PAGE 409

Pronounced Ko-lee'sa   fas'see-ay"ta   *Popular name,* Striped Gourami

Colisa lália (HAMILTON-BUCHANAN) TEXT PAGE 410
Pronounced Ko-lee'sa lal'e-a *Popular name,* Dwarf Gourami

Colisa làbiòsa (DAY) TEXT PAGE 411
Pronounced Ko-lee'sa lay'bee-o"sa *Popular name,* Thick-lipped Gourami

Trìchogáster trichópterus (PALLAS) (Blue type)   TEXT PAGE 412
Pronounced Try'ko-gas''ter try-kop'te-rus   *Popular name,* Three-spot Gourami

Trìchogáster leèri (BLEEKER)   TEXT PAGE 413
Pronounced Try'ko-gas''ter   leer'eye   *Popular name,* Pearl Gourami

Photo by Sharad R. Sane, M. Sc.

Colisa Chuna   **TEXT PAGE 414**

Pronounced Ko-lee′sa   *Popular name,* Sunset Gourami

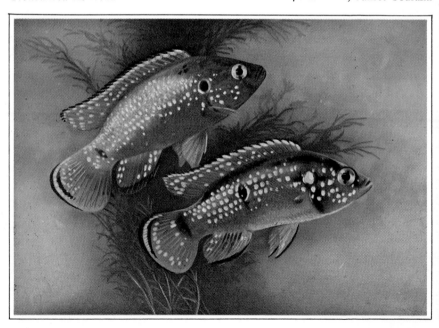

Hémichròmis bimáculàtus GILL   **TEXT PAGE 428**

Pronounced Hem′mee-crow″miss   by-mak′you-lay″tus   *Popular name,* Jewel Fish

Haplochròmis Múlticolor (HILGENDORF)   TEXT PAGE 431

Pronounced Hap'low-krow"miss mul"te-col'or *Popular name,* Egyptian Mouthbreeder

Pelmatochròmis kribénsis BOULENGER   TEXT PAGE 438

Pronounced Pel-ma'to-krow"miss   kree-ben'sis   *Popular name,* Kribi Cichlid

Etròplus maculàtus (BLOCH) TEXT PAGE 439
Pronounced E-tro'plus mac'you-lay"tus *Popular name,* Orange Cichlid

Photo by Wolfsheimer

Nannacara anomala REGAN TEXT PAGE 442
Pronounced Nan'-na-car'-a a-nom'-a-la *Popular Name,* Golden-eyed Cichlid

Cichlasòma meèki (BRIND)   TEXT PAGE 446
Pronounced Sick'la-so"ma meek'eye   *Popular name,* Firemouth

Æquidens cúrviceps E. AHL   TEXT PAGE 452
Pronounced Ee'kwi-denz kur'vi-seps   *Popular name,* Blunthead Cichlid

Cíchlasòma séverum (HECKEL.)   **TEXT PAGE 447**
Pronounced Sick'la-so"ma   sev'e-r-rum   *Popular name,* Deacon

Cíchlasòma bìocellàtum REGAN   **TEXT PAGE 450**
Pronounced Sick'la-so"ma   by'o-sell-ay"tum   *Popular name,* Jack Dempsey

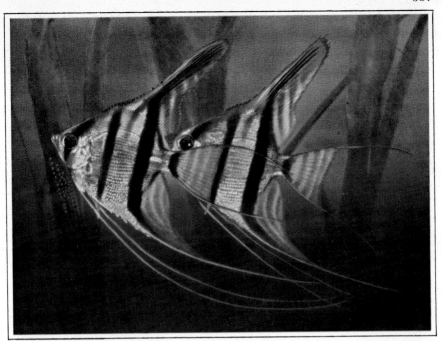

Pterophyllum scalare (LICHTENSTEIN)
Pronounced Ter'-o-fill"lum ska-la're

TEXT PAGE 457

Popular names, Angel Fish and Scalare

Angel fish and young.

Æquidens portalegrénsis (HENSEL)   TEXT PAGE 453
Pronounced Ee'kwi-denz por'tal-e-gren"sis   *Popular name,* "Port"

Apistográmma ramírezi MYERS AND HARRY   TEXT PAGE 468
Pronounced A-pis'toe-gram"ma rah-meer"ez-eye   *Popular name,* Ram

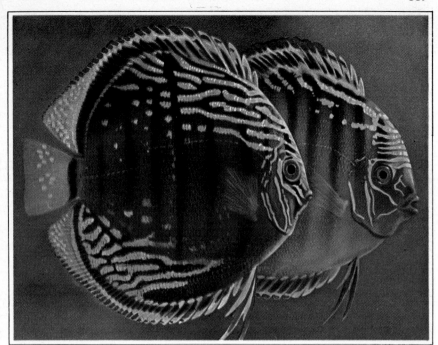

Symphysodon discus (HECKEL) TEXT PAGE 464
Pronounced Sim-fy'so-don dis'kus

Amphiprìon percùla (LACÉPÈDE) TEXT PAGE 473
Pronounced Am-fi-pry'on per-kew'la *Popular names,* Clownfish, Anemone Fish

Chánda lála (HAMILTON-BUCHANAN) TEXT PAGE 476
Pronounced Chan'da la'la *Popular name,* Glassfish

Bràchygòbius xánthozònus (BLEEKER) TEXT PAGE 488
Pronounced Bray'kee-go"bee-us zan'tho-zo"nus *Popular name,* Bumble Bee Goby

Scátophàgus ärgus (PALLAS)
Pronounced Scat'o-fay"gus ar'gus

TEXT PAGE 480

Popular name, Spotted Scat

Ptéroïs vòlitans (LINNAEUS)
Pronounced Ter'o-iss   vo'le-tans

TEXT PAGE 492

Popular name, Lionfish or Turkeyfish

A List of Reference Indexes

How to Use Location Maps

"Western" in front, "Eastern" in back of book

UNDER the heading given each fish in the text will be found the words "Location Map," followed by certain key letters and figures. These refer to the same letters and figures in the margins of the maps designated. Where the lines extending from those key letters and figures cross each other is an exact or approximate point known to be inhabited by that particular species of fish.

It will, of course, be understood that a species is seldom confined to a single spot, although in many instances collections have thus far been made from but one point. Where the distribution of a species is either wide or scattered, there are sufficient location-points (and text explanations) given so that the reader will easily understand what is meant.

Most collections have been made from streams and pools quite too small to show on anything less than a huge map. This accounts for the fact that in many places no water appears to be near the point indicated.

In a few instances commercial collectors of new species have not reported exactly where fishes were gathered, but we are, nevertheless, able to closely approximate where they are found. The great majority of locations have been described by scientists, and are accurate.

Continents, for the sake of clearness, are shown as large as space permits, regardless of their respective sizes. In the Western Map their relative positions are ignored, except for the line of the Equator, which is continuous and correct, although considerably contracted between South America and Africa.

The alphabet for our particular purpose proved to have less than half enough characters, but by utilizing capitals and small letters (and a few odd signs for seldom-used spots), we managed to have enough. This is mentioned to make sure that the reader always notes whether it is a capital or a small letter that is referred to in the key combination.

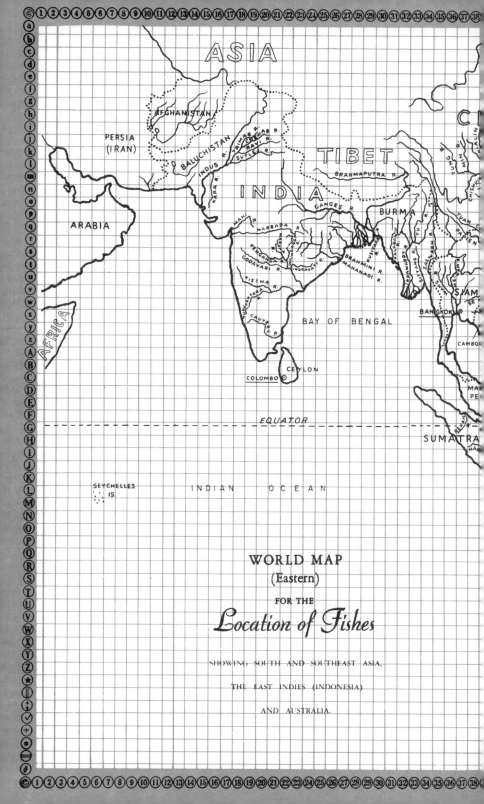

WORLD MAP
(Eastern)

FOR THE

Location of Fishes

SHOWING SOUTH AND SOUTHEAST ASIA,

THE EAST INDIES (INDONESIA)

AND AUSTRALIA.